D1276739

Common Core Progress

English Language Arts

7

Sadlier School

Common Core
Progress™
English Language Arts

For additional online resources, go to sadlierconnect.com.

William H. Sadlier, Inc.
9 Pine Street
New York, NY 10005-4700

Printed in the United States of America.
ISBN: 978-1-4217-3057-8
1 2 3 4 5 6 7 8 9 WEBC 17 16 15 14 13

CONTENTS

continued next page

R.9, RL.7.4, RL.7.5, RL.7.6, RL.7.10, SL.7.1.a, SL.7.1.c–d

L.7.5.a

RL.7.4, RL.7.5, RL.7.6, L.7.5.a

Unit 6

Text Types and Purposes: Write Evidence-Based Texts

W.7.2, W.7.2.a–f, W.7.4, W.7.5, W.7.9, W.7.10

L.7.1.b, L.7.2

SL.7.1.a–d, SL.7.3, SL.7.4, SL.7.6

W.7.2, W.7.2.a–b, W.7.2.f, W.7.4, W.7.5, W.7.9, W.7.9.b, W.7.10, L.7.1.b, L.7.2, RI.7.10

Unit 7

Reading Informational Text: Craft and Structure

RI.7.4, RI.7.5, RI.7.6, RST.7.6, RI.7.9, RI.7.10, RST.7.3, RST.7.5, RST.7.6, RST.7.7, RST.7.8, SL.7.1.a–d

L.7.4.a

RL.7.4, RI.7.5, RI.7.6, L.7.4.a

W.7.2, W.7.2.a–f, W.7.4,
W.7.5, W.7.6, W.7.7, W.7.10,
WHST.7.2.a–f

L.7.1.a, L.7.1.c

SL.7.1.a–d, WHST.7.2.a–c

W.7.2, W.7.2.a–f, W.7.4, W.7.5,
W.7.6, W.7.10, L.7.1.a, L.7.1.c

RL.7.7, RL.7.9, RL.7.10, SRL.7.11,
L.7.1.a, SL.7.1.c, SL.7.1.d

L.7.5.c

RL.7.7, RL.7.9, RL.7.10, L.7.5.c

W.7.1, W.7.1.a–e, W.7.4, W.7.5,
W.7.6, W.7.7, W.7.9, W.7.9.b,
W.7.10, WHST.7.1, WHST.7.1.a–e

continued next page

L.7.2.a, L.7.3.a

SL.7.1.a–d, SL.7.6

W.7.1, W.7.1.a–e, W.7.4, W.7.5,
W.7.6, W.7.7, W.7.8, W.7.9,
W.7.9.b, W.7.10

Unit 11 | Reading Informational Text:
Integration of Knowledge and Ideas

RI.7.7, RI.7.8, RI.7.9, RI.7.10,
RH.7.6, RH.7.7, RH.7.8, RST.7.2,
RST.7.8, SL.7.1.a, SL.7.1.c,
SL.7.1.d

L.7.5.b

RI.7.7, RI.7.8, RI.7.9, L.7.5.b

W.7.2, W.7.2.b, W.7.4, W.7.5,
W.7.6, W.7.7, W.7.8, W.7.9,
W.7.9.b, W.7.10, L.7.1, L.7.1.f–g,
L.7.2, L.7.2.a–c, L.7.3, L.7.3.a,
L.7.3.c, L.7.4.c, L.7.4.d, SL.7.1.a,
SL.7.1.c, SL.7.4, SL.7.5, SL.7.6

Welcome

You have an exciting year ahead of you! You will be reading fascinating texts in a variety of genres, including short stories, plays, poems, speeches, historical accounts, movie reviews, magazine articles, and Web articles. You'll read about topics as varied as space travel, exploring in the Amazon, GPS satellites, building the Transcontinental Railroad, and rainforest deforestation. Along the way you'll learn and practice reading skills and strategies that will help you better understand what you read.

Writing is important, too. This year you'll study how successful writers tell stories, explain events, present research, and give opinions. You'll have the opportunity to apply writers' skills and techniques when writing your own stories, essays, and reports about important technologies, historical figures and events, and more.

This book, **Common Core Progress**, will guide you on the path to improvement in reading and writing—and perhaps in school. That's why it's called *progress*.

Have a great year!

Introducing UNIT 1

In this unit about courageous actions, you will see how key ideas and details help shape a literary text. Literary texts can be entertaining, but they can also make you think in new ways. Authors communicate a text's central idea, or theme, by providing details that engage the reader. Sometimes the author states the theme directly; at other times, you will use details in the textto draw inferences about the theme. You will also look at how elements of a story combine and interact to communicate the author's ideas.

Literary texts cover many genres, including realistic fiction, historical fiction, drama, and myth. In this unit, you will read an example of each. Within each of these texts, you will meet someone who found the courage to overcome obstacles or explore new worlds. Think about how each story is driven by the main character's reaction to the challenges he or she faces. Ask yourself how the author communicates the key ideas or themes. Finally, pay attention to the important details in the text. How do these key details bring both the story and the theme to life?

Progress Check — Can I?

Before Unit 1		After Unit 1
☐	Find evidence that supports an author's ideas, including inferences drawn from details that the author provides.	☐
☐	Determine the main theme of a text, and analyze how an author develops it.	☐
☐	Summarize a text.	☐
☐	Analyze how setting, characters, and plot interact within a text.	☐
☐	Use affixes to help determine the meanings of unfamiliar words.	☐

HOME◆CONNECT...

When writing a literary text, authors combine the use of explicit ideas, or those that are clearly stated, and **inferred** ideas, or those the reader must discover. As you read the selections in this unit with your child, help him or her discover the meaning beneath the author's words. Questions like, "What does she mean when she says that?" or "Why did he just take that action?" can help your child **draw inferences**.

Authors write with a purpose, which usually centers on a **theme**, or overall message. As you read with your child, encourage him or her to think about the theme.

Analyzing **literary elements**, including **character, plot,** and **setting,** leads to an understanding of the key ideas and details that make a story meaningful. As you read, ask your child to identify key elements of literature. Questions like "Who is your favorite character, and why?" or "Where does the story take place?" will prompt your child to analyze the author's purpose. Help your child summarize the text: Read a section and then ask, "What just happened in the story?"

Activity: Learn about someone who has overcome adversity to accomplish a goal. Help your child research an impressive person, either on the Internet or at a local library. Talk with your child about why this person is a courageous figure and what helped him or her overcome life's obstacles.

IN THIS UNIT, YOUR CHILD WILL...

- Read four literary selections, including realistic fiction, historical fiction, a play, and a myth.
- Identify details that support an author's stated ideas.
- Draw inferences by analyzing implied ideas and use textual evidence to support inferences.
- Analyze a text to determine its theme.
- Summarize the text.
- Analyze the main elements of a drama and how they affect each other.
- Use affixes to figure out the meanings of unfamiliar words.
- Compare and contrast ideas across four selections on the theme of courageous actions.

NOTE: All of these learning goals for your child are based on the Grade 7 Common Core State Standards for English Language Arts.

WAYS TO HELP YOUR CHILD

Help your child identify key details. In regular conversation, ask your child about the events of his or her day. See if your child can identify the most important points about these events. If your child has difficulty leaving out unimportant details, ask questions that will help him or her find the most salient points of a personal story.

ONLINE

For more Home Connect activities, continue online at sadlierconnect.com

Reading Literature: Key Ideas and Details

Essential Question:
How do authors use literary details to create text?

RL.7.1

WORDS TO KNOW

affected

diagnosis

feat

lurch

tumultuous

Sometimes an author's ideas are directly stated in a text, and sometimes they are implied, or suggested. Use clues in the text to **draw inferences** about implied ideas.

CITE EVIDENCE

A Sometimes authors state an idea explicitly, or directly, in a text. In this text, the author speaks through a first-person narrator named Ellie. According to Ellie, what is one of the major obstacles in Gertrude Ederle's swimming career? Find the stated idea, and underline it.

B Sometimes authors expect readers to **draw an inference**—that is, make an educated guess—about ideas in a text. You can draw inferences by thinking carefully about details in the text. Put a box around the paragraph whose details help you infer how Ellie feels about Gertrude Ederle.

Courage in the Water

(Genre: Realistic Fiction)

1   The boat **lurches** wildly as I stand looking up at the gray sky. Concerned, I search the water before me, squinting for some glimpse of the swimmer ahead. I know she is out there, but I don't see how anyone can keep going with the seas so rough. We are getting closer to our destination; at least half of the 21-mile journey is already gone. However, the pounding wind and **tumultuous** waves must be taking quite a toll on our swimmer.

2   Suddenly, I feel a tap on my shoulder. I turn to see my father smiling down at me, his expression animated as he gestures ahead. He looks pointedly at me and then slowly says, "There she is—look where I am pointing."

3   I follow the direction of his arm and see a red bathing cap bobbing above the waves. I let out a yell of excitement: "That's it, Trudy, you can do it!" Even though I know she can't hear my words of encouragement, I still can't contain my enthusiasm. It's hard for me to believe I am here, watching Gertrude Ederle attempt to swim the English Channel. Not only is she the first woman to try such a **feat**, she faces even more difficult odds. Like me, Trudy lives with partial deafness. She may not be able to hear everything around her, but she has never let it stand in her way.

RL.7.1

"She may never hear again . . . "

4   Last year, when I was twelve, my little brother and I both came home from school feeling poorly. I can still remember walking into my father's grocery store that day in 1925, and my head felt as if it was going to explode.

5   My mother took one look at me, and I could hear the panic in her voice when she said, "Ellie, are you all right?" When I didn't answer, she told my father to run for the doctor and then took my brother and me upstairs to our apartment above the store.

6   The doctor said we had the measles—and that it was one of the worst cases he had seen in years. For a while, my family wasn't even sure if I would pull through. My brother and I are tough, though, and within a few weeks, we had made it through the worst.

7   Unfortunately, it wasn't all good news. At first, I thought maybe I had a cold along with the measles; everything sounded muffled inside my head. The city noises outside my window were quieter, and when people spoke, I had a hard time understanding them. Finally, I told my father about the muffled sounds. He gave me a look of concern and sent for the doctor again.

8   It didn't take the doctor long to give me a **diagnosis**. "The disease has **affected** her hearing," he told my parents. "The loss of hearing will continue, gradually, and it could become complete. In truth, she must face the fact that she may never hear again."

9   After my parents told me what the doctor had said, I panicked. How could I lose my hearing? Would I never hear my parents or my little brother talk to me again? I went back to bed and wouldn't leave my room, telling my parents that I thought the measles had returned.

CITE EVIDENCE

C What does the author explicitly state about the cause for Ellie's hearing loss? Put an asterisk by the sentence that gives that information.

D You can infer that Ellie will lose her hearing before the author states it explicitly. Circle the paragraph where you first understand what is going to happen to Ellie's hearing.

E Double underline the sentences that tell you how Ellie's hearing loss made her feel. Which words and phrases help you draw an inference about Ellie's feelings?

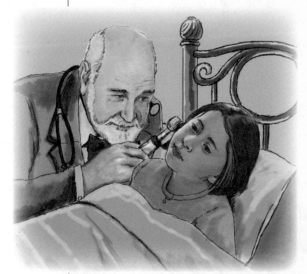

Comprehension Check

Based on what you have read, will Ellie's feelings about her hearing loss change during the course of the story? Which details from the story help you make this inference?

DRAWING INFERENCES

Guided Instruction

Courage in the Water *continued*

RL.7.1

WORDS TO KNOW

certification

endurance

inspiration

onlooker

related

CITE EVIDENCE

A The author explicitly states what Gertrude Ederle is trying to achieve. Put a box around the paragraph in which the newspaper story identifies her goal.

B Think about Ellie's conversation with her father. Why does he bring her the newspaper? Underline a sentence that helps you infer the answer.

10   Still, I couldn't fool my father. One night, after a long day at the grocery store, he came into my room, holding a newspaper. "Here," he said, "I thought you might like to read the cover story." The story was about a young woman, only 19 years old, named Gertrude Ederle, or "Trudy," as the papers called her. She was a well-known American swimmer who had already broken records in distance swimming and had decided to become the first female to swim the English Channel.

11   The story described her Channel crossing and how she had trained for months, working to develop her muscle strength and **endurance**. It **related** how she finally made her attempt at the crossing, beginning in France early in the morning, with a boat full of **onlookers** and reporters following her as she swam through the desperately rough waters. Finally, the story told of her failure—how, seven miles away from her destination, she just couldn't take it anymore.

12   But the story didn't end there. Instead of giving up, Trudy had decided to try again. Now, she was in a race against three other women, each trying to accomplish what only five men in history had ever done. And then I read the last paragraph: The reporter talked about how Trudy had overcome amazing odds, including a battle with measles as a child that left her partially deaf.

13   When I finished reading the article, I looked up at my father. "This says Gertrude Ederle is partially deaf," I said, "but she is still one of the most famous swimmers in the world. She's even trying to swim the English Channel!"

14   "That's true," my father answered. "Funny, I don't see Gertrude Ederle lying in bed all day, feeling sorry for herself. It appears to me that she isn't going to let anything stop her, even a hearing loss."

15   I thought about this for a while; then, finally, I spoke. "Father," I said, "I think it might be time for me to get over my measles. I'd like to become a swimmer. What do you think?"

16   "Well," he slowly replied, "I think that's a fine idea.'"

"The Right Motivation . . . "

17   When my father puts his mind to something, he gets it done. One week later he had me enrolled in a swimming **certification** course for girls. He made me a bargain: If I would work on learning to lip-read, and maybe even learn some sign language, he would pay for as many swimming classes as I wanted. That was all the motivation I needed.

18   I took to swimming like a fish. I never feel so free as when I am in the water, working all of my muscles at once, focusing on nothing but the destination in front of me. In the water, my hearing loss doesn't matter. As long as I count my laps, I am no different from anyone else around me.

19   Early on, Trudy became my **inspiration**. I read everything I could find about her life. I learned that she was a native New Yorker, just like me, and that her parents were immigrants from Germany. I learned how, at age eight, she had almost drowned in a pond near her grandmother's house. The accident gave her the motivation she needed to learn to swim, so she started learning from her father.

CITE EVIDENCE

C What activity will help Ellie deal with her hearing loss? Circle the two sentences in which Ellie states this explicitly.

D Reread paragraphs 17 and 18. What inferences can you draw about the benefit of swimming (1) as Ellie's father sees it and (2) as Ellie sees it? Underline the details that help you draw these inferences.

Comprehension Check

What inference can you draw based on information in the text about Ellie's interest in Gertrude Ederle's life?

DRAWING INFERENCES

Guided Practice

WORDS TO KNOW

attempt

crewman

meet

tugboat line

CITE EVIDENCE

A The author provides explicit details about Gertrude Ederle's career before the Channel swim. Put a box around the paragraph that gives this information.

B With a partner, draw and discuss an inference about how the effect of Gertrude Ederle's accomplishments on Ellie's life is obvious even to other people. Underline details that help you draw this important inference.

Courage in the Water *continued*

20   Whenever I looked around me at the younger girls in my class, who had already been swimming longer than I, I remembered Trudy. She didn't start swimming with proper form until she was 15, but that never stopped her. At 19, she won a gold medal at the Paris Olympics. A year later, she became the first woman to swim the length of New York Bay, even breaking the men's record!

21   Six months after my first swimming class, I won my first **meet**. You might have thought I was Gertrude Ederle, swimming at the Olympics, the way my parents and brother cheered me on. When I got out of the pool, my coach gave me a big hug. "You did great!" she exclaimed. "You must have had some inspiration out there today!"

22   I looked at my father and grinned. "Well, maybe I just had the right motivation."

The Chance of a Lifetime

23   I have been a swimmer ever since, and I have been following Gertrude Ederle's story every day, reading eagerly as the newspapers tell of her daily training, her decision to hire a new swimming coach, and her struggles to find enough money to **attempt** the swim again. Then, about three weeks ago, my father came home with a big smile on his face. My mother gave him a curious look and asked, "Why are you grinning with such mischief in your eyes?"

24   "I have a surprise," my father replied.

25   My father then explained that he had contacted his cousin in France, who worked as a **crewman** for a **tugboat line**. It seemed this cousin would be working on the tugboat *Alsace*, which was set to follow Trudy Ederle on her second attempt to swim the English Channel.

26   "Oh, Father!" I cried. "Can he take pictures? Will he be able to meet Trudy?"

27   "Better still," my father said, "for he has invited all of us to France for a vacation. Furthermore, he has permission from his captain for you and me to ride along on the *Alsace*!"

28   I couldn't believe it. This was truly the chance of a lifetime!

Comprehension Check

1. Use your understanding of the story to draw an inference about the characters. Why does Ellie spend her time learning about the life of Gertrude Ederle?

    a. Ellie wants to beat Gertrude Ederle's record.

    b. Ellie relates to Gertrude Ederle's struggles and successes.

    c. Ellie needs something to do while she is recovering from the measles.

    d. Ellie is an avid reader of newspapers.

2. Which of these details does the author state explicitly in the story?

    a. Gertrude Ederle hired a new swimming coach after her first Channel crossing attempt.

    b. It is the goal of Ellie's life to meet Gertrude Ederle in person.

    c. Ellie's father is worried about her feelings after her hearing loss.

    d. Ellie learns to overcome challenges through swimming.

3. Based on text details, you can infer that Ellie's father is taking her to France because

    a. he knows that Ellie has always wanted to visit France.

    b. he hopes that Ellie will become a reporter when she is older.

    c. he wants Ellie to meet his cousin.

    d. he wants Ellie to meet her hero.

4. Draw an inference about Ellie's decision to learn to swim. Based on details from the story, why does Ellie decide to become a swimmer?

    a. She is afraid of being around water and unable to swim.

    b. She thinks that her father wants her to become a swimmer.

    c. She knows that her hearing loss will not stop her from being a swimmer.

    d. She wants to prove that she is as good as Gertrude Ederle.

5. Discuss with a partner how making inferences helps you better understand the story, especially with respect to Ellie's character.

_____

_____

_____

Independent Practice

Courage in the Water *continued*

WORDS TO KNOW

elements

encountered

jovial

perseveres

CITE EVIDENCE

A Draw an inference about why, in paragraph 31, Ellie refuses to leave the deck during Gertrude Ederle's swim. Underline a sentence in paragraph 30 that helps you make this inference.

B Circle a detail that explicitly states Ellie's reaction to Gertrude Ederle's success. What can you infer about what her success means to Ellie?

"From France to England . . . "

29   And that's how I came to be standing here, cheering Trudy on in the middle of the English Channel. It hasn't been an easy journey. We left Cape Gris Nez, France, at about 7:00 this morning. The air around us was cold, and my father's cousin said the water would be about 61 degrees. With all of us watching, as well as a boat full of reporters and photographers, Trudy covered herself in all kinds of different greases and oils (to protect against the cold and the jellyfish) and got into the water.

30   The **elements** have not helped, and we have **encountered** some severe storms throughout the trip. My uncle said that some waves were almost 20 feet high! Trudy's coach keeps asking her if she needs to stop, but she **perseveres**. Sometimes, we can hear her singing "Let Me Call You Sweetheart" as she swims, her strokes keeping time with the beat. Sometimes, we join her! The reporters on the boat behind us are a **jovial** group, and they often break into song with "Yes, We Have No Bananas" or "East Side, West Side," trying to keep Trudy's spirits up. Everyone is so thrilled; and although I can't hear everything they say, I can feel the excitement building the closer we get to France.

31   We have been on board the ship for 14 hours, and I have stayed on deck the whole time. My father keeps asking me to come below, just for a time, but I have refused. And so, he has stayed with me, battling the wind and the waves as we watch Trudy move carefully through the water.

32   Finally, my father's cousin leans in to tap us on the shoulder. "We are almost there," he says, waiting until I can see his lips. "She has almost made it."

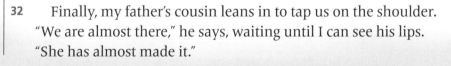

33   It's 9:00 at night, and so dark that we can see Trudy only through the tugboat's onboard lights. I lose sight of her for a moment, and then turn to look at him, trying to read his lips. "Has she made it?"

34   "She's made it!" my father says. "From France to England—she's done it!"

35   And, even though I can't hear them, I add my voice to the cheers that I know must be coming from the shore.

Comprehension Check   (MORE ONLINE) **sadlierconnect.com**

1. What explicit reason does the author give for Gertrude Ederle's covering herself in grease and oil before entering the water?

   a. It protects her against the cold.

   b. It makes her faster in the water.

   c. It wards off sharks.

   d. It keeps the salt water from burning her skin.

2. Which inference can you draw, based on your answer to question 1?

   a. Seawater is less comfortable for swimming than fresh water is.

   b. Cold water presents difficulties for swimmers.

   c. The English Channel is home to dangerous sea creatures.

   d. Long-distance swimming is not an Olympic event.

3. Ederle's coach probably offers her the chance to quit swimming because

   a. Ederle did not complete her first Channel attempt.

   b. there is an increased threat of jellyfish.

   c. daylight is fading and night is falling.

   d. the sea conditions are very rough.

4. Which of these is the most reasonable inference about the historical importance of Gertrude Ederle's accomplishment?

   a. It took Ederle two tries to complete the swim.

   b. Ederle had many reporters following her.

   c. Ederle was the first woman to complete the swim.

   d. Ederle could swim despite being partially deaf.

5. What inference can you draw about the lesson that Ellie learns from this experience? Cite evidence from the text to support your answer.

_____

_____

_____

_____

RL.7.2

WORDS TO KNOW

armory

diplomatic

exchange

merchant

statesman

Most authors develop at least one main **theme**, or central message, in each text. Paying attention to and **summarizing** key details can help you analyze the theme or themes of a text.

CITE EVIDENCE

A One way to begin thinking about the main **theme** of a story is to look for ideas that appear early on, and then see which of those ideas the author develops. In paragraph 4, double underline a pair of sentences whose ideas you think the author will develop.

B Does the author develop the ideas you chose? On this page, find and circle the paragraph that develops those ideas.

The Courage of John Adams
(Genre: Historical Fiction)

1   "All hands on deck! All hands on deck!"

2   I am lying in my small hammock belowdecks when I hear the cry echo through the cabin area. All around me, men jump up and begin readying themselves. I turn to Silas, who sleeps in the hammock next to mine, and ask, "What do you think is going on?"

3   "I'm not sure, but we have had so many calls for 'all hands' on this trip that I'm starting to think I should just sleep on deck! I wonder if the lookout has spotted one of those British ships we encountered earlier."

4   We get our clothing straightened out and quickly move to our positions on deck. When the cry comes for "all hands," it usually means something important or even dangerous is about to happen. I wait, in high expectation, for one of the officers to address us. Already, this voyage has been far more exciting than I could have anticipated. I cannot imagine what will happen next.

5   "Men," a first officer's voice rings down the deck, "a ship has been spied by our lookout, within the path of our voyage. It is not known whether the ship is friendly, nor if the crew could intend to do us harm. However, Captain Tucker has decided to give chase, as he believes we may be facing a British **merchant** ship. All crew members are ordered to arm themselves in preparation for battle, but do not fire upon the other ship until you are given orders."

6   As we move to the ship's **armory**, I hear Silas call out from behind me, "Samuel!"

7   I stop and wait for him to catch up.

8 "Samuel, can you believe this? This trip gets more and more exciting! Do you think they will let us fight?"

9 "I don't think so, Silas," I reply. "If they do let us fight, it will be because our crew has been overwhelmed. So, let us hope it doesn't come to that."

10 "But you will fight if necessary?" Silas asks.

11 "Of course I will, but I'd rather it not be necessary. Remember our cargo, Silas. . . . "

12 Silas nods solemnly. "Who could forget?"

13 We get in the back of the line at the armory; for although Silas and I are considered officers-in-training, we are at the bottom of the ship's hierarchy in instances like these. Most officers assume that 14-year-old boys will not be able to fight as well as grown men. Silas and I disagree, but we would sooner jump ship than argue with a first officer.

14 As I look around at the crew members readying the ship, I see, off to the right, the "precious cargo" being carried by our ship. John Adams, **statesman** and Revolutionary leader, and his son, John Quincy, boarded the *Boston* with us a month ago. Mr. Adams is on a **diplomatic** mission to France, although his presence on board is supposed to be kept in greatest secrecy. Mr. Adams himself doesn't seem to realize his own importance, as he has often ignored the captain's requests to remain in his cabin and has joined the crew in every dangerous situation we have faced. Right now, Mr. Adams appears to be arguing with his son.

15 Silas, too, notices the **exchange**. "What do you think Mr. Adams is saying to his son?"

16 I think for a moment. "Well, if it were my father and me, he would be telling me to get back to our cabin, in case there is a fight. And I would be telling him that I am old enough and as capable of fighting as he is."

CITE EVIDENCE

C In paragraph 14, the author develops the theme by introducing a character who will be connected to that theme. Put a box around the name of that character.

D When you give a **summary**, you restate the key details of a text in your own words. Summarizing a story, then, can help you focus on the author's main theme or central idea. How would you summarize paragraphs 15–16? Underline three details that you would include in the summary.

Comprehension Check

Based on information in the text, the main theme of this story might have something to do with fighting. Support that idea by summarizing the story so far.

ANALYZING THEME

Guided Instruction

RL.7.2

WORDS TO KNOW

frigate

outfitted

routine

skirmish

CITE EVIDENCE

A When you summarize, remember that not every detail is really important. Underline one detail in paragraph 21 and one detail in paragraph 22 that seem important enough to include in a summary.

B In paragraph 23, put an asterisk by the sentence that explains why a fight might be necessary. How does this explanation develop an important story idea?

17   We watch them for another moment. Finally, the younger Adams turns and walks away, although I notice he does not move as if to return to his cabin.

18   "It appears that he will be allowed to stay," I tell Silas.

19   "Well, we will see how long that lasts," Silas replies. "Mr. Adams is a statesman. He won't be taking up arms once the fighting starts."

20   "We don't even know if there will be any fighting! And I think you're wrong, Silas. When we chased that British **frigate** a few weeks ago, Mr. Adams stood with the first officers—don't you remember?"

21   Our turn in line is up before Silas can answer. We are **outfitted** with minor weapons and are told that they are for protection purposes only. As we expected, we are instructed not to enter into a **skirmish** unless specifically ordered to do so.

22   A call of "all hands" also means that we are to be at the ready until such time as those of us who are supposed to be off-duty are released. Silas and I take up positions on watch, maintaining our place on the ship's deck, as we move closer to the sails in the distance.

23   When I was assigned to the *Boston*, I was told we would be sailing on a **routine** trip to Europe. In all honesty, there isn't any such thing as a "routine" trip anymore. Every time we set sail, we run the risk of encountering a British ship. And since the Revolution began, neither side can ignore the other. Even when we confront merchant ships, we must engage. Merchant and trade vessels could be carrying supplies to British troops and if we can stop them, we weaken the British army.

RL.7.2

24   Of course, once Mr. Adams and his son boarded our ship, the trip became anything but "routine." We are responsible for taking one of America's great statesmen safely to Europe. If Mr. Adams can persuade the French to join us as allies against the British, it could help to bring an end to the war.

25   Early on, it was obvious this trip would be different. The weather became rough almost as soon as we left port. Most of the ship's crew, and all of her passengers, were taken ill. The cabin area was full of sick people, and some thought the captain might make us turn back. We continued on, however, and most of us eventually were back up and working.

26   Then we sailed into the midst of three British ships, and we thought we would be overtaken. After a short skirmish with one of the ships, the British vessel turned and disappeared. None of us were sure why she turned, until we were met with the storm that came upon us shortly thereafter.

27   During the storm, the *Boston* was battered and tossed by violent waves and pounded by the wind and rain. The *Boston* was hit by lightning, and one of the crewmen was injured. He later died from his wounds. Taken together, the events of this trip have caused a great amount of apprehension throughout our journey, and having Mr. Adams and his son aboard has increased our concerns significantly.

28   As we continue giving chase to the ship ahead, I start to make out the outline of her sails. Silas, too, is paying close attention to our approach.

CITE EVIDENCE

C In paragraph 24, the author uses Samuel's words to explain why John Adams is an important passenger on the *Boston*. Put a box around the sentence that summarizes his importance.

D Reread the final sentence of paragraph 27. Then, in paragraph 26, underline two events to which Samuel refers. Think about how these events also have to do with the theme of fighting in this story.

Comprehension Check

How does summarizing the story help you understand the author's central idea, or theme?

ANALYZING THEME

Guided Practice

RL.7.2

WORDS TO KNOW

broadside

countenance

gallantly

helm

tailwind

vessel

CITE EVIDENCE

A With a partner, summarize the events of paragraphs 29–37. Underline five key details that should be included in your summary.

B The theme of paragraphs 29–37 can be found in paragraph 37. Put an asterisk next to the sentence that expresses the theme of this section.

29   "Samuel," he asks, "did you notice that the captain is directly bearing down upon that **vessel**? We usually approach other ships with our **broadside** visible. What do you think is going on?"

30   "I think it makes perfect sense. There is no way to hide our approach, but we can hide our guns. If we come at them directly, then they may not realize who we are until it is too late."

31   We make a loop around the deck, keeping watchful eyes open. Suddenly, I spot Mr. Adams talking to the officer on duty at the ship's armory.

32   "Silas," I whisper, "do you see Mr. Adams over at the armory? I wonder what that is all about!"

33   "I'm sure he is getting outfitted for the possible skirmish ahead. After all we have been through, Mr. Adams doesn't strike me as the type to hide in his cabin."

34   We have made good time chasing the unknown vessel ahead. Smooth seas and a good **tailwind** have given us the advantage, and we can distinctly see the ship in front.

35   "At the ready, men!" we hear one of the officers call. Silas and I quickly get into position. My heart is pounding nervously. Even though I am an officer-in-training, my actual combat experience is limited. Despite the fact that we are at war with the British, I have not yet been involved in a real battle.

36   We pull up within fighting distance. Suddenly, there is a wrenching sound in the air, and then I feel the ship shaking around me. Everyone jumps into action, and I hear Silas shout, "They've fired on us!"

37   For some reason, in the midst of the chaos, I look for Mr. Adams. At first, I can't see his distinctive **countenance** anywhere. And then I see him, standing proudly at the ship's **helm**, weapons drawn. Statesman or not, right now he is one of us, ready to fight as **gallantly** for his country as anyone else on board. I take heart and feel a surge of pride. I, too, am ready to fight for my freedom.

Comprehension Check

1. On these two pages, the author develops the main theme by

 a. raising questions about what Captain Tucker will do.

 b. creating a conversation between Samuel and Mr. Adams.

 c. having the story's characters face an actual battle.

 d. showing the surrender of the British ship.

2. In the story, when the British vessel fires on the *Boston*, John Adams

 a. goes in search of his son.

 b. prepares to fight alongside the crew.

 c. urges the captain to hide the ship's guns.

 d. reports to the ship's armory.

3. Which statement best summarizes the story's plot so far?

 a. John Adams teaches his son to fight aboard a ship.

 b. An American ship captures a British vessel during the Revolutionary War.

 c. A teenager learns a lesson by watching an American hero.

 d. Two officers-in-training become friends during a battle.

4. Samuel's comments in paragraph 37 suggest which of these central ideas?

 a. Brave people will sacrifice safety for the sake of freedom.

 b. Even diplomats can be good soldiers.

 c. It is important to be prepared for any situation.

 d. Few people understand what courage really means.

5. Discuss how the encounter between the *Boston* and the British ship helps illustrate an important story idea. Share story details that support your answer.

_____

_____

_____

_____

_____

The Courage of John Adams *continued*

RL.7.2

WORDS TO KNOW

authorized

bemoans

cargo

commandeer

patriot

CITE EVIDENCE

A Summarize how Captain Tucker is able to avoid a naval battle with the British ship *Martha*. Underline details that support your summary.

B Put an asterisk by the sentence in paragraph 42 that emphasizes the result of fighting, rather than the fight itself. How does this sentence develop the main theme of this story?

38 However, before I can even draw my weapon, the cry of "Stand down!" roars through the ship. Captain Tucker has turned the *Boston* to her broadside, and we are preparing to return fire on the British vessel.

39 That simple decision changes the course of our encounter. Once the captain of the opposing ship sees our broadside and notes the amount of firepower we can easily access, he immediately surrenders. Our officers board his vessel, **commandeer** all weapons and supplies on board, and take prisoner every member of the crew.

40 As we explore the deck, it becomes apparent that Captain Tucker's decision to give chase was the correct one. The British ship *Martha* is a Letter of Mark, meaning that it is a privately owned ship that the British government has **authorized** to attack and capture enemy vessels—in this case, the *Boston*. On board, we find significant weaponry, as well as a substantial amount of valuable **cargo**. Truly, had we not given chase, the *Martha* would have attacked us, forcing us into a more costly engagement.

41 We bring the ship's crew on board and continue on our journey to Europe. The officers release us from our "all hands" just as I am to begin my watch. Silas, ever the adventurer, **bemoans** the fact that we did not get to fight in a battle with the British. I, on the other hand, am both relieved and, for the first time, ready for the next steps.

42 There will be other battles in which I will be forced to take up arms against my enemies. However, seeing Mr. Adams ready and willing to fight for our country gives me the confidence I need to

RL.7.2

continue. As we sail on toward Europe, I look off into the horizon. I may not know what my future holds, but I know that with dedicated **patriots** like John Adams at our helm, it will be a glorious future, indeed.

Comprehension Check   MORE ONLINE sadlierconnect.com

1. What idea is most clearly expressed by the captain's order for his crew to stand down?

   a. Even when you are weaker than your enemy, you still can win.

   b. There is a time to fight, but there also is a time to show restraint.

   c. Defending your country is important.

   d. Even the most important people can fail in a moment of weakness.

2. There can be more than one way to express the theme or central message of a story. Based on the full text of the story, which of these statements best describes this story's theme?

   a. Personal principles can overcome fears.

   b. Only soldiers should be allowed to fight.

   c. Statesmen do not make good soldiers.

   d. All of the above.

3. How do Samuel's feelings after a battle is avoided help express the theme?

   a. His fears underscore the theme of keeping young people away from the dangers of war.

   b. Because he is young, he cannot understand the issues behind the war.

   c. He is relieved but knows that he will be able to fight in the future if necessary.

   d. None of the above.

4. How does the character of Silas help reinforce a central idea of the story?

   a. His relationship with Samuel shows the importance of friendship.

   b. His words illustrate the dangers of training young people to become officers.

   c. His excitement about the battle supports the idea that only cowards prefer peace.

   d. His adventurous (and slightly foolish) spirit helps highlight the change in Samuel's feelings about fighting.

5. In your own words, give a summary of the story, choosing the details that best support the story's theme. At the end, state that theme.

   _____

   _____

   _____

   _____

Guided Instruction

RL.7.3

WORDS TO KNOW

chart

manifest

passage

qualifications

In fiction, the elements of **setting, plot, and characters interact** to create an engaging story that communicates the author's theme.

CITE EVIDENCE

A In a play, or **drama**, the **setting** (time and place) of the play is typically explained at the beginning of the act or scene. Put a box around the words that describe the setting of Act I, Scene 1.

B In a drama, the dialogue (spoken words) of the **characters** is indicated with the name of the character who is speaking. Circle the name of the first character to speak.

Into the Unknown

(Genre: Multi-Act Play)

CAST OF CHARACTERS

MUNGO PARK, a Scottish explorer

THE BUTLER

DR. JOHN LAIDLEY, an Englishman living in Africa

JOHNSON, Dr. Laidley's African former servant, who will be joining MUNGO PARK as his guide

ACT I, SCENE 1

1 **SETTING:** *The time is 1795. MUNGO PARK, a Scottish explorer, is at home in his study. There are bookshelves lining the walls, filled with old, academic volumes. There is a desk in one corner, and a comfortable couch in the middle of the room. MUNGO PARK paces the floor as he reads a letter.*

MUNGO PARK *(murmuring)*: . . . "It has been weeks since we have heard anything from Major Houghton" . . . *(He stops pacing, and looks up.)* As if Major Houghton's situation has anything to do with me! *(He returns to the letter, murmuring and pacing again.)* . . . "However, we are quite satisfied with your **qualifications**" . . . "we wish to recommend you to Dr. John Laidley, currently working in an English factory in Gambia." *(looking up again)* Gambia! That will put me right in line to travel the Niger River. If all goes well, I may be the one to finally **chart** the course of that river, and, with any luck, even discover the exact location of the city of Timbuktu!

(PARK walks purposefully to his desk, picks up a small bell, and rings it. THE BUTLER appears at the door to the library.)

BUTLER: Yes, sir?

5 **PARK:** The Royal Society has approved my request to travel to Africa and will provide me with the necessary arrangements once I'm there. I should like to begin preparations for the trip immediately, and I will need to book the **passage** for Africa. I trust you can handle the arrangements?

BUTLER: Of course, sir. I will inquire about the passage directly.

(The stage lights come down.)

SCENE 2

(The stage lights come up, revealing PARK, once again in his study. This time, he is sitting at his desk, studying a variety of papers spread out in front of him. A tap is heard at the door.)

PARK: Come in!

10 **BUTLER:** Sir, the passage has been booked. You sail from Portsmouth on the twenty-second of May, aboard the ship *Endeavor*.

PARK: Thank you very much for making the arrangements. What type of vessel is the *Endeavor*, and who captains it?

BUTLER: I believe, sir, that the *Endeavor* is a trading vessel. It is primarily known for its trade in beeswax and ivory, and its main point of arrival is in West Africa. According to the ship's **manifest**, the captain is a Mr. Richard Wyatt.

PARK: Thank you for that excellent information. It sounds as though the *Endeavor* will do nicely. Of course, with just a few weeks to go, there is little time to be lost!

(The stage lights come down.)

ACT II

15 **SETTING:** *PARK is sitting at a small table in Africa, writing in a journal. A gas lamp on the table gives off a soft glow, and a glass of water sits next to the lamp. There is a bed next to the table. PARK is reading aloud as he writes.*

CITE EVIDENCE

C The scene between Mungo Park (who was a real-life adventurer) and his butler gives information on the **plot**, or what is going to happen during the play. Underline the dialogue that gives information about when and how Park will travel.

D In Act I, Scene 1, the author (also known as the playwright) tells readers about the setting for the next part of the play. To what location in Africa will Park travel? Put a box around the character dialogue that the author has included to explain this.

Comprehension Check

The setting changes between Act I and Act II. How does that change help move the plot of the drama forward?

ANALYZING LITERARY ELEMENTS

Guided Instruction

Into the Unknown *continued*

RL.7.3

WORDS TO KNOW

dispatched

duty

inclement

intact

trade route

CITE EVIDENCE

A In Act II, the author advances the plot through spoken descriptions of various places. Which character speaks these descriptions? Underline each place that this character describes.

B In some dramas, the setting has a strong effect on the characters. Put an asterisk by two sentences that show that the story events are affected by the African setting.

PARK: July 2, 1795. We sailed from Portsmouth on May twenty-second under sunny skies, with little prospect of **inclement** weather. On June 4th, I caught my first glimpse of the mountains of Mogadore, on the coast of Africa. On June 21st, after a fairly pleasant journey with smooth seas, our ship arrived at Jillifree, a small town on the banks of the River Gambia. Jillifree is located in the kingdom of Barra, known for its extensive trade in salt. The king of Barra commands a considerable amount of land and maintains control over the entire salt trade for the region. The **trade route** through Jillifree has been established as a main thoroughfare in the kingdom of Barra. Consequently, the king of Barra collects large trade **duties** on every vessel that docks at Jillifree. The governor of Jillifree handles the collection of these duties, so we did not have the opportunity to see the king himself.

(PARK clears his throat, takes a drink from his glass, and continues writing.)

PARK: We stayed in Jillifree only one day, departing for the town of Vintain, on the northern side of the River Gambia, on the 23rd. Vintain is well known for exporting high-quality beeswax; it is much frequented as a trade destination for European merchants. We stayed two days in Vintain, leaving on the 26th for the town of Jonkakonda. The trip along the river was not nearly so pleasant as the first portion of the journey. In this area, the river is quite muddy, and the vessel had to be towed through some of the more treacherous areas.

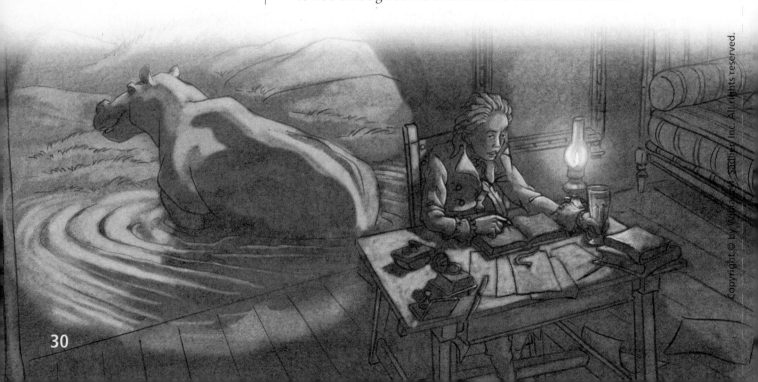

RL.7.3

(PARK pauses, smiles to himself, and continues writing.)

20 **PARK:** Although this part of the journey was tedious, it did present some interesting opportunities for study of the native wildlife. The river is home to a variety of different species of fish, none of which can be found in Europe. Further, the river houses both hippopotami and alligators, making for an interesting—and somewhat dangerous—journey. Our journey from Vintain took us, in total, six days. We are now here in Jonkakonda, where I have recently **dispatched** a letter to Dr. Laidley, informing him of my arrival.

(PARK closes his journal and gets up from his table. He stretches and yawns.)

PARK: Well, perhaps I will call it a night. I do hope to hear from Dr. Laidley soon—perhaps tomorrow.

(PARK reaches over to the lamp as if to douse it, and the stage lights dim.)

ACT III

SETTING: *At DR. LAIDLEY's house in Pisania, a small village near Jonkakonda, MUNGO PARK sits in a wicker recliner, a blanket covering his body and a scarf around his neck. He is almost asleep but wakes up often to cough. As the scene begins, DR. LAIDLEY walks into the room.*

25 **DR. LAIDLEY** *(cheerfully)*: Good morning! And how's our patient today?

PARK *(hoarsely)*: Feeling much better, thank you. I'm sure I will be up and ready to proceed with our journey soon.

DR. LAIDLEY: I wouldn't count on it, Park. I'm not sure you really understand the extent of your illness. These African fevers can be fatal, and you barely pulled out of yours with your senses **intact**.

PARK: I don't quite understand, Dr. Laidley.

CITE EVIDENCE

C Toward the end of Act II, the author introduces an important new character. Double underline that character's name.

D It is clear that an important plot event occurs between Act II and Act III. What event is it? Circle the dialogue that explains it.

Comprehension Check

How would you describe the way that characters, setting, and plot are working together to help you understand this drama?

Guided Practice

Into the Unknown *continued*

RL.7.3

WORDS TO KNOW

climate

delirium

recuperate

relapse

solace

torrential

CITE EVIDENCE

A Discuss with a partner how the dialogue between Mungo Park and Dr. Laidley helps readers understand more about Mungo Park's character. Underline evidence to support your ideas.

B In paragraph 32, Mungo Park describes three setting details that reveal his feelings about living in Africa. Put an asterisk next to each.

DR. LAIDLEY: Delirium, man! You've had a very severe fever—tossing and turning, not knowing where you are or to whom you were speaking. If you think you can begin this journey any time soon, you are sorely mistaken.

30 **PARK:** I cannot believe I have been so sick just from spending one night out, observing the eclipse.

DR. LAIDLEY: It's certainly not unheard of. Your body is unaccustomed to the **climate** here, even after a month with us. You are still getting used to living in Africa. I must say, however, that your mastery of the Mandingo language is becoming quite impressive.

PARK: Thank you for your kind words. But truly, I am hoping to try at least a short walk around the village tomorrow, with an eye to increasing my stamina and distance each day. I am feeling so much better, and I am ready to be off. It is only your company that has kept me going. These **torrential** rains, during the day, followed by oppressive heat at night, are almost more than a body can bear! And the constant croaking of those frogs! There must be dozens of species. I don't know how you do it, Laidley.

DR. LAIDLEY: If it is any **solace**, you do become used to it, over time. I believe your fever has prevented you from becoming better accustomed to your surroundings. When one is sick, everything seems that much more difficult to bear. . . . Well, Park, do as you will, but I can't help but advise against it. Your body still needs to **recuperate**. If you should **relapse**, you won't be able to start until the new year, at the earliest.

PARK: I'm sure I'll be fine. In fact, I have no doubt we will be leaving for the next leg of our journey within the month.

35 *(The stage lights dim.)*

Comprehension Check

1. What do Mungo Park's complaints in Act III tell readers about the setting of the drama?

  a. Africa's conditions are very hard on people who are not used to them.

  b. Africa is a dangerous place to live because it makes everyone sick.

  c. Dr. Laidley's house is very uncomfortable.

  d. Park complains only about his illness, not about the setting.

2. The dialogue between Dr. Laidley and Mungo Park advances the plot in Act III because readers learn that

  a. no time has passed between Acts II and III.

  b. Mungo Park has taken some time off from his journey to relax.

  c. Mungo Park has been ill and cannot yet continue his trip.

  d. Dr. Laidley has taken Mungo Park to a hospital.

3. What does Dr. Laidley's dialogue reveal about his character?

  a. He is afraid of the African interior and is content to stay at Pisania.

  b. He is very adventurous and wants to join the expedition.

  c. He is jealous of Mungo Park's determination to keep going.

  d. He is knowledgeable about Africa but also rather cautious.

4. Which statement best describes the relationship between character and plot in Act III?

  a. Mungo Park's unhappiness shows that he should have stayed at home.

  b. Mungo Park's determination indicates that the story of his exploration will continue.

  c. Dr. Laidley's arguments prove that Mungo Park was right to risk coming to Africa.

  d. All of the above.

5. Which element of literature is most important for understanding Act III: plot, character, or setting? Compare answers with a partner, and cite evidence for your answer.

_____

_____

_____

Independent Practice

RL.7.3

WORDS TO KNOW

accompany

incomparable

naïve

venture

CITE EVIDENCE

A Circle the name of the character the author introduces in Act IV. Why is this character important to the plot?

B Think about the plot events that have occurred between Act III and Act IV, leading to Mungo Park's delay. Then put a box around the dialogue that gives that information.

Into the Unknown *continued*

ACT IV

SETTING: *In DR. LAIDLEY's house, it is now December. MUNGO PARK is standing in the center of the room, dressed in traveling clothes. He is speaking with JOHNSON, an African man who will* **accompany** *him on his journey.*

PARK: Well, Johnson, I believe we are set. I must say, I am disappointed to be leaving so late. Who would have anticipated that it would be December before we could begin?

(As JOHNSON nods, DR. LAIDLEY suddenly enters the room.)

DR. LAIDLEY: Why, I would have, of course! I told you it could be the new year before you set off, Park!

40 **PARK:** Well, on that count you were right. The fever had a deeper hold on my body than I realized. Then when the river rose, we couldn't travel.

DR. LAIDLEY: I ask you again, Park, are you sure you want to take on this journey? You know what happened to Major Houghton—

PARK: No one really knows what happened to Major Houghton.

DR. LAIDLEY: Don't be **naïve**. Houghton has disappeared, and I believe he fell victim to one of the wars between the local villages. *(grimly)* And I fear the same may happen to you, Park.

PARK: I will be careful, Doctor. I have a fairly decent grasp of the language, and I understand the respect that must be shown to the chiefs and kings of each village. Besides, I have an excellent guide in Johnson.

45 **DR. LAIDLEY:** He's **incomparable**—none better, no doubt about it. Do you think you can get our man back alive, Johnson?

JOHNSON: Yes, Doctor. I will do my best. The path we travel is difficult and dangerous, but we will be cautious and courageous.

DR. LAIDLEY: Well then, gentlemen, I guess that's all I can ask. But do be careful, Park. I hope you are ready for this **venture**.

PARK: I believe I am, Doctor. Thank you so much for your kind hospitality. And now, Johnson, let us begin our grand adventure!

(Stage lights go dark; house lights come up.)

Comprehension Check   (MORE ONLINE) sadlierconnect.com

1. The dialogue in Act IV reveals that Major Houghton

   a. had a successful trip through Africa.

   b. left on a similar trip and is now missing.

   c. was able to send a letter to Dr. Laidley.

   d. will be acting as Mungo Park's guide.

2. What do readers learn about the character of Johnson in Act IV?

   a. He is considered an excellent guide.

   b. He once worked for Major Houghton.

   c. He is uncomfortable about guiding Mungo Park.

   d. He has been giving Mungo Park advice on his trip.

3. What are the three main setting locations in this play?

   a. a village in Gambia, Vintain, and Jonkakonda

   b. the Niger River, Timbuktu, and Dr. Laidley's home in Pisania

   c. Mungo Park's home, his lodging in Jonkakonda, and Dr. Laidley's home

   d. the *Endeavor*, Mungo Park's home, and the African interior

4. How does the author indicate plot advancement between the acts of this drama?

   a. by using an outside narrator

   b. by creating dialogue and changes in setting

   c. by introducing new characters

   d. by having characters speak directly to the audience

5. Think again about your answer to the second Cite Evidence question on page 34. How else have plot, character, and setting worked together to keep Mungo Park from pursuing his goal? Be specific.

   _____

   _____

   _____

   _____

   _____

Theseus and the Minotaur

(Genre: Myth)

1   King Minos of Crete was a cruel and harsh ruler. He was also a powerful ruler, and his army incited fear in everyone who encountered it. All of the city-states surrounding the island of Crete lived in fear of King Minos's forces. And King Minos, being a power-hungry and brutal king, took great pleasure in abusing his power and in forcing the rulers of these city-states to do whatever he might ask.

2   King Minos had two possessions of which he was very proud: his labyrinth, and the terrible monster that ruled it—the Minotaur. The Minotaur was a fearsome monster, half-man and half-bull, that lived at the center of the labyrinth. The labyrinth itself was a kind of prison. When King Minos took people captive, he sent them into the labyrinth, knowing that they stood very little chance of finding their way out. The labyrinth had many twists and turns, causing anyone venturing into it to become hopelessly lost and trapped inside.

3   If, by chance, someone did manage to navigate the labyrinth and arrive successfully at its center, the Minotaur would be there, waiting. There, the weary prisoner would be forced to battle the Minotaur, and no one ever survived.

4   The city-state of Athens lay directly across the sea from Crete, and King Minos often turned his cruel eye toward Athens. Every year, King Minos demanded that Athens send seven young men and seven young women as sacrifices to the Minotaur. If Aegeus, the king of Athens, refused Minos's demand, Minos would send his armies to destroy Athens.

5   Theseus was the prince of Athens but also the son of Poseidon, god of the sea. King Aegeus had adopted Theseus as the heir to the throne of Athens, and he loved Theseus dearly. Theseus, however, was angered by the king's willingness to send Athenian citizens to their death.

6   "Father," Theseus argued, "we cannot allow King Minos to take our young men and women as sacrifices to the Minotaur. Minos is not our king, and we owe him nothing."

7   "My son," King Aegeus answered, "Minos is far more powerful than we are. Should we refuse his sacrifice, he will destroy Athens with his powerful army."

8   Theseus knew he must do something to try to stop King Minos. So, when the time came for King Aegeus to send the seven young men and women to Crete, Theseus spoke up.

9   "Father," Theseus exclaimed, "it is time to end our oppression by King Minos of Crete! I, myself, will volunteer as one of the fourteen. I will travel to Crete, enter the labyrinth, and battle the Minotaur!"

10   King Aegeus was greatly distressed by his son's decision. "But, Theseus, no one can survive a battle with the Minotaur, especially after traveling through the mysteries of the labyrinth. I cannot allow you to do this foolish thing!"

11   "Do not worry, Father," Theseus assured him. "I will return. And after I have defeated the Minotaur, we will finally be free of this terrible threat."

12   King Aegeus saw that he could not dissuade his son from his decision. "Go, then, if you must," he told Theseus. "Defeat Minos's horrible monster, and return to Athens a hero."

13   So Theseus set sail for the island of Crete, along with the six other young men and the seven young women chosen as sacrifices to the Minotaur. When they arrived at the palace, King Minos was eager to send them into the labyrinth.

14   "Ah, another crop of men and women here to feed my Minotaur!" the cruel king exclaimed.

15   Theseus immediately stepped forward. "I am Theseus, son of Poseidon and prince of Athens. I will enter the labyrinth and defeat your miserable monster."

16   King Minos thought for a moment. "If you are the prince of Athens, you must be the son of Aegeus, not the son of Poseidon. Before I will allow you to enter the labyrinth, you must first pass a test."

17   With that, King Minos threw his ring into the sea. "Theseus, son of Poseidon," he roared, "if you are truly who you say you are, dive into the sea and bring back my ring!"

18   Theseus paused only a moment, asking for Poseidon's help in locating the ring, and plunged into the water.

19   As Theseus swam down into the sea, he saw a shadowy figure ahead of him. Through the depths of the ocean, he heard a female voice calling to him.

20   "Theseus, noble son of Poseidon," the voice said, "I am Thetis, nymph of the sea. I am here to assist you on your quest. I come to bring you the ring of Minos."

21   As Theseus swam closer, he saw a beautiful woman floating just below him. Her hair was green, and it floated gently in the current like seaweed. Her eyes were gray, and they reminded Theseus of gray storm clouds building over the ocean. In her hand sat Minos's ring.

22   She held out the ring to Theseus and said, "Take this ring back to Minos, so that you may begin your quest into the labyrinth. But, as a word of advice from your father, remember to trust Princess Ariadne. She understands the workings of the labyrinth, and she will help you on your quest."

23   Theseus thanked the sea nymph and swam quickly back to the surface of the sea. He burst forth from the water and held the ring aloft like a trophy.

24   "Minos," Theseus called, "I bring your ring, and I have passed your test. Now, I will enter the labyrinth and defeat your gruesome monster!"

25   "Perhaps," answered King Minos, "and perhaps you will make a tasty meal for my Minotaur. However, it would be poor sport for my Minotaur if I were to serve you up wet and tired from your trip into the sea. Tonight you and your companions will sleep in comfort as guests in my house; then tomorrow, you will enter the labyrinth."

26   That night, as Theseus lay down to sleep, he heard a knock on his door. King Minos's daughter, Princess Ariadne, was waiting outside his room. Impressed by Theseus's noble actions, she had fallen in love with the hero.

27   "Theseus," she whispered, "I am Ariadne, daughter of Minos. I am pleased by your willingness to die for your people, and I wish to help you. I have a gift for you."

28   Ariadne gave Theseus a ball of string. "The trick of my father's labyrinth lies not just in finding the center and beating the Minotaur. The most difficult part of your journey will be finding your way out of the labyrinth, but I have an antidote for your problem, Theseus. You can use this string to mark your path and find your way out."

29   "Thank you so much, Princess," Theseus replied. "Should I defeat the Minotaur, I will certainly owe you my life."

30   Ariadne smiled at Theseus and said, "Should you defeat the Minotaur, and emerge from the labyrinth, you must promise to take me with you back to Athens. My father is a cruel man. If he discovers that I helped you, he will surely have me killed."

31   "I give you my word," Theseus answered.

32   The next morning, Minos and his guards brought Theseus and his companions to the entrance of the labyrinth. Princess Ariadne was there, waiting. She gave Theseus a sympathetic look as the guards opened the gates to the labyrinth and, with a deceptive smile, shoved him inside.

33   The journey through the labyrinth was difficult, as Theseus traveled through dangerous, shifting passages, expecting to encounter the Minotaur at any moment. However, Theseus was prepared, and he held tightly to Ariadne's string, trailing it behind him to mark his path. Finally, Theseus found himself in the center of the labyrinth. There, in a wide room, stood the terrible creature. The Minotaur let out a terrifying bellow and instantly attacked.

34   Theseus felt the Minotaur's massive arms grab his legs and lift him high above the ground. As Theseus looked into the Minotaur's gaping mouth, he saw an opportunity. He swung his arms around and grasped the Minotaur around the neck, holding tightly as the Minotaur struggled against him. After what seemed like hours but was really only moments, the Minotaur collapsed, lifeless, against the ground.

35   During the struggle, Theseus had dropped the end of Ariadne's string, and now he panicked, searching the ground frantically. Finally, he spotted the thread and, with a sigh of relief, began the difficult journey back through the labyrinth.

36   When Theseus felt the string becoming taut, he knew he was close to the entrance of the labyrinth. He paused to collect his thoughts. He had defeated the Minotaur. His beloved home of Athens would be safe forever from Minos's cruel monster. As he pushed the gate open, Theseus quietly thanked Poseidon. "Lord Poseidon," he whispered, "you have seen me through this far, and I thank you. Now please see me and my companions safely away from Minos's island, so that we may return home in triumph."

Comprehension Check

1A. The character of King Minos can best be described as

    a. merciless and violent.

    b. generous and compassionate.

    c. thoughtful but foolish.

    d. fair and honest.

1B. Which phrase from the text supports the answer to Part A?

    a. "far more powerful than we are"

    b. "sleep in comfort as my guests"

    c. "pleased by your willingness to die for your people"

    d. "took great pleasure in abusing his power"

2A. What can you infer about the way that King Aegeus and King Minos think about each other?

    a. The two kings see each other as equals.

    b. King Aegeus considers his kingdom to be more powerful than that of King Minos.

    c. King Aegeus is afraid of King Minos's power.

    d. King Minos is afraid of King Aegeus's power.

2B. Which sentence from the text best supports the answer to Part A?

    a. "Minos is not our king, and we owe him nothing."

    b. "Defeat Minos's horrible monster, and return to Athens a hero."

    c. "Ah, another crop of men and women here to feed my Minotaur!"

    d. ". . .he will destroy Athens with his powerful army."

3A. Which of the following themes is supported by the text?

    a. Courageous actions will be rewarded.

    b. Power is more important than principles.

    c. Always respect your elders.

    d. Never trust strangers.

3B. Which detail from the text supports the answer to Part A?

    a. Princess Ariadne falls in love with Theseus.

    b. Both Thetis and Ariadne help Theseus in his mission.

    c. Theseus drops Ariadne's string.

    d. Minos uses the threat of the Minotaur to hold onto his power.

4A. Based on the myth, what can you infer about Princess Ariadne's relationship with her father, King Minos?

    a. She loves and respects her father.

    b. She believes her father is right in his actions toward Athens.

    c. She fears her father and does not share his violent tendencies.

    d. She wants to take over the throne from her father.

4B. Which detail from the text does NOT support the answer to Part A?

    a. Ariadne begs Theseus to take her away from Crete.

    b. Thetis urges Theseus to trust Ariadne.

    c. Theseus says he will owe Ariadne his life.

    d. Ariadne tells Theseus how to return from the labyrinth.

5A. Based on the story, which statement best describes the character of Theseus?

    a. He will fight to defeat injustice.

    b. He is afraid of those with power.

    c. He wants to rule like Aegeus.

    d. None of the above.

5B. Which words from the text best support the answer to Part A?

    a. "'Do not worry, Father,' Theseus assured him. 'I will return.'"

    b. "'We cannot allow King Minos to take our young men and women.'"

    c. "However, Theseus held tightly to Ariadne's string, trailing it behind him to mark his path."

    d. "His beloved home of Athens would be safe forever."

6. Based on the actions of Theseus, what can you infer are the most important qualities in a hero? Support your answer with evidence from the text.

_____

_____

_____

_____

7. Based on Theseus's exchange with Thetis, what can you infer about Poseidon?

_____

_____

8. How does King Minos's labyrinth help illustrate the theme of the story?

_____

_____

_____

9. Write a paragraph summarizing this myth. Remember to include only those key details that are most important to the myth's plot and theme. Use a separate piece of paper if you need more space for your answer.

_____

_____

_____

_____

_____

_____

10. Below are three themes that are represented in the story of Theseus and the Minotaur.

- Bravery and good deeds will be rewarded with success.

- A person must be willing to take a stand against tyranny.

- Difficult tasks can be made easier with help from others.

A. Underline the theme that best represents the author's main message, in your opinion.

B. Write two facts that provide evidence to support the theme that you have chosen.

_____

_____

_____

_____

_____

Analyze Literary Elements

RL.7.1, RL.7.2, RL.7.3, RL.7.9, SL.7.1.a, SL.7.1.c–d

In this unit you've read a work of realistic fiction, a work of historical fiction, a drama, and a myth. Think about the elements of literature you have studied: character, setting, plot, and theme. In the chart below, list details that help you understand the author's use of these elements in each selection. Use a separate sheet of paper if you need more room to write. Then choose one element and write a brief essay about how the authors develop that element in the four selections. Refer to what the texts say explicitly and to inferences that you draw from the texts. Be sure to cite evidence for your ideas. Be prepared to discuss your ideas with the class.

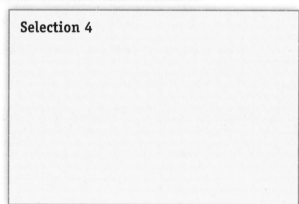

Selection 1

Selection 3

Skillful development of character, setting, plot, and theme allows an author to entertain readers and give them something to think about.

Selection 2

Selection 4

Return to the Essential Question

How do authors use literary details to create text?

In small groups or as a class, discuss the Essential Question. Think about what you have learned about drawing inferences, determining themes, and analyzing literary elements in a text. Use evidence from the four texts in this unit to answer the question.

Greek and Latin Affixes

L.7.4.b

Guided Instruction Knowing common Greek and Latin affixes, or word parts that can be added onto a word root, can help you determine the meaning of unfamiliar words. You can define a word based on its affix.

Affix	Origin	Meaning
ab-	Latin	away / not
ante-	Latin	before / above
anti-	Greek	opposing
con- / com-	Latin	together / with
intra-	Latin	within
-ive	Latin	with a tendency to
-ize	Greek	to become
-(i)ous	Latin	full of
pre-	Latin	before
pro-	Latin	tending toward
syn- / sym-	Greek	together / with

Examples:

- ***antidote*** *(Greek: dote comes from a root meaning "something given"
  + anti- = "something given [to be] against something")*
  *. . . I have an **antidote** for your problem, Theseus.*

- ***massive*** *(Latin: mass is "size" or "weight" + -ive = "with a tendency to have weight or size")*
  *Theseus felt the Minotaur's **massive** arms grab his legs . . .*

Guided Practice Find and write the words from paragraphs 32 and 33 of "Theseus and the Minotaur" that match these definitions.

1. full of danger _____

2. with a tendency to deceive _____

3. people who travel together _____

4. was ready beforehand _____

Independent Practice Here are other words formed with Greek and Latin affixes. On separate paper, define and write a sentence for each word.

abnormal   antedate   idolize   intramural   prediction

RL.7.1, RL.7.2, RL.7.3, L.7.4.b

Read the following realistic fiction texts that include implied ideas, central themes, and interactions of story elements. Then answer the questions on pages 45 and 46.

The Drummer's Courage

1   Musket fire shatters the day around me as I stand at attention, my drum in position. The cadences I played yesterday, the ones I know perfectly, seem to have disappeared from my mind! I cannot remember even the call forward! Our unit has received notice that the Redcoats are heading this way. The commander has made it very clear that I am to be ready to move at a moment's notice and that I must know the cadences to lead and rally the troops.

2   I look around at the men getting ready for battle. Certainly, we are not so well portioned as the British, as we have neither fancy uniforms nor abundant supplies. Our winters have been hard, and we have struggled against little food and abundant sickness. Nevertheless, we soldier on.

3   Suddenly, a hush sweeps over the chaotic encampment. I look around for the source of the disturbance and see one of our sentinels riding in at breakneck speed. He is waving his arm and frantically shouting, "The Redcoats are on their way! They will arrive within the next quarter-hour!"

4   The encampment is enveloped in a wall of sound, but this time with a purpose. Men gather their muskets and ready their bayonets. I watch the soldiers around me, so willing to die for what they believe is right, and suddenly everything comes back into focus. I pick up my drum, and the rally cadence falls naturally from my fingers. We are going into battle, and I am ready.

The Story of Hua Mulan

1   Hua Mulan was a courageous young woman who, when the time came to fight for her family, answered it without hesitation. Hua Mulan lived in ancient China in a time when each family was expected to provide a son to fight in the Emperor's armies. If the family had no son, then the father, as head of the household, would have to serve.

2   Hua Mulan had no brothers who could serve. When the Emperor's forces demanded a son from Hua Mulan's parents, she knew that her father would have to fight.

3   Hua Mulan's father had trained her in the weapons and skills necessary for battle. So, to protect her father's life and honor, Hua Mulan disguised herself as a man and enlisted in the Emperor's army.

4   Because of her skill in battle, Hua Mulan's true identity was never discovered. For twelve years, she fought for the Emperor. For twelve years, she was promoted and honored for her skill. When her time in the army was over, Hua Mulan chose not to demand accolades or reveal the truth. Instead, she quietly returned home to her family—the silent and courageous hero.

Circle the letter next to the best answer choice.

1A. What can you infer about the drummer's feelings at the beginning of "The Drummer's Courage"?

    a. He feels well prepared for battle.

    b. He is anxious about his duties.

    c. He does not want to be the drummer.

    d. He is excited to march with the troops.

1B. Which comment from "The Drummer's Courage" supports the answer to Part A?

    a. "Nevertheless, we soldier on."

    b. " . . . the ones I know perfectly, seem to have disappeared from my mind!"

    c. " . . . is enveloped in a wall of sound, but this time with a purpose."

    d. "We are going into battle, and I am ready."

2A. Which of these is NOT a theme of "The Story of Hua Mulan"?

    a. Women can fight in battle as well as men can.

    b. You should put your family above yourself.

    c. Those in power are always right.

    d. Some of the greatest heroes are the quietest.

2B. What information from the text supports the answer in Part A?

    a. Hua Mulan violates the Emperor's law to protect her father.

    b. Hua Mulan protests against the Emperor's treatment of women.

    c. Hua Mulan is not a very good soldier.

    d. None of the above.

3A. Which words best describe the character of the drummer in "The Drummer's Courage"?

    a. lazy but optimistic

    b. loyal and determined

    c. confused and depressed

    d. unwilling to work hard

3B. Which phrase from the text supports the answer to Part A?

    a. "I look around for the source of the disturbance"

    b. "I watch the soldiers around me, so willing to die for what they believe is right"

    c. "I pick up my drum, and the rally cadence falls naturally from my fingers."

    d. "The commander has made it very clear that I am to be ready to move at a moment's notice"

4A. The setting of "The Drummer's Courage" is

    a. a Civil War battlefield.

    b. a World War II battlefield.

    c. a Revolutionary War battlefield.

    d. a World War I battlefield.

4B. What evidence from "The Drummer's Courage" supports the answer to Part A?

    a. The narrator describes the use of muskets and bayonets.

    b. A sentinel is riding a horse to break news.

    c. The narrator refers to "Redcoats" and "the British."

    d. All of the above.

RL.7.1, RL.7.2, RL.7.3, L.7.4.b

5A. Which detail helps communicate the theme of "The Story of Hua Mulan"?

   a. Hua Mulan takes her father's place.

   b. Hua Mulan has no brothers.

   c. Hua Mulan refuses all accolades.

   d. Hua Mulan has been trained in weapons.

5B. Which statement from the text best supports the main theme, as determined in Part A?

   a. "Hua Mulan was a courageous young woman"

   b. "For twelve years, she fought for the Emperor."

   c. "So, to protect her father's life and honor, Hua Mulan disguised herself as a man"

   d. "the father . . . would have to serve."

6A. What is the meaning of the affix in the word *commander* from "The Drummer's Courage"?

   a. before / above

   b. together / with

   c. away / not

   d. full of

6B. Based on your answer in Part A, what is the best definition of the word *commander* in the text?

   a. someone in charge of an activity

   b. one who brings soldiers together

   c. the head of the army

   d. a high-ranking soldier

7. How does Hua Mulan's character shape the plot of "The Story of Hua Mulan"?

_____

_____

_____

8. Write a brief paragraph summarizing the "The Story of Hua Mulan."

_____

_____

_____

9. What inference can you draw about the treatment of women in ancient China, based on evidence from "The Story of Hua Mulan"?

_____

_____

_____

10. How are the drummer and Hua Mulan alike? How do they differ?

_____

_____

_____

Introducing UNIT 2

In this unit about people who take courageous actions, you will learn how to write a nonfictional narrative. A nonfictional narrative presents a real event or experience in the form of a story. Even though the event or experience actually happened, the text reads like a short story or novel. As a result, the narrative shares some literary elements with fiction, including characters, dialogue, and descriptive details.

As you prepare to write a nonfictional narrative, do some research to make sure that your details are accurate. Then, as you write, create a sequence of events that unfolds naturally. Establish a point of view. Develop the events and engage readers by creating interesting characters and using effective pacing. Include transition words and phrases to connect events or to indicate a change in the story's setting. Use precise words and sensory language to describe events and experiences. Finally, provide a strong conclusion that wraps up the story in an interesting way and leaves readers with a final thought.

Progress Check *Can I?*

Before Unit 2 / **After Unit 2**

☐ ☐ Engage readers by introducing interesting characters and establishing a point of view.

☐ ☐ Base a narrative on factual evidence that I have researched.

☐ ☐ Organize a sequence of plot events.

☐ ☐ Use dialogue, pacing, and description to develop a narrative.

☐ ☐ Connect details by using transition words or phrases.

☐ ☐ Use precise words and phrases and effective sensory language.

☐ ☐ Provide a satisfying conclusion to a narrative.

☐ ☐ Identify and use various kinds of phrases and clauses.

☐ ☐ Use word relationships to learn new words.

HOME ◆ CONNECT...

- Learn how to write a narrative about a real event, using descriptive details and a clear sequence.

- Establish a point of view and organize a sequence of events that unfolds naturally.

- Use dialogue, pacing, and description to develop a narrative.

- Use transitions to show a sequence of events or a shift in setting.

- Use precise words and sensory language to describe action and convey experiences.

- Provide a conclusion that wraps up the narrative in a satisfying way.

- Identify and use various kinds of phrases and clauses.

- Analyze and work with synonyms, antonyms, and analogies.

NOTE: All of these learning goals for your child are based on the Grade 7 Common Core State Standards for English Language Arts.

In this unit, your child will learn to **write a nonfictional narrative**. This type of writing presents a real event or experience, but it is written like a fictional story, with **characters**, **dialogue**, **description**, and **action**. A nonfictional narrative also includes **precise language** and **sensory language** that make the story come to life for readers. Help your child develop a stronger grasp of this kind of writing by identifying nonfictional narratives in print or online. Discuss the stories the writers tell, including the **research** that the writer probably did, the way the narratives are structured, and the kinds of details that are included.

Do a little research on your own, if needed, and then tell your child a story about a real event from history that will be familiar to him or her. Tell the story with the events in proper **sequence**. Try to include **dialogue** and **description** to make the story come to life. In addition, give your narrative a strong **conclusion** that provides a final thought about the true-life event. Have your child respond by telling you a story about an event that he or she has learned about at school.

On the Go: As you walk through your neighborhood, talk about courageous actions in everyday life—for example, someone putting out a kitchen fire or confronting a bully. Choose an action that really happened; then work together to research the event (perhaps through an interview). Create a flow chart that shows the step-by-step order of events. Discuss how you could use this chart to write a nonfictional narrative about the courageous action.

WAYS TO HELP YOUR CHILD

Have your child practice presenting events in a logical sequence. For example, you might ask, "What happened first? Next? After that? At the end?" Help your child record and review the answers, deciding which are most important to include and how to add lively details to them. Encourage your child to write and share a nonfictional narrative about the event.

ONLINE

For more Home Connect activities, continue online at sadlierconnect.com

Text Types and Purposes: Write Nonfictional Narratives

Essential Question:
How can writers create an effective narrative?

W.7.3, W.7.3.a–b

CREATING AN ORGANIZATIONAL STRUCTURE

Riley used a graphic organizer like the one below to plan her nonfictional narrative.

Title: _____
Characters: _____
Setting: _____
Sequence of Events: _____

Conclusion: _____

TITLE

- Gives readers a clue about the real-life event in the narrative

POINT OF VIEW

- Tells the story from a particular perspective. Riley tells this story from the perspective of someone who is not part of the story. In other words, the story has a third-person point of view.

DESCRIPTIVE DETAILS

- Help readers envision the characters and the setting. For example, Riley writes that Edmund Hillary was "a tall, lanky beekeeper."

Read a Student Model

Riley is a student in Ms. Kim's seventh-grade Language Arts class. Ms. Kim gave Riley's class an assignment to write a nonfictional narrative about a real person who has done something courageous. Ms. Kim expects students to create well-researched, accurate narratives. The narratives should have a clear sequence of events and include descriptive details and sensory language. Think about a courageous person from history to write about in your own nonfictional narrative.

To the Top of the World

Staring at the face of the mountain, Edmund Hillary stood at the base of Mount Everest, about to tackle the greatest challenge of his life: reaching the world's highest peak. One of many slopes along the Himalayas, Everest straddles the border between Nepal and Tibet. At more than 29,000 feet, its summit is "the top of the world." Other people had attempted the climb, but no one had yet made it to the top.

It was the spring of 1953, and a team of mountain climbers was determined to reach the top of Everest. A member of the team, Edmund Hillary was a tall, lanky beekeeper from New Zealand. At 16, he had taken a school trip to a national park, had seen a 9,000-foot volcano, and had become an avid climber. Now, on May 29, he was about to climb the highest mountain of them all.

At 6:30 in the morning, Hillary and teammate Tenzing Norgay made preparations for a final climb. A villager from the valley below, Norgay often scaled very high altitudes. The two men were at a ridge camp near the top; the rest of the team was at base camp or smaller camps down the mountain. Hillary and Norgay gathered ice axes and ropes and added cans of oxygen to their packs. The air was very thin near the top of the mountain, so they needed to make sure they had enough oxygen to breathe. With all their equipment packed, they were ready. Now there was only one way to go: up!

The last 400 feet were very steep, which made the climb tough and grueling. Attached together with ropes, the two climbers took turns cutting steps into the side of the massive mountain. One wrong step and they would both fall. If that happened, a rescue team could never reach them, and they would die on the mountain. A fierce wind howled in their ears and clawed at their faces. The ice axes felt heavy in their hands as they hacked at the snow. Hillary had a lot of experience, so he knew how to find footholds. He was very fit after years of climbing, so he had a lot of energy and endurance. He also had a lot of courage, and he needed every bit of it to make such a difficult, dangerous climb.

Close to the top, Hillary and Norgay came to a smooth rockface. There were no bumps or ridges to use as footholds, and it would be impossible to cut steps into this 40-foot sheet of ice. At first, they were unsure how to continue.

TRANSITIONS

Use transition words and phrases to connect events or show a shift in the setting. In this paragraph, *At 6:30 in the morning* is a transition, shifting the setting to the moment of the climbers' departure.

Circle two transition phrases in the third paragraph on this page.

PACING

Riley uses description to slow down the pace of her narrative and action to speed it up. Varying your pace keeps your reader interested.

Underline the two sentences in the second paragraph where the pace slows down.

SENSORY LANGUAGE

Include details that show what the characters saw, heard, or felt. Here, *A fierce wind howled in their ears* shows what Hillary and Norgay heard as they climbed. Sensory language helps bring the characters' experiences to life for readers.

Box two other examples of sensory language in this paragraph.

WRITE NONFICTIONAL NARRATIVES

W.7.3.b, W.7.3.d–e, W.7.9

DIALOGUE

Include dialogue to make the characters more realistic and to make the narrative read like a fictional story.

Underline the dialogue in paragraph 1 on this page.

PRECISE LANGUAGE

Use precise language that names exact details, such as *At 11:30 in the morning.* Also, use precise verbs to describe actions specifically, such as the verb *embraced.*

Put an asterisk next to three precise verbs in this paragraph.

CONCLUSION/RESEARCH

Riley wraps up her nonfictional narrative with a conclusion. It reflects on the real-life event and leaves readers with a final thought. Here, as throughout the narrative, Riley depends on facts that she has researched to keep her story accurate.

Underline the final thought in this narrative. Where might Riley have done research to find this information?

The two climbers surveyed the mountain, searching for some way to go forward. Then one of them spotted a small space packed with snow off to the right. Could they climb it? Would it hold their weight? "What do you think?" Norgay asked. "That will do," Hillary replied. Norgay drove his ice axe into the space to anchor Hillary, who wedged into the gap then forced himself up, pulling Norgay after him.

At 11:30 in the morning, they reached the peak, and the firm cone of snow was big enough for both climbers to stand on. Filled with joy and relief, they embraced each other. Gazing into the distance, they could see the snow-covered ridges of the Himalayas for a hundred miles in all directions. As Hillary snapped photographs with his trusty camera, Norgay waved flags that represented Britain, Nepal, India, and the United Nations.

However, they could stay for only about 15 minutes because they were low on oxygen. Turning to his teammate, Hillary said, "Let's go," and back down the mountain they went. News of their amazing achievement quickly spread around the world. Both Hillary and Norgay would become world famous as the men who had "conquered Everest." In the years to come, Hillary would make other expeditions to the Himalayas, but never again would he climb to "the top of the world."

W.7.3.a–e, W.7.4, W.7.5, W.7.10

Use this graphic organizer to plan a nonfictional narrative for the Common Core Review on page 59. Then write your first draft on a separate sheet of paper. Keep your point of view in mind. Remember to use description and dialogue as well as precise words and sensory language. In addition, think about which transition words and phrases might be helpful.

Title: _____

Characters: _____

Setting: _____

Sequence of Events: _____

Conclusion: _____
_____

L.7.1, L.7.1.a

Function of Phrases and Clauses

Guided Instruction A **phrase** is a group of words that function together as a single part of speech. A **clause** is a group of words that has both a subject and a predicate. Some clauses can also function as a single part of speech.

- A **noun phrase** can do anything a one-word noun can do. It can function as the subject of a sentence or as different kinds of objects.

  The mountain-climbing rope has a grappling hook. (subject, direct object)

  I gave my friend a book about the historic climb. (indirect object, object of a preposition)

- A **prepositional phrase** has a preposition and an object. It can function as an adjective or an adverb.

  We could barely see the stage from our seats in the last row. (adverb [modifies could see], adjective [modifies seats])

- A **verb phrase** can do anything a one-word verb can do. Verb phrases indicate certain times, or tenses, when actions or states of being happen.

  We have been excited about this speaker for some time.
  (state of being [present perfect])

  She will speak on the challenges of a Mount Everest climb. (action [future])

  Now everyone is watching her great slide presentation. (action [present progressive])

  Keiko would have come, but she is feeling sick today. (action [past conditional], state of being [present progressive])

- An **independent clause** can stand alone. It can be written as a separate sentence.

  Max talked to the speaker later, and he got her autograph.

- A **dependent clause** cannot stand alone. It cannot be written as a separate sentence, but it does have a function: it can function as a noun, an adjective, or an adverb. A dependent clause at the beginning of a sentence should be followed by a comma.

  After we get home, Max will tell us about their conversation.
  (adverb [modifies will tell])

  We will enjoy hearing whatever he tells us. (noun [direct object])

  Of all of us, he is the one who is most interested in Mount Everest.
  (adjective [modifies one])

L.7.1, L.7.1.a

Guided Practice Identify the kind of phrase or clause that is underlined in each sentence. If the phrase or clause functions as a part of speech, explain its function.

1. The soccer players <u>have been practicing</u> for three hours.

2. During storms, my dog Comet always hides <u>under my bed</u>.

3. <u>Before Marisol performs</u>, she does several breathing exercises.

4. Rachel and David played <u>that difficult piano duet</u> beautifully.

5. Clouds are gathering, and <u>we probably will see rain soon</u>.

6. A man <u>in a blue plaid shirt</u> just joined the ticket line.

7. <u>What we are having for dinner</u> is anyone's guess.

8. Shall we ride our bikes <u>on the city's new bike path</u>?

Independent Practice Write five original sentences. Three sentences should include a phrase, and the other two should include a dependent clause.

1. _____

2. _____

3. _____

4. _____

5. _____

Word Relationships

Guided Instruction **Synonyms**, **antonyms**, and **analogies** all reveal word relationships. Understanding word relationships can help readers learn new words or better understand familiar words.

- **Synonyms** are words that have the same meaning or a similar meaning. Synonyms must be the same part of speech, such as two nouns or two adjectives.

  After the game, my sneakers were <u>caked</u>, or <u>covered</u>, with dirt.

  As seen from the moon, Earth looks <u>fragile</u> and <u>delicate</u>.

  That <u>gown</u> is an especially formal <u>dress</u>.

- **Antonyms** are words with opposite meanings. Antonyms must be the same part of speech. Words and phrases such as *not*, *but*, and *instead of* sometimes signal that antonyms appear in a sentence.

  We thought the hike would be <u>leisurely</u>, but it was <u>grueling</u>.

  Instead of taking the <u>long</u> route, we went the <u>short</u> way home.

  Although the broken glass seemed like a <u>major</u> clue, it turned out to be <u>unimportant</u>.

- An **analogy** is a kind of word equation based on the relationship between pairs of words. To understand an analogy you first identify the relationship between the first pair of words; then you apply that relationship to the second pair of words. Example:

  PLEASED : DELIGHTED :: hesitant : reticent

  Read this as "*Pleased* is to *delighted* as *hesitant* is to *reticent*." When you identify that the words *pleased* and *delighted* are synonyms, you will know that the words *hesitant* and *reticent* must also be synonyms. You can tell this even if you are not sure what *reticent* means. Here is another example:

  STRONG : WEAK :: calm : boisterous

  Read this as "*Strong* is to *weak* as *calm* is to *boisterous*." When you identify that the words *strong* and *weak* are antonyms, you then know that the words *calm* and *boisterous* must be another pair of antonyms.

  Sometimes you may be presented with an analogy that is missing a part, as in

  TINY : ENORMOUS :: wild : _____

  To solve this analogy you first identify that *tiny* and *enormous* are antonyms. Then look for a word that is the antonym of *wild*, such as *tame*. *Tame* completes the analogy.

L.7.5.b

Guided Practice Circle the synonyms or antonyms in each sentence. On the line, write whether the words are synonyms or antonyms.

1. The procession, or parade, started on Elm Street. _____

2. Shawn exercises in the evening, but I prefer a morning routine. _____

3. Although people call her a nervous person, I think she is easygoing. _____

4. While I watched a science program, my brother viewed a movie. _____

5. That green banana looks even less appetizing than that unripe peach.
   _____

6. Grandpa always says, "One person's trash is another person's treasure."
   _____

Independent Practice Fill in the blank in each sentence with a synonym or antonym for the underlined word.

1. In sewing class, Karina made an outfit that looked simple but was actually very
   _____ .

2. The science presentation left Malcolm feeling _____ and bewildered.

3. That tasty pineapple was very _____!

4. The documentary we watched about Russian history was _____ —not boring at all!

Solve the analogies below. Then create two analogies of your own. One should include pairs of synonyms, while the other should include pairs of antonyms.

5. ENTHUSIASTIC : EAGER :: kind : _____

6. GREEDY : GENEROUS :: rude : _____

7. _____ : _____ :: _____ : _____

8. _____ : _____ :: _____ : _____

SL.7.1.a–d, SL.7.3, SL.7.4, SL.7.6

Discuss the Essential Question

How can writers create an effective narrative?

Prepare for a class discussion about the Essential Question by responding to the questions below. Support your point of view with reasons and examples.

1. What is the sequence of events in Riley's nonfictional narrative?

_____

_____

_____

_____

2. What literary elements did Riley include to bring the story to life?

_____

_____

3. How did Riley connect ideas and events in her narrative?

_____

Use your notes to discuss the Essential Question in small groups or as a class. Use the rules for being a good speaker and a good listener in the checklist below.

Did I :

☐ Build on ideas expressed by others and express my own ideas clearly?

☐ Come to the discussion prepared and stay on the topic?

☐ Help define individual roles during discussions?

☐ Revise my own views when presented with new evidence or information?

☐ Distinguish claims that are supported by reasons and evidence from claims that are not?

☐ Present relevant claims and other ideas in a logical manner?

☐ Speak in an appropriate volume, pronounce words clearly, and use eye contact?

☐ Use formal English when appropriate?

W.7.3, W.7.3.a–d, W.7.9

Read this draft introductory paragraph from a student nonfictional narrative, and answer the questions below.

> (1) The year was 1963, and Valentina Tereshkova was about to do what no woman had ever done before: travel into outer space. (2) She was a cosmonaut in the Soviet Union's space program, which was competing with the U.S. agency NASA in a "space race." (3) After Yuri Gagarin became the first person to travel into space in 1961, she determined, "I would love to do that," so she volunteered. (4) Valentina was not a pilot; she had made more than a hundred parachute jumps.

1. This narrative is told from the point of view of

  a. a Soviet official.

  b. an American official.

  c. an outside narrator.

  d. an American astronaut.

2. Which of the following would be effective sensory language for this paragraph?

  a. It was an historic time for the world.

  b. Her heart pounded with excitement.

  c. People around the world admired her.

  d. Both cosmonauts were very brave.

3. Which is an example of a precise verb from the text?

  a. was

  b. done

  c. became

  d. determined

4. Based on this introduction, which event would best fit in this narrative?

  a. Tereshkova's training

  b. NASA designing its spaceship

  c. the reaction of other astronauts

  d. Gagarin's flight into space

5. Based on this introduction, which detail would NOT fit in this narrative?

  a. a description of a rocket

  b. a description of a parachute

  c. a description of a spacesuit

  d. a description of the NASA offices

6. Which transition word or phrase would best fit in the middle of sentence 4?

  a. meanwhile,

  b. however,

  c. in addition,

  d. for example,

W.7.3, W.7.3.e, W.7.4, W.7.5, W.7.9, W.7.10, L.7.1, L.7.1.a, L.7.5.b

Read these next two paragraphs from the student nonfictional narrative, and answer the questions below.

> (1) Two years later, Valentina was ready to make the leap into space. (2) Dressed in an orange spacesuit, she strapped into her seat on board a space capsule, or ship, called the *Vostok 6*. (3) As the engines fired, roaring in her ears, she bravely declared, "Hey, sky! Take off your hat; I'm coming!" (4) The rocket lifted off and hurled the capsule into space.
>
> (5) Valentina spent three days in space, orbiting Earth. (6) As she circled the planet forty-eight times, she noted the amazing scene beneath her. (7) Finally, gripping the controls tightly to keep the capsule steady, she dropped out of orbit and headed back toward the planet's surface. (8) After reentering the atmosphere, she ejected from the falling capsule and parachuted to the ground. (9) The landing was bumpy and her face was bruised, but she made it back safely.

7. Circle two words in sentence 2 that are synonyms.

8. Write the phrase in sentence 4 that functions as an adverb. _____ What kind of phrase is it, and what does it modify? _____

9. Underline a dependent clause in sentence 6. Rewrite it as an independent clause.

_____

10. Write a concluding paragraph for this nonfictional narrative.

_____

_____

_____

Assignment: On a separate sheet of paper, provide a final draft of the nonfictional narrative you began on page 53. Use what you learned about phrases and clauses and about word relationships in the Language section of this unit. Think about how you and your classmates answered the Essential Question. Check your graphic organizer to make sure you presented events in a logical sequence. Be sure to use precise words, sensory language, and transitions where needed. End with a conclusion that provides readers with a final thought.

Introducing UNIT 3

In this unit about exploring new frontiers, you will learn about the key ideas and details of informational text. The purpose of informational text is to communicate ideas. The authors of these texts communicate their key ideas—also known as central ideas—and support them with details. Some of these central ideas are directly stated. Others are hinted at, and you will have to draw inferences to find them. Finally, the author will explain how the people, events, and ideas described in the text interact with and influence each other.

Informational text can take different forms, including speeches, interviews, feature articles, and policy statements. In this unit, you will find examples of each. Some informational texts are related to subjects you study in school, such as history and science. Scientific texts can include technical information that can be very specific and detailed. Summarizing an informational text is a good way to check your understanding.

Before Unit 3

Progress Check *Can I?*

After Unit 3

☐   Draw inferences from a text.   ☐

☐   Determine the central ideas of a text.   ☐

☐   Summarize a text.   ☐

☐   Analyze the relationships among people, events, and ideas in a text.   ☐

☐   Describe the conclusions drawn by a text's author.   ☐

☐   Analyze and cite evidence from technical texts.   ☐

☐   Use Greek and Latin roots to determine word meanings.   ☐

HOME✦CONNECT...

- Read four informational selections, including a speech, an interview, a feature article, and a policy statement.

- Learn new academic and content-area vocabulary.

- Draw inferences by analyzing implied ideas.

- Identify ideas that are central to the meaning of the text.

- Summarize texts and identify conclusions.

- Analyze interactions among people, events, and ideas in a text.

- Use Greek and Latin roots to determine word meanings.

- Compare and contrast ideas across four selections on the theme of new frontiers.

NOTE: All of these learning goals for your child are based on the Grade 7 Common Core State Standards for English Language Arts.

The purpose of an informational text is to communicate information. However, authors do not always state their ideas directly. Sometimes authors expect the reader to **draw inferences** to pick up on implied ideas. Help your child by showing him or her how to connect the dots in everyday conversations to find unstated messages.

Not all of the information included by authors in informational texts is of equal importance. Students will practice finding the **central ideas of a text**. Help your child practice this skill by having him or her create new titles or headlines for news articles, using the fewest words possible to express the key information.

Another way authors communicate is by setting up **interactions between people and events**. Readers need to consider how people can affect events by making choices, and how events can affect people by creating opportunities or obstacles. You can help your child by talking about people in history or players in a sporting event. Talk about how a different person might respond to the same events, or how different events might change a person.

WAYS TO HELP YOUR CHILD

Help your child learn to identify important information. In conversations, ask your child to summarize what the other person has said. See if he or she can restate the important ideas and pick up on ideas that are implied. If your child misses important stated or implied ideas, ask questions that will help him or her notice these points.

> **ONLINE**
> **For more Home Connect activities, continue online at** sadlierconnect.com

Activity: Create a fact file on a "frontier" that is not well explored: the ocean floor, the interior of the earth, deep space, or even the human brain. With your child, do a search on the Internet for information and images. See if you can design an experiment that would add new knowledge about this area.

Reading Informational Text: Key Ideas and Details

UNIT 3

Essential Question:
How can readers find and analyze central ideas in a text?

RI.7.1

WORDS TO KNOW

democracy

emerged

reeling

satellite

Sometimes an author's ideas are directly stated in a text, and sometimes they are implied. Use clues in the text to **draw inferences** about implied ideas.

CITE EVIDENCE

A Sometimes an author will state an idea directly, or explicitly. Consider why the United States and the Soviet Union were in competition with each other. Find the stated idea in paragraph 1 and underline it.

B When you are looking for an answer that is not explicitly stated, you must **draw an inference** based on evidence in the text. What was so unusual about using rockets to get into space? This idea isn't stated. Put an asterisk next to each piece of information that tells how rockets had been used previously. How does this information help you make an inference?

A Man on the Moon

(Genre: Explanatory Text with Speech)

1   The Space Race started after World War II. The United States and the Soviet Union had **emerged** from the war as the two most powerful countries in the world. They had different systems of government. The United States was the champion of **democracy**, while the Soviet Union was a defender of communism. Both countries wanted their form of government to succeed in countries around the world. The two countries competed for allies, weapons, and power.

2   Both countries wanted to develop rocket technology for their own power and protection. The United States had an early victory by being the first to develop the nuclear bomb, but space was the next frontier. Although the Germans had been the first to develop modern rocket technology, rocket science had begun long before the war.

A Brief History of Rockets

3   The first rockets were developed in China in the 12th century. The Chinese had already invented gunpowder and fireworks. These rockets were weapons that were an extension of that technology.

4   The technology spread through Asia, and then to Europe, when India used gunpowder rockets against the invading British. Britain then used them against the United States, as the lyrics to "The Star-Spangled Banner" relate: "And the rockets' red glare/The bombs bursting in air . . . "

a V-2 rocket, used during World War II

RI.7.1, L.7.6

5   In 1898 a Russian schoolteacher, Konstantin Tsiolkovsky, proposed the idea of using rockets to explore space. Although deaf from childhood, Tsiolkovsky was an active inventor, and he developed the math that made modern rocket science possible.

6   The next great advance in rocket science came from an American, Robert H. Goddard. He experimented with liquid fuel for rockets. In 1926 Goddard tested the idea. The flight lasted for only two-and-a-half seconds and landed about half a football field away. Goddard's experiments continued, though, and his work changed how high and fast rockets could fly.

7   Hermann Oberth, another great rocket pioneer, published a book in 1923 about rocket travel into outer space. His writings inspired many small rocket societies around the world. In Germany, members of the Society for Space Travel experimented with rocket designs that eventually led to the development of the V-2 rocket, used by Germany during World War II.

8   After the war, the United States and the Soviet Union captured many unused V-2 rockets. Many German rocket scientists came to the United States. Others went to the Soviet Union.

The Soviet Union Pulls Ahead

9   On October 4, 1957, the Soviet Union launched *Sputnik I*, the world's first artificial **satellite**. It was about the size of a beach ball, weighed about as much as an adult male, and orbited Earth in less time than it takes to watch a movie.

10   The *Sputnik* launch crossed a new frontier for human beings— entering space. Its success captured the world's imagination. It also caught America off guard. Not only had they lost the race to space, but Americans also feared that the Soviets would now be able to launch nuclear missiles from Europe to the United States.

11   While America was still **reeling** from the news, the Soviets chalked up another victory. On November 3, *Sputnik II* carried a dog into space. It was the first animal to orbit Earth.

CITE EVIDENCE

C How were the Soviets able to launch *Sputnik I*? Circle the paragraph that gives you some clues.

D Put a box around the word in paragraph 10 that means "an area that forms the edge of settled territory." If you're not sure what word this is, use a dictionary to look up all the unfamiliar words in the paragraph until you find it.

E Double underline a sentence that gives clues about how Americans felt about the Soviet Union at this time. Which words and phrases most helped you to make an inference?

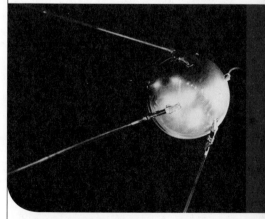

Sputnik I **was the first artificial satellite.**

Comprehension Check

What inferences can you make about the effect of war on the development of space technology?

DRAWING INFERENCES

A Man on the Moon *continued*

RI.7.1, RH.7.1

WORDS TO KNOW

affirmatively

enterprise

exploit

instrument

orbit

CITE EVIDENCE

A In science, one discovery or accomplishment often leads to another. Underline the sentences that help you infer why Americans started thinking about sending a man to the moon.

B Which American accomplishment would lead to bringing astronauts safely back from space? Double underline this. Explain how you used this information to make your inference.

C A primary source is an original source, a printed or recorded document from the time period being written about. Put an asterisk next to the part of the text that is taken from an actual historical record.

America Rallies

12   A few months later, in January 1958, the United States launched *Explorer I*. This satellite carried some scientific **instruments**. The data gathered from this mission led to the discovery of magnetic radiation belts around Earth. Then, in July 1958, Congress passed a law that created the National Aeronautics and Space Administration (NASA). The United States was determined to win the Space Race.

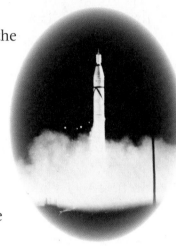

To the Moon!

13   The moon was the next frontier. The Russians again were leading the way. They crash-landed the spacecraft *Luna 2* on the surface of the moon in 1959. Then they sent *Luna 3* in orbit around the moon to photograph its "dark side"—the side that is always turned away from Earth. That was the first time anyone had seen it.

14   Meanwhile, the United States launched two monkeys into space and recovered them from a splash landing in the Atlantic Ocean.

15   The Russians then stunned the world by sending the first human into space. Cosmonaut Yuri Gagarin entered Earth's **orbit** in *Vostok I*. About a month later, the United States launched astronaut Alan Shepard into space on *Freedom 7*.

16   The United States was ready to make a bold move ahead. President John F. Kennedy had a plan, and he shared it in a speech to the United States Congress on May 25, 1961. He asked the nation to pull together to meet the challenge of putting a man on the moon.

From President John F. Kennedy's Speech to Congress, May 25, 1961

17   Now it is time to take longer strides—time for a great new American **enterprise**—time for this nation to take a clearly leading role in space achievement, which in many ways may hold the key to our future on Earth. . . .

RI.7.1

18   Recognizing the head start obtained by the Soviets with their large rocket engines, which gives them many months of lead-time, and recognizing the likelihood that they will **exploit** this lead for some time to come in still more impressive successes, we nevertheless are required to make new efforts on our own. For while we cannot guarantee that we shall one day be first, we can guarantee that any failure to make this effort will make us last . . . But this is not merely a race. Space is open to us now; and our eagerness to share its meaning is not governed by the efforts of others. We go into space because whatever mankind must undertake, free men must fully share. . . .

19   . . . I believe that this nation should commit itself to achieving the goal, before this decade is out, of landing a man on the moon and returning him safely to the Earth. No single space project in this period will be more impressive to mankind, or more important for the long-range exploration of space; and none will be so difficult or expensive to accomplish . . . But in a very real sense, it will not be one man going to the moon—if we make this judgment **affirmatively**, it will be an entire nation. For all of us must work to put him there. . . .

20   Let it be clear . . . that I am asking the Congress and the country to accept a firm commitment to a new course of action, a course which will last for many years and carry very heavy costs . . . If we are to go only half way, or reduce our sights in the face of difficulty, in my judgment it would be better not to go at all.

Comprehension Check

How does reading the excerpt from President Kennedy's speech help you understand the rest of the selection up to this point?

CITE EVIDENCE

D Why does President Kennedy think America should put a man on the moon? Put a box around his reasons.

E What are some "difficulties" that could come from trying to put a man on the moon? Circle a paragraph whose information helps you answer this question. Why does Kennedy not explicitly state the potential difficulties he hints at here?

JFK asks Congress to support the space program.

DRAWING INFERENCES

Guided Practice

A Man on the Moon *continued*

WORDS TO KNOW

brink

communism

module

tense

CITE EVIDENCE

A How did political tension on the ground influence the Space Race? Underline the answer in the text.

B Why were the Soviets being secretive about their efforts to send a man to the moon? Put an asterisk at the beginning of the paragraph that helps answer this question. Discuss with a partner what you can infer about the Soviet failure to reach the moon.

Spying Eyes in the Sky

21   While the United States was working on a manned lunar mission, events on the ground were getting **tense**. The United States and the Soviet Union were getting into conflicts as the Soviets helped **communism** to spread. American airmen spotted Soviet missile sites being built in Cuba. With Cuba only a short distance from Florida, missiles fired from these sites could easily strike the United States. Meanwhile, the Americans had a missile base in Turkey near the Soviet border. For two weeks, the Cuban Missile Crisis threatened the world with nuclear war. Eventually, both countries stepped back from the **brink**.

22   Still, there was a lot of mistrust. Space missions gave both countries another way to spy on each other from the air. Both countries soon developed "spy satellites" that would allow them to photograph and monitor each other from space.

Reaching for the Moon

23   Although the Soviets dominated early in the space race, things were about to change. The Americans did not seem to be making progress, but they were. Each NASA mission built on the previous one.

24   The Soviets said publicly that they were not trying to reach the moon, but they worked covertly on that project as well. Their efforts were less successful, though. As it turns out, the Soviets were using many smaller engines while the Americans were using a few large ones. In the end, the Soviets never did put a man on the moon.

Lunar Landing

25   *Apollo 11*, the American mission that would land the first men on the moon, was made up of several parts. The *Saturn V* rocket would power it into space. The *Columbia* command **module** would take the astronauts into lunar orbit. The *Eagle* lunar module would be the part that landed on the moon's surface.

26 The voyage began on July 16, 1969. Aboard *Apollo 11* were Neil Armstrong, Michael Collins, and Edwin "Buzz" Aldrin, Jr. Everything went as planned. After reaching lunar orbit, Armstrong and Aldrin boarded the *Eagle* and landed it on the moon on July 19, with Armstrong famously reporting, "The *Eagle* has landed." As Armstrong descended the ladder to become the first person to set foot on the moon, he said, "That's one small step for man, one giant leap for mankind."

Comprehension Check

1. America had fallen behind the Soviet Union because

   a. the Soviets put a man in space first.

   b. the Soviets reached the moon with a spacecraft first.

   c. the Soviets launched the first satellite.

   d. all of the above

2. What issue about putting an American on the moon worried President Kennedy?

   a. America could not afford the cost.

   b. The Soviets were too far ahead.

   c. Putting people on the moon was technologically impossible.

   d. Americans would not pull together.

3. Which of the following would be a primary source about the first moon landing?

   a. a textbook chapter about rocket development

   b. a film clip of Armstrong and Aldrin landing on the moon

   c. an encyclopedia entry about the Cuban Missile Crisis

   d. an audio recording explaining NASA's missions in the year 2013

4. What does *covertly* in paragraph 24 mean?

   a. secretly

   b. carefully

   c. quickly

   d. seriously

5. How has drawing inferences helped you understand the text? Specifically, how do you better understand the connection between the Space Race and politics? Confer with a partner and use evidence from the text to support your answer.

   _____

   _____

   _____

   _____

   _____

   _____

DRAWING INFERENCES

Independent Practice

A Man on the Moon *continued*

RI.7.1

WORDS TO KNOW

dwindling

joint

meteoroid

stockpiling

CITE EVIDENCE

A Why was docking the two crafts in space hard to do? In paragraph 28, put an asterisk next to the stated reason.

B Why did the astronauts have to leave the *Eagle* behind? Underline the clue that helps you infer the answer. Why was this an important moment in the Space Race?

Getting Home from the Moon

27   The *Apollo 11* mission was not complete until the astronauts returned safely home. After studying and taking samples on the moon's surface, Armstrong and Aldrin got back into the *Eagle* and launched it into the lunar sky. Everything would have to function properly, or they would be stranded on the moon with no way home.

28   Meanwhile, Collins had been orbiting in the *Columbia* ever since Armstrong and Aldrin had left in the *Eagle*. The plan was for the *Eagle* and the *Columbia* to dock in space. The measurements and timing had to be exact. Millions of people watched on television and cheered as Armstrong and Aldrin joined Collins. They had done it! The astronauts separated the two crafts and let the *Eagle* drift away into space.

29   The final rocket had just enough thrust to get the *Columbia* out from the moon's orbit. The astronauts splashed down in the Pacific Ocean on July 24. The mission was accomplished, and President Kennedy's challenge had been answered.

Other Apollo Missions

30   In all, six Apollo missions (*Apollo 11, 12,* and *14–17*) sent people safely to the moon, giving humanity a wealth of scientific data and lunar samples. Experiments included the study of soil, **meteoroids**, heat flow, magnetic fields, solar wind, and more.

31   *Apollo 13* captured photographs but did not land on the moon due to a malfunction. An explosion occurred in space. Pilot John L. Swigert, Jr. calmly reported to Mission Control, "Houston, we've had a problem." The whole world held its breath until the astronauts made it back home after overcoming mechanical difficulties and **dwindling** supplies.

From Competition to Cooperation

32   After years of competition, the Soviet Union and America planned a **joint** mission. It was a symbol of hope and goodwill for people at a time when wars were being fought over communism and the superpowers were **stockpiling** nuclear weapons.

33 On July 17, 1975, the *Apollo* and *Soyuz* crafts docked in space. The hatch opened, and *Apollo* commander Thomas P. Stafford and *Soyuz* commander Alexey A. Leonov shook hands. People back on Earth dared to hope for peace.

Comprehension Check

MORE ONLINE sadlierconnect.com

1. The word *malfunction* means

   a. machine failure.

   b. pilot error.

   c. carelessness.

   d. natural disaster.

2. Which can you infer from the text?

   a. The Apollo 13 disaster changed the way NASA built rockets.

   b. The joint mission ended conflict between the U.S. and the Soviet Union.

   c. Congress unanimously supported President Kennedy's proposal.

   d. none of the above

3. A recording of the *Apollo 13* astronauts talking to Mission Control in Houston is an example of

   a. scientific data.

   b. a primary source.

   c. a secondary source.

   d. explanatory text.

4. What is the central idea of the text?

   a. America always wins at everything.

   b. The Soviets had better technology.

   c. The United States and the Soviet Union competed in a "Space Race" in the 1960s.

   d. Space exploration is more important than competing for superior technology.

5. Would humans have reached the moon if the United States and the Soviet Union had not been competing? Give reasons for your answer, using both explicit and implicit evidence from the text. Continue writing on another sheet of paper if you need more space for your answer.

_____

_____

_____

_____

_____

_____

DETERMINING CENTRAL IDEAS

Guided Instruction

RI.7.2

WORDS TO KNOW

assumed

fateful

flight deck

solar array

stowage

tragedy

A text's **central ideas** are the most important ideas the author wants you to understand. Look for ideas that are repeated or stressed in the text.

CITE EVIDENCE

A Circle the information in paragraph 5 that tells the purpose of the shuttle mission. Would this information be a **central idea** in an article or encyclopedia entry on Barbara Morgan? Explain.

B How does Barbara Morgan stress her feelings about going to space? Underline the words that she lists. What do these words have in common? How are these words important to the central ideas of the text?

Barbara Morgan, Teacher and Astronaut

(Genre: Interview)

1   Barbara Morgan was selected as a backup candidate for NASA's Teacher in Space Program in 1985 and trained with Christa McAuliffe and the *Challenger* space shuttle crew. However, she remained behind when that **fateful** shuttle exploded, killing everyone onboard. Afterward, Morgan **assumed** the duties of NASA's Teacher in Space.

2   Morgan spent 20 years working with NASA on the ground but only made her first trip to space in 2007 aboard *Endeavor* space shuttle flight STS-118.

3   Here is part of a longer interview Morgan gave right before this mission. She was about to be the first Teacher in Space to blast off since the horrible *Challenger* **tragedy** in 1986.

Preflight Interview

4   **NASA:** Barbara, STS-118 will mean a lot of things to a lot of people, but probably not more than it will for kids around the world who will be watching you as you fly in space. How would you describe the mission to kids and what your role and duties are on the flight?

5   **MORGAN:** Well, my first word would be "exciting." Actually, it's more than a word. Exciting, interesting, amazing, and fun. We are going to the International Space Station; we call it an assembly mission. We are going to the International Space Station to help finish building it. In our cargo bay, or in the back end of the shuttle, we're taking up a couple of big pieces that are part of the station. One is part of the support structure that's going to hold more of the **solar arrays**, and one is the **stowage** platform that's going to hold a bunch of spare equipment that will be used eventually on station.

RI.7.2

6   Those are two of our major things that we're going to be doing. We'll be transferring all the things over that they need and bringing the things that they don't need back home with us. I'll have many different duties, so I'll just tell you about a couple of them. I'll be one of the robotic arm operators, so I'll be using the space shuttle arm and the space station arm to help us move some of these pieces of equipment as we attach them onto the station. And I'll be helping on the **flight deck**, coming home, or during what we call "entry" of the space shuttle back to Earth.

7   **NASA:** Kids always love spaceflight. What should they pay particular attention to on your flight? What should they be looking for? And ultimately, what do you think they're going to learn from this mission?

8   **MORGAN:** You're going to laugh at this, but what I really want them to do is to pay attention to themselves and to look very deep within themselves and dig up all the questions that they can that they have about our world, our universe, and about space exploration. Because this is all about learning, and we're here to help and we want to know from them—what is it that they really want to know and learn? Because this is their future and it's open-ended for them. I also hope that they'll see an ordinary person doing the things that they can be doing.

CITE EVIDENCE

C A **summary** is made up of central ideas without a lot of details. Double underline the sentence in Morgan's response that does the best job of summarizing the mission. How would you summarize what Morgan says in the rest of the paragraph about her duties on the shuttle?

D Being aware of key, or important, words as you read will help you determine central ideas. What does Morgan say is the key reason kids should pay attention to her mission? Circle the key word in her answer.

Comprehension Check

Why is Barbara Morgan so excited about this mission?

Barbara Morgan in the weightlessness of space

DETERMINING CENTRAL IDEAS

Guided Instruction

RI.7.2

WORDS TO KNOW

documented

long-standing

seize

tribulation

CITE EVIDENCE

A Paying attention to repeated words is important in determining the central ideas of a text. Circle the word in paragraph 10 that expresses Morgan's main reason for signing up with NASA.

B What two things did Christa McAuliffe accomplish, according to Morgan? Underline them. Summarize Morgan's views of McAuliffe.

9 **NASA:** Let's go back a little bit in history and trace the path that took you to this point in your career, from teacher in McCall, Idaho, to astronaut. Why did you sign up to do this in the first place all those many years ago?

10 **MORGAN:** Well, when the Teacher in Space program was started, I was sitting at home, it was after school, it was about five o'clock . . . and the President came on the news and announced that they were going to send a teacher in space. I shot straight up and said, "Wow!" As you know, teachers all across the country did! What a great opportunity! Because as teachers, we're always looking for opportunities to bring the world to our classroom, to gain more experiences, gain more knowledge about our world so that we can make our classroom a better place for our kids. And, it was a tremendous opportunity. And, as all teachers, we don't pass up those opportunities.

11 **NASA:** That summer day in 1985 when you and your fellow candidates were at the White House and Christa McAuliffe was announced as the Teacher in Space, you were announced as her backup, what feelings did you have?

12 **MORGAN:** We were all really excited and really thrilled to be doing what we were doing. Christa was, is, and always will be our "Teacher in Space," our first teacher to fly. She truly knew what this was all about—not just bringing the world to her classroom—but also helping . . . helping to show the world what teachers do and what all the good teachers do across our country day in and day out.

13 **NASA:** Isn't that really the whole point of you flying in space as an Educator Astronaut, to show that there are no boundaries to kids, that there are no limitations, that the opportunities are there if they would just wish to **seize** them?

14 **MORGAN:** Absolutely.

15 **NASA:** Certainly the **tribulations** have been well **documented** over the past two decades, most recently the *Columbia* accident. After that, after all of this, and after reliving the *Columbia* accident and all of the memories and the shadows of *Challenger* all over again, did it cause you at all to rethink your goal to fly in space, and to fly as an educator to carry out this **long-standing** dream of yours, of Christa, of your fellow educators?

RI.7.2

16 **MORGAN:** I'm going to answer that in a couple of ways because both *Challenger* and the *Columbia* have caused me to think, and it caused all of NASA to think. First of all, it caused us to think about what are we doing wrong, and how can we make it better, how can we make spaceflight safer because it is risky business, but we want to make it as safe as we can. All the astronauts, all of NASA, have been working really hard and will continue to work hard to try to make spaceflight as safe as we can possibly make it. It also caused me to really think, both *Challenger* and *Columbia*, about what's really important. In both situations, we had kids watching adults, and they watch adults. Kids learn a lot from watching adults. It's not just what we say, but it's what we do, and, kids were watching to see what the adults do in a terrible, terrible situation. What I thought was really important for kids to see is that we figure out what's wrong, we fix it, and we move on, and we keep the future open for our young people. And I just thought that that was really important, and feel that's really important today. I'll feel that's important forever.

CITE EVIDENCE

C Double underline some of the conclusions that NASA drew from the *Challenger* tragedy.

D Put a box around Morgan's key point about the most important thing to come from the *Challenger* tragedy.

E Put an asterisk next to the sentences that show Morgan's emphasis on the key point she made. Summarize Morgan's ideas about why her "long-standing dream" of flying in space is important.

Comprehension Check

Why might Barbara Morgan be afraid to fly into space? Is she?

Guided Practice

Barbara Morgan, Teacher and Astronaut *continued*

RI.7.2

WORDS TO KNOW

chemist

decade

perceived

singular

CITE EVIDENCE

A How can you tell how Morgan feels about learning? Underline evidence in paragraphs 18 and 20.

B How does Morgan emphasize the benefits over the risks of space exploration? With a partner, count the benefits and put an asterisk by each of them. Does Morgan convince you that the benefits outweigh the risks? Explain.

17 **NASA:** One of the things I'm struck by is that the roles are reversed: the teacher is being taught how to fly in space here, and has been over the course of all these years. Is Barbara Morgan a good student?

18 **MORGAN:** I hope I'm a good student. One thing is, like anything else, the more you put into it, the more you're going to get out of it. Actually, yes, I've been a student here at NASA, but, teachers are also students in their own classroom. That's one of the challenges and one of the rewards of being a classroom teacher is that you're there helping other people learn, and every day you're learning yourself.

19 **NASA:** Why is it worth the risk for humans to fly in space? And, what is really the benefit of the risk of putting an educator in space?

20 **MORGAN:** The risks are the same for an educator or a physician or an engineer or a pilot or a **chemist**, anyone else who flies in space. We're doing it to learn. We're doing it to explore; we're doing it to discover. We're doing it to help make this world a better place, and we're doing it to help keep those doors open for our young people so that they can, they can do it, too.

21 **NASA:** What kind of a support system is in place in your family to go through two **decades** of this **singular** goal of yours?

22 **MORGAN:** Well, my family knows that space exploration is really important. My husband and both our boys would love to fly, too.

23 **NASA:** What do you see as the similarities between what astronauts and teachers do, and how will your mission be **perceived** as a benefit for the education process in schools, do you think?

24 **MORGAN:** Astronauts and teachers learn and share; they explore; they discover; and then they go learn and share some more. And that's what this is all about.

Comprehension Check

1. What are two of the central ideas in Morgan's interview so far?

   a. learning and opportunity

   b. risk and reward

   c. assembly and cargo

   d. limitations and boundaries

2. How does Morgan develop the idea that she is a student as well as a teacher?

   a. by explaining how she will share her experiences in space when she returns to the classroom

   b. by describing how important a role model Christa McAuliffe was to her

   c. by comparing herself to a physician, an engineer, a pilot, and a chemist

   d. by reminding the interviewer that she learns from her students as much as they learn from her

3. One conclusion that readers can draw about Morgan is that she looks to the future with a sense of

   a. uncertainty.

   b. excitement.

   c. worry.

   d. overconfidence.

4. Which is the best summary of the interview so far?

   a. Morgan loves learning and teaching.

   b. Morgan was lucky not to be on the *Challenger* shuttle.

   c. Morgan is a teacher who is excited to go into space.

   d. Morgan is a mother with a supportive family.

5. How does Morgan's conclusion about the similarities between teachers and astronauts help you understand one of the central ideas of the text? Use evidence from the text. If you need more space to write, continue on another sheet of paper. When you are finished, compare answers with a partner.

_____

_____

_____

_____

_____

_____

DETERMINING CENTRAL IDEAS

Independent Practice

Barbara Morgan, Teacher and Astronaut *continued*

RI.7.2

WORDS TO KNOW

inherent

momentary

propelled

sustenance

telescope

CITE EVIDENCE

A What were the two main experiences that inspired Morgan as a child? Underline that information.

B Put an asterisk by places in paragraph 28 that show Morgan's positive attitude. What central idea of the text do these examples point to?

25 **NASA:** Did you just have an **inherent** interest in space at all? Did you follow the Neil Armstrong thing that so many astronauts say **propelled** them to want to specifically become an astronaut?

26 **MORGAN:** Absolutely, I was always interested in looking up at the stars when we'd go camping and as a Girl Scout. My folks, when we were very young, got us a little **telescope** for Christmas, and we had that out and would look up at the stars. I was always interested in what's out there. And then, yes as the space program was being born, we were glued to the TV when we first landed on the Moon and the flights leading up to that, and yes, that was very much a part of my growing up. I didn't even consider that that would be something that I could do, so that wasn't part of what I thought I would be doing. Part of that, too, was because the [lack of] opportunities then for women. I'm so glad now that's not the case anymore.

27 **NASA:** What kind of a mark do you think you will have left on education when this is all said and done? Is it going to be a lasting mark, or is this just a **momentary** blip on the radar screen in history? How can you make your flight an impact flight that will have **sustenance** for years to come with the lessons that you will have provided from the mission itself and what you're going to be doing up in orbit?

28 **MORGAN:** NASA's been doing excellent education, both on the ground and from orbit. By "education" I mean providing opportunities for students and teachers to get involved and to both experience and to contribute to space exploration goals. This is just one of many, many steps along the way. I really look forward to coming back and helping with what comes next, and what comes next, and what comes next. Education is never-ending. It can get better and better and better.

29 **NASA:** In that sense, is education very much like space itself—limitless? No boundaries?

30 **MORGAN:** Absolutely.

31 **NASA:** Barbara Morgan, educator astronaut, mission specialist, shuttle *Endeavour*, STS-118, thank you so much.

32 **MORGAN:** Thank you.—www.nasa.gov

Comprehension Check

(MORE ONLINE) **sadlierconnect.com**

1. Which words show that Morgan is interested in being part of a team?

   a. *women* and *history*

   b. *contributing* and *helping*

   c. *education* and *program*

   d. *interested* and *opportunities*

2. Based on this passage, what can you conclude about Morgan?

   a. She is fearless.

   b. She learns quickly.

   c. She is calm under pressure.

   d. She is enthusiastic about her job.

3. Which of the following would NOT be necessary in a summary of the text?

   a. Morgan wants to inspire children to learn.

   b. Morgan hopes to bring attention to her fellow teachers and their work.

   c. Morgan's husband and sons are very supportive of her goals.

   d. Morgan became a Teacher in Space in 1986.

4. Education is a central idea of this interview. How does Morgan define it?

   a. getting involved in an experience

   b. studying quietly alone

   c. reading books on different subjects

   d. learning from role models

5. Think again about the central ideas of this text. What makes Morgan a good representative for NASA's Teacher in Space program? Give reasons, using evidence from the text.

   _____

   _____

   _____

   _____

   _____

RI.7.3, RST.7.1

WORDS TO KNOW

circumference

compound

dissipate

mass

plummet

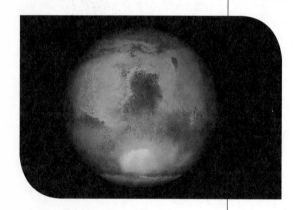

> Analyzing a text means understanding how its people, events, and ideas relate to and influence each other.

CITE EVIDENCE

A **Analyzing a text** means paying close attention to its details. Underline the information about the distance between planets that is important to consider when planning a mission to Mars.

B Which weather and atmospheric conditions will influence how astronauts prepare for Mars's climate? Put asterisks by two pieces of relevant information.

Destination Mars

(Genre: Feature Article)

1   After landing on the moon, landing on a planet seems to be the next logical step. Of our two neighbors, Venus and Mars, Mars is the logical choice. The surface of Venus is too hot—hot enough to melt metal. Mars is colder than Earth, which is less challenging. Even so, nearly 50 years after landing on the moon, we still haven't made it there!

2   Mars is visible in the night sky and has been known to humans since ancient times as the Red Planet. It is red because its surface is full of iron oxide, the same **compound** that colors blood and rust. In fact, the planet was named after the ancient Roman god of war due to its blood-red color.

3   Mars is the fourth planet from the sun, which makes it Earth's next-door neighbor. It's not a close neighbor, though, since Mars is about 36 million miles away from Earth at the closest point in their orbits. When the two planets are at their furthest distance, on opposite sides of the sun, Mars is closer to 250 million miles away. Obviously, then, any mission to Mars would have to be timed to take advantage of the shorter distance.

No Place Like Home

4   Mars, being farther from the sun, is colder than Earth. Although its temperatures can reach 80 degrees Fahrenheit at the warmest point on the warmest day, it can also **plummet** to more than 100 degrees below zero. The coldest place that humans regularly inhabit is Oymyakon, Russia. There the average winter temperature is minus 58 degrees Fahrenheit. On Mars the temperature drops dramatically because the atmosphere is thinner than on Earth. A thinner atmosphere allows heat to **dissipate** quickly. The atmosphere here on Earth holds heat in and also protects us from certain kinds of radiation; the thinner atmosphere on Mars does not.

5   It's not only the cold temperatures and radiation that can harm humans on Mars. The atmosphere on Mars is missing oxygen, which means that the air is poisonous for Earthlings to breathe. Humans would need to have life-support systems, radiation protection, and defense from below-freezing temperatures to survive on Mars.

What Goes Up

6   Mars is smaller than Earth. The **circumference** around Earth's equator is about 25,000 miles, while the circumference around Mars is about 13,000 miles. Therefore, another big difference between the two planets is connected to the force of gravity on each. As Earth is bigger and has more **mass**, the gravity on Earth is stronger than the gravity on Mars. On the Red Planet, you would be able to jump higher and throw a ball farther, which would make you much better at basketball! Your shape wouldn't look any different, but your weight would be reduced by about one-third. You might even be an inch or so taller with less gravity pulling you toward the planet's center. However, there would be a big price to pay if you ever returned to Earth.

7   The force of Earth's gravity pushing on us creates muscle strength even when we are still. When the force of gravity is reduced, your muscles don't have to work as hard, so they begin to shrink. This includes your heart, which is also a muscle. You might feel like Superman going from Earthling gravity to Martian gravity, but the reverse could be deadly!

8   Considering all the differences between the two planets, any mission that included humans would have to be very carefully planned.

Comprehension Check

Why is planning a manned trip to Mars so much more difficult than sending robot probes?

CITE EVIDENCE

C What would astronauts need to explore the surface of Mars? Double underline that information.

D Circle the evidence that shows that Mars is smaller than Earth. Why does this fact matter? Underline the word that answers this question.

E When analyzing a text, focus on how important ideas impact the people involved. What issues related to gravity could be problematic for astronauts? Put a box around that information.

Guided Instruction

Destination Mars *continued*

RI.7.3, RST.7.1

WORDS TO KNOW

genre

invigorating

isolated

marshal

philanthropist

suborbital

CITE EVIDENCE

A How is the Mars Society contributing to future exploration of Mars? Underline this information.

B What tools did the researchers use to measure the crew's stress and mood responses? Circle that information.

Training on the Ground

9   A group called the Mars Society is preparing for human exploration of Mars. The Mars Society is using small research bases established in desert terrains on Earth to study how people might live and work on Mars. As part of this project, a team of college students stayed at the Mars Desert Research Station in Hanksville, Utah. These students were there to research factors that might affect a team's stress levels and mood while **isolated** together inside a small living space for two weeks.

How Do We Measure Stress and Mood?

10   The first thing the team had to do was figure out how to measure the crewmembers' state of mind. One tool used was a questionnaire that asked crewmembers how they felt. Another was a computer assessment for measuring such functions as attention span, memory, reaction time, and decisionmaking. Scales and profiles gave descriptions the team could match to observable behaviors. Lastly, the team could measure physical indicators, such as blood pressure and heart rate. One of the goals was to see which tools worked best.

Does Music Reduce Stress?

11   One member of the team performed a study on the effect of music. The experiment exposed subjects to five different **genres** of music. These were played twice over a 10-day period. For three days no music was played. Those music-free days came at the beginning, middle, and end of the experience. The preliminary results showed that the crewmembers had the lowest blood-pressure measurements and heart rates on the days when country music was played, even though several crewmembers claimed to dislike that type of music. All of the crewmembers preferred days with some kind of music rather than no music at all.

Does Exercise Improve Mood?

12   Another factor studied was the effect of exercise on mood. In a Mars mission, exercise would be important to combat muscle loss, an effect of reduced gravity. The experiment compared the effects on mood after an advanced workout versus the effects after a moderate workout. The results first showed a negative reaction to the advanced workout and a positive reaction to the moderate workout. Over time, however, those feelings reversed. The advanced workout felt less intense over time and the moderate workout became less **invigorating**. Preliminary conclusions show that increasing workout intensity keeps workouts satisfying.

Beyond NASA

13   The Mars Society is not the only private group to get involved in space innovation. In the past, governments were the only organizations that could **marshal** enough money, talent, and resources to pull off such a large endeavor. Today, both private companies and individuals are funding space projects.

14   The era of private manned space travel began in 2004. The brainchild of a **philanthropist**, engineer, and pilot, *SpaceShipOne* was the first privately developed reusable launch vehicle and winner of a $10 million prize. A reusable vehicle is the key to making space trips more affordable.

15   This means it's only a matter of time before space tourism becomes a workable business. Space tourism began when a few wealthy people paid millions for a ride into space. A Russian spaceship took these privileged passengers to the International Space Station. Soon companies will offer **suborbital** rides to anyone with a few hundred thousand dollars or so to spare.

CITE EVIDENCE

C Double underline the factor that experiments show might reduce stress and improve the mood of Mars explorers.

D What new technology is necessary for space tourism to become a real business? Circle your answer.

E Put a box around the information that tells how space tourism got started.

The International Space Station

Comprehension Check

Based on your analysis of the text, how long will it take before humans are able to overcome the issues involved with traveling to Mars? Explain your answer.

ANALYZING TEXTS

Guided Practice

RI.7.3, RST.7.1

WORDS TO KNOW

cosmic

disorder

entrepreneur

impaired

scout

CITE EVIDENCE

A People who travel to Mars might have to worry about their thinking skills. Underline two reasons that support this idea.

B With a partner, consider the private missions to Mars (paragraphs 18–20). Put asterisks by the differences between the two missions. Then discuss which mission is more likely to succeed.

Destination Mars *continued*

Danger Ahead

16   Mars is the dream destination of many would-be space travelers. However, there are two big issues: the psychological effects of extreme isolation and the dangers of **cosmic** radiation. Mars500 was designed to test the effects of a simulated Mars voyage. An international crew was sealed in a spaceship-like environment for 520 days and monitored. Most of the crew developed sleep **disorders** that caused **impaired** thinking.

17   Experiments done with cosmic radiation showed that certain particles cause brain damage in mice. Of course, we can't be sure radiation would affect people the same way. Unfortunately, it's difficult to protect astronauts from these particles, since the particles can travel through almost anything.

Against the Odds

18   Despite these risks, a U.S. millionaire and rocket scientist has started the Inspiration Mars Foundation. Its goal is a manned mission to Mars in 2018. The plan is to fly by Mars rather than land on the planet. The voyage would last about 500 days. The Foundation is looking for a married couple to serve as the crew. Many have already applied. The group still needs to raise more money to make the mission happen.

19   A company founded by a Dutch **entrepreneur**, Mars One is taking a different approach. This group plans to generate the money it needs by turning the mission into a reality show. The ambition is greater, as well, since this group plans to start a human colony on Mars by 2023. Tens of thousands of people have already applied for a one-way ticket to the Red Planet. The company is planning its first launch, of equipment only, for 2016.

20   Two years later, a rover will **scout** the best location, and six living units will be sent up in 2021, according to the plan. In

2023, the first humans would land! Of course, the plan can work only if people around the world remain interested in watching this mission on TV, since the mission depends on money generated by television advertising.

21   Because it's so risky, NASA is not planning on any manned trips to Mars until 2030.

Comprehension Check

1. How does understanding different organizations' plans for private Mars missions help readers?

   a. Readers can better understand how much such a mission will cost.

   b. Readers can explore the problems with each organization's plan.

   c. Readers can imagine traveling to Mars on one of the missions.

   d. Readers can consider different solutions to the challenges of a Mars mission.

2. Of all the organizations preparing for a trip to Mars, which has the most problems to solve?

   a. the Mars Society

   b. Mars One

   c. NASA

   d. the Inspiration Mars Foundation

3. We can't be sure if cosmic radiation will harm humans because

   a. no experiments have been conducted.

   b. the results were negative.

   c. the results were positive.

   d. the experiment wasn't conducted on humans.

4. The dates in 2016, 2018, and 2023 were probably chosen because

   a. that's when Mars and Earth will be closest.

   b. that's how long it will take to raise the money needed.

   c. that's how long it will take to get ready.

   d. that's when the space radiation will be reduced.

5. Why might the ideas in this text influence people to choose one of the private companies instead of NASA? Discuss your answer with a partner, citing text evidence.

_____

_____

_____

_____

_____

_____

Independent Practice

Destination Mars *continued*

RI.7.3, RST.7.1

WORDS TO KNOW

artifact

deposit

refined

sedimentary

transmitted

CITE EVIDENCE

A Did the Soviets rush the *Mars 2* mission? Underline evidence you can use to answer this question.

B Put asterisks by details that tell you how each mission built on the one before it. Discuss what the progress of unmanned Mars missions reveals about NASA's goals.

Robots in Space

22   Even though NASA is not ready to plan a manned mission to Mars, it has sent many probes and rovers to study the planet. Over the years, these machines have become more **refined** and complex. You might even call them robots. Here's a short history of what has been accomplished so far.

23   *Mars 2*, the first unmanned craft that made it to the Red Planet, was sent up by the Soviets in 1971. The mission failed when *Mars 2* was destroyed in a crash landing, but it became the first human **artifact** left on another planet.

24   NASA had the first successful landing with the Viking Program in 1975, which included *Viking 1* and *Viking 2*. Each craft had an orbiter and a lander. All parts performed better than expected and **transmitted** data from the Martian orbit and ground for several years.

25   In 1996, NASA's *Pathfinder* delivered a micro-rover called *Sojourner* to the surface. This mission, building on what was learned from *Viking*, was much more efficient and cost the government much less.

26   Large rovers *Spirit* and *Opportunity* followed, reaching Mars in 2003. As information about the planet was gathered, the missions became more specific. *Spirit* was designed to explore the Gusev Crater and look for evidence that liquid water may have once been present there. *Opportunity* was designed to explore the Meridiani Planum, an area that includes iron-rich mineral **deposits**.

27   The rover *Opportunity* discovered a rock with markings that scientists think may have been made by flowing water because they look similar to markings on certain **sedimentary** rocks here on Earth. In 2007 the *Phoenix* mission explored the polar region of Mars and the next year was able to confirm the existence of frozen water in the soil.

28   The most recent rover to go to Mars is *Curiosity*, which was sent in 2012. It has already retrieved a core sample that includes all the necessary building blocks for life! Yet another robotic mission is planned for 2016. The InSight mission will drill down into the surface to learn more about the planet's core.

29   It will be interesting to see whose boots walk the dusty red soil first. Will it be NASA's slow and steady progress, or one of the bold space entrepreneurs?

Comprehension Check

MORE ONLINE sadlierconnect.com

1. Why has NASA sent so many unmanned missions to Mars?

    a. They haven't landed successfully.

    b. They haven't found evidence of life yet.

    c. Astronauts fear the Red Planet.

    d. They keep making new discoveries.

2. What led to the discovery of water on Mars?

    a. exploring the polar region

    b. seeing the markings on rock

    c. digging into the planet's core

    d. finding iron-rich mineral deposits

3. Which Mars mission will benefit most from the discovery of water?

    a. a fly-by mission

    b. a colony mission

    c. a rover mission

    d. a 500-day mission

4. The discovery by *Curiosity* means that

    a. there was definitely life on Mars.

    b. there is life somewhere on Mars.

    c. there is no more to learn about possible life on Mars.

    d. there is more to learn about possible life on Mars.

5. Would the *Curiosity* mission have been as successful if the other missions had not gone before it? Explain your answer, using evidence from the text.

_____

_____

_____

_____

_____

_____

_____

Our National Space Policy

(Genre: Explanatory Text and Policy Statement)

1   Part of every U.S. president's job is to set space policy. During the election season, presidential candidates talk about their goals for space exploration. Voters decide if they agree with those goals. Space policy may not seem like an important issue during an election because other issues get a lot more attention in the media.

2   In fact, some people are not in favor of more space exploration. They feel that the government has more important business and should focus on helping people. Space programs cost the government many millions of dollars, taking money away from other things government could be doing. However, people might be surprised to learn what else we get for that money in addition to knowledge and a sense of achievement.

3   In order to pull off a mission to space, a huge amount of research needs to be done.

This research takes place in all kinds of areas, such as engineering, biology, weather, communications, computer technology, and more. Many inventions that come out of this research have applications beyond the space program. Here are a few benefits that have come from the space program. Some of these advances were developed by NASA, and some were developed by private companies that were commissioned by NASA.

For Your Health

4   NASA, along with doctors and a technology company, developed a lifesaving heart pump for patients awaiting heart transplants. The ventricular assist device (VAD) can keep people alive and active until an organ donor is found.

5   Before the invention of the ear thermometer, taking your temperature meant sitting for several minutes with a mercury-filled glass tube under your tongue. Modern ear thermometers, developed with NASA's assistance, take your temperature in two seconds. They use the same infrared-detection technology that astronomers use to measure the temperature of distant stars.

6   Originally created for NASA, space robotic technology is now adding comfort and function to artificial limbs. Advances include artificial muscle systems with robotic sensing and movement. In addition, NASA's temper foam technology can be used to create natural-looking limbs that have the soft feel of flesh. The foam also provides cushioning that makes prosthetics more comfortable for people to wear.

For Safety and Convenience

7   Speaking of temper (memory) foam, you may have seen the mattresses or pillows that spring back when you touch them. That foam was developed by NASA to improve safety during crashes. It's now being used in safety features for cars, airplanes, amusement park rides, sports equipment, and more. The primary quality of the foam is its ability to absorb energy, which can soften impacts. That feature also makes it very comfortable to sink into. It is even used to make luxurious dog beds!

8   A tool company used *Apollo* and *Gemini* mission technologies to make cleaning easier. NASA required a portable, self-contained drill capable of extracting core samples from below the lunar surface. A computer program optimized the design of the drill's motor and reduced its need for power. That computer program made the cordless miniature vacuum cleaner possible.

For the Environment

9   A NASA-sponsored coalition of companies, government groups, universities, and nonprofits helped create improvements to solar power cells, making them both lighter and more effective. These new solar cells allow people to reduce the costs and pollution associated with traditional energy sources. The coalition's original goal was to create solar power sources without adding weight to unmanned aircraft.

10   NASA technology is being used to clean petroleum-based pollutants from water. The basic technology is thousands of microcapsules—tiny balls of beeswax with hollow centers. Water cannot get inside the microcapsule, but oil is absorbed right inside. The beeswax spheres float on the water's surface. In this way, oil spills can be captured before they settle into the water, damaging sea life and the ocean floor.

11   Water purification is an important part of space missions. Water is heavy to carry, so any water carried onboard needs to be recycled multiple times. NASA engineers in collaboration with private companies developed a water purification system for the astronauts living on the International Space Station. This system can turn wastewater from respiration, sweat, and urine into drinkable water. It's also used to help people all over the world who lack clean water. The system can provide drinkable water from even badly polluted sources.

12   Did you know NASA's excess rocket fuel can be used to destroy land mines? Instead of dumping this fuel as waste, NASA shares it with a company that gets rid of land mines. A device with a battery-operated electric match ignites solid rocket fuel placed on the mine. The fuel burns a hole in the mine's case and also burns up the explosive inside, so the mine is safely disarmed.

A man searches for land mines.

Our National Space Policy *continued*

And More!

13   Space technology has contributed to improvements or new products in all kinds of fields, from photography and art restoration to infant care and clothing manufacturing. In addition, NASA advances spurred technology that has led to smaller and smaller electronic devices, such as cell phones.

14   All these new products are great for individuals, but they also help the economy in general. New companies are created, and more people are hired. Of course, part of their paychecks goes to buy more things. In a way, then, some of the money spent on space exploration makes its way back to us all.

15   Probably the greatest benefit of the space program is its ability to inspire children's imagination. By motivating students to study science, technology, engineering, and math, our society will advance. The wonders of tomorrow will come from the students we are educating now. They will make devices that we cannot even imagine today.

16   So what is NASA's mission? It's inside the United States Space Policy document. These are the guidelines that were given to NASA by President Obama.

Guidelines for Space Science, Exploration, and Discovery

• NASA shall set far-reaching exploration milestones. By 2025, begin crewed missions beyond the Moon, including sending humans to an asteroid. By the mid-2030s, send humans to orbit Mars and return them safely to Earth.

• NASA shall continue the operation of the International Space Station (ISS), in cooperation with its international partners, likely to 2020 or beyond.

• NASA shall seek partnerships with the private sector to enable safe, reliable, and cost-effective commercial spaceflight capabilities and services for . . . the ISS.

• NASA shall implement a new space technology development working with industry, academia, and international partners . . . that can increase the capabilities, decrease the costs, and expand the opportunities for future space activities.

• NASA shall conduct research and development in support of next-generation launch systems, including new U.S. rocket engine technologies.

• NASA shall maintain a sustained robotic presence in the solar system to: conduct scientific investigations of other planetary bodies; demonstrate new technologies; and scout locations for future human missions.

• NASA shall continue a strong program of space science for observations, research, and analysis . . . to enhance knowledge of the cosmos, . . . understand the conditions that may support the development of life, and search for planetary bodies and Earth-like planets in orbit around other stars.

- And NASA shall pursue capabilities . . . to detect, track, catalog, and characterize near-Earth objects to reduce the risk of harm to humans from an unexpected impact on our planet and to identify potentially resource-rich planetary objects.

Going to an Asteroid?

17   Did you notice the goal of sending humans to an asteroid by 2025? NASA is also working with the University of Arizona on a mission called OSIRIS-REx in which a robot probe would approach and take samples of an asteroid named Bennu. Then the probe would tow the asteroid into the Moon's orbit, where astronauts can study it.

18   Bennu is a 500-ton asteroid in a near-Earth orbit. That might sound enormous, but Bennu is small enough to burn up in Earth's

atmosphere. It is rated 0 on the Torino Scale, used to measure how dangerous an asteroid might be to Earth. The OSIRIS-REx mission may help us learn to deflect more dangerous asteroids in the future.

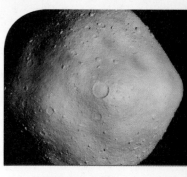

The asteroid Bennu

19   Bennu is also rich in carbon, the building block of life on Earth. Scientists hope that it may help answer questions about why Earth is abundant in carbon, unlike other planets.

20   In less than 100 years, humans will have gone from gazing at the stars to capturing asteroids—and the possibilities for future knowledge from and exploration of space are as boundless as the universe itself.

Comprehension Check

1A. The space technology we use is mostly developed by

  a. NASA.

  b. private companies.

  c. NASA and private companies working together.

  d. neither NASA nor private companies.

1B. What phrase from the text supports the answer to Part A?

  a. "new companies are created"

  b. "a NASA-sponsored coalition"

  c. "originally created for NASA"

  d. "NASA technology"

2A. What can you infer about most advances in new space technology?

  a. They are a result of problem solving.

  b. They are a result of wasteful spending.

  c. They are an attempt to recycle waste.

  d. They are lucky accidents.

2B. What sentence from the text best supports the answer to Part A?

  a. "Did you know NASA's excess rocket fuel can be used to destroy land mines?"

  b. "NASA technology is being used to clean . . . pollutants from water."

  c. "Modern ear thermometers . . . take your temperature in two seconds."

  d. "[Memory] foam was developed by NASA to improve safety."

3A. Which of the following is a main idea that is supported by the text?

    a. Space exploration is very expensive.

    b. Some people are not in favor of a space policy.

    c. It's important to have a space policy.

    d. all of the above

3B. What detail from the text best supports the answer to Part A?

    a. Other issues get more attention than space policy.

    b. The U.S. president sets space policy.

    c. NASA's mission is stated in the Space Policy document.

    d. The space program inspires students to study science and engineering.

4A. What is the main reason for having a space policy?

    a. to advance consumer products

    b. to set goals for exploration and research

    c. to make rules for how to treat alien life

    d. to spend more money helping people

4B. What detail from the text does NOT support the answer to Part A?

    a. "NASA shall continue a strong program of space science . . ."

    b. "NASA shall seek partnerships with the private sector . . ."

    c. "NASA shall set far-reaching exploration milestones."

    d. "NASA shall conduct research and development in support of next-generation launch systems . . ."

5A. Which part of the nation's policy addresses asteroids?

    a. "maintain a sustained robotic presence in the solar system"

    b. "detect, track, catalog, and characterize near-Earth objects"

    c. "seek partnerships with the private sector"

    d. "continue the operation of the International Space Station"

5B. Which words from that part of the policy are a clue to answer Part A?

    a. "near-Earth objects, impact"

    b. "Earth-like planets, life"

    c. "decrease costs, expand opportunity"

    d. "launch systems, engine"

6. What is the key quality of temper (memory) foam, and why does it have so many uses? Explain.

_____

_____

_____

7. What is an asteroid, and why does NASA want to study one?

_____

_____

_____

8. Summarize how the OSIRIS-REx mission to study an asteroid is supposed to work.

_____

_____

_____

9. Write a paragraph summarizing the text that tells how events in space research have positively affected everyday people's lives. Explain your answer using evidence from the text. Use a separate piece of paper if you need more space for your answer.

_____

_____

_____

_____

_____

_____

_____

10. Below are three claims that one could make based on the United States Space Policy.

- The United States is mainly committed to protecting its own interests in space.

- The United States supports cooperative efforts in the exploration of space.

- The United States intends to transfer responsibility for space exploration from the government to private organizations.

A. Underline the claim that is supported by the most relevant and sufficient evidence within the Space Policy excerpt.

B. On a separate piece of paper, write two facts that best provide evidence to support the claim you underlined in Part A.

Support a Claim

RI.7.9, SL.7.1.a, SL.7.1.c–d, SL.7.3

In this unit you've read an explanatory text and speech about the Space Race, an astronaut interview, a feature article about going to Mars, and guidelines from the United States Space Policy. Think about the claim below and how these selections might support that claim. In the chart, list key details and important points from the texts to use as evidence. Then write a brief essay in which you use the information in the chart to support the claim. Use a separate sheet of paper if you need more room to write. Be prepared to discuss your ideas with the class.

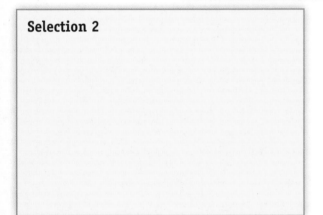

Selection 1

Selection 3

CLAIM: The United States has benefited in many ways from the space program.

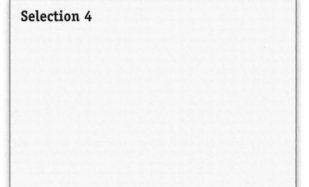

Selection 2

Selection 4

Return to the Essential Question

How can readers find and analyze central ideas in a text?

In small groups or as a class, discuss the Essential Question. Think about what you have learned about drawing inferences; determining central ideas; and analyzing interactions among people, events, and ideas in a text. Use evidence from the four texts in this unit to answer the question.

Greek and Latin Roots

Guided Instruction Knowing common **Greek and Latin roots** can help you determine the meaning of unfamiliar words. See if you can recognize an unfamiliar word's root (the core of the word). Some words have more than one root.

Root	Origin	Meaning
astro / aster	Greek	star
cosmo	Greek	universe
lab	Latin	work
lun	Latin	moon
micro	Greek	small
miss / mit	Latin	send
naut	Greek	sailor
port	Latin	carry
sol	Latin	sun
techno	Greek	skill
therm	Greek	heat
trans	Latin	across

Examples:

- **atmosphere** (Greek: *atmo* is "air," *sphere* is "ball or globe")
  The **atmosphere** is like a globe of air around Earth.

- **manufacture** *(manu* is Latin for "hand," *fact* is Latin for "make")
  Before machines, to **manufacture** something was to make it by hand.

Guided Practice Use the Greek and Latin roots from the chart above to complete the sentences below.

1. The astro _____ trained and was ready for her space mission.

2. Solar panels are a green energy _____ logy.

3. The plan is to capture an _____ oid and put it in _____ ar orbit.

Independent Practice What other words with Greek and Latin roots can you find in the Close Reading selection? Write them on another piece of paper. Are there any other words you know with these roots? Add them. Write three sentences using some of the words on your list.

RI.7.1, RI.7.2, RI.7.3, L.7.4.b

Read the following texts that include implied ideas; multiple central ideas; interactions among people, events, and ideas; and words with Greek and Latin roots. Then answer the questions on pages 97 and 98.

Going Up: Space Elevator

1   For the entire space age so far, we have depended on rocket technology for getting out of the grip of Earth's orbit. Rockets have to burn a tremendous amount of fuel to overcome the force of Earth's gravity. It is one of the most difficult and expensive parts of space travel. What if there were another way?

2   The space elevator was once an idea in a science-fiction story, and now some engineers think it is possible. From a platform in the sea, a cable would stretch into space. Climbing machines attached to the cable would transport people and supplies into Earth's orbit for much less money than it costs to send up spacecraft.

3   The trick is to find a substance strong enough to use to make the cable. Carbon nanotubes are the material being considered. A carbon nanotube is a configuration of carbon atoms arranged in a pattern like a soccer ball. Carbon nanotubes are nearly as light as air and are as flexible as plastic, but they are also 100 times stronger than steel. Although carbon nanotubes are incredibly strong when woven into small strands, engineers are still working on longer strands. They are trying to weave a thread made of millions of carbon nanotubes. It's like trying to weave a rope from a pile of powder.

4   In the meantime, one of the companies working on this problem is going to try to build a space elevator on the moon first. They believe it will work with existing technology. The moon's gravity is much weaker than Earth's, and without an atmosphere, the moon has no weather. So, it might become a shortcut from the International Space Station to the moon.

5   Some people are less optimistic about the carbon nanotube breakthrough necessary to tether a space elevator to Earth. However, that's not the only issue that makes the idea of a space elevator unlikely.

Going Nowhere: Space Elevator

1   The motion from solar wind, the gravitational pull of the sun and moon, and the climbers themselves could cause the cable to vibrate like a plucked guitar string. Of course, there could be a way to dampen the cable's motion, but that's more technology to develop.

2   Another issue is that satellites and space junk could crash into the cable. New satellites could have technology that would allow them to dodge the cable, but existing satellites and space junk would be a risk. Despite these issues, even skeptics admit that the idea just might work on the moon.

RI.7.1, RI.7.2

Circle the letter next to the best answer choice.

1A. Which of the following would a space elevator make unnecessary?

   a. rockets

   b. orbiting satellites

   c. travel to the moon

   d. the International Space Station

1B. What details from "Going Up: Space Elevator" support the answer to Part A?

   a. Carbon nanotubes are difficult to weave together.

   b. Orbiting satellites might crash into the space elevator.

   c. A space elevator might be built on the moon.

   d. People have always used rockets to get out of Earth's orbit.

2A. Which of the following is a reasonable inference, based on both texts?

   a. There is no way that a space elevator can ever be made to work.

   b. Any alternatives to the space elevator would have to solve the same basic problems.

   c. A space elevator is the only way to transport things into space inexpensively.

   d. Humans will never stop searching for a way to travel into space more cheaply.

2B. What information from the texts supports the answer in Part A?

   a. A space elevator will be easier to build on the moon.

   b. Rockets are expensive and burn a lot of fuel.

   c. A cable would be attached to a platform in the sea.

   d. Scientists have to find a way to dampen the cable's motion.

3A. Which of the following is a central idea of "Going Up: Space Elevator"?

   a. Carbon nanotubes are 100 times stronger than steel.

   b. The space elevator might be a shortcut from the ISS to the moon.

   c. The space elevator is an idea from science fiction.

   d. The space elevator might be easier to build on the moon.

3B. What detail from the text supports the answer to Part A?

   a. The gravitational pull of the sun could make a cable vibrate.

   b. Some people think it is possible to build a space elevator.

   c. The moon has no atmosphere and no weather.

   d. Climbing machines would move up and down a cable.

4A. What is a quality of carbon nanotubes that makes them a good option for a space elevator cable?

   a. They are inexpensive.

   b. They are arranged in a pattern.

   c. They have almost no weight.

   d. They are made from powder.

4B. What evidence from "Going Up: Space Elevator" supports the answer to Part A?

   a. A carbon nanotube is a configuration of carbon atoms.

   b. Carbon nanotubes are nearly as light as air.

   c. Carbon nanotubes are 100 times stronger than steel.

   d. Carbon nanotubes are hard to weave into long strands.

RI.7.1, RI.7.2, RI.7.3, L.7.4.b, L.7.6

5A. Which claim about nanotube technology is supported by both texts?

    a. This technology is ready to use.

    b. This technology has not been proven.

    c. This technology cannot possibly work.

    d. This technology is too expensive to build.

5B. Which statement provides evidence for the claim above?

    a. The idea comes from a science-fiction story.

    b. Carbon nanotubes are being considered.

    c. Engineers are still working on longer strands.

    d. It's like trying to weave a rope from a pile of powder.

6A. Which word from "Going Up: Space Elevator" contains the Latin roots for *across* and *carry*?

    a. *International*

    b. *transport*

    c. *technology*

    d. *nanotubes*

6B. Choose the idea from the text that could be expressed using the answer to Part A.

    a. A space elevator would be less expensive than using rockets.

    b. Solar wind can make a space cable vibrate.

    c. Carbon atoms can be arranged in a pattern.

    d. The space elevator would be used to take materials into space.

7. What breakthroughs in technology might improve the space elevator's chances?

_____

_____

8. Briefly summarize "Going Up: Space Elevator."

_____

_____

_____

9. What inference can you draw from "Going Nowhere: Space Elevator" about how soon a space elevator might exist on Earth? Support your inference.

_____

_____

_____

10. What would be the biggest impact of a space elevator? Explain.

_____

_____

_____

Introducing UNIT 4

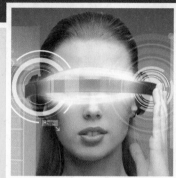

In this unit about new frontiers in technology, you will learn how to write an informative/explanatory essay. In this type of essay, your primary purpose is to communicate information—that is, to explain something that your readers may not know.

Your essay should be complete and well presented. Break your topic down in a way that will help readers grasp it better. Explain each important point clearly, and connect the points with transitions. Include facts, details, and examples to support your ideas. Consider strategies such as defining, comparing, and cause-effect analysis to help explain the topic. Headings and graphics, too, can help make information clear.

Progress Check *Can I?*

Before Unit 4 / **After Unit 4**

- Introduce a topic clearly.
- Use an appropriate strategy to organize ideas and information.
- Use formatting and graphics to make information clear.
- Develop a topic with facts, details, and examples.
- Use a formal style in my writing.
- Include appropriate transitions to link ideas.
- Choose precise language.
- Use commas correctly when punctuating phrases and clauses.
- Recognize and correct misplaced modifiers.
- Understand and use figurative language.

HOME◆CONNECT...

In this unit, your child will learn to **write to explain or inform** effectively. Your child will **organize** relevant facts and details and share them clearly. Help your child with these skills by working together to **select and analyze the content** of good examples of informative writing. You may wish to point out well-written explanations in newspaper or magazine articles, manuals, and other nonfiction sources. Together, discuss how the explanations are developed and why they are clear.

Help your child acquire knowledge about topics that spark his or her interest. Together, look for and discuss print sources and reliable online sources of information. Ask questions to prompt more comprehensive explanation; for example, ask your child what he or she learns from **quotations, examples**, and **graphics** in the text. Encourage your child to use **precise language** when responding and to link ideas with **transitions**.

Activity: Explore with your child the unit theme: "New Frontiers in Technology." Together, research and discuss areas in which people are pushing the boundaries of knowledge and innovation in areas such as genetic research, alternative energy, and robotic technology. You and your child might choose one area of exploration and create a timeline that shows major milestones and breakthroughs in that field, ending with anticipated next steps for the future.

IN THIS UNIT, YOUR CHILD WILL...

- Learn to write an informative/explanatory text that introduces a topic, organizes information logically, and ends with a conclusion.

- Use facts, details, and examples to develop a topic.

- Use text features such as headings and graphics to help communicate information.

- Include transitions to link ideas.

- Choose precise language and a formal style.

- Use commas correctly with phrases and clauses.

- Recognize and correct misplaced modifiers.

- Understand and use figurative language.

NOTE: All of these learning goals for your child are based on the Grade 7 Common Core State Standards for English Language Arts.

WAYS TO HELP YOUR CHILD

Have your child practice communicating information about topics he or she already knows well. For example, you might ask for step-by-step instructions for operating an electronic device, or your child might share information about a sport, hobby, or other interest. Talk about the information that your child shared and where you need more information to answer your remaining questions.

ONLINE

For more Home Connect activities, continue online at sadlierconnect.com

Text Types and Purposes: Write Informative/ Explanatory Texts

Essential Question:
How can writers present information effectively?

W.7.2, W.7.2.a–b, W.7.2.e, WHST.7.2, WHST.7.2.a–b, WHST.7.2.e

CREATING AN ORGANIZATIONAL STRUCTURE

Alex used an outline like the one below to organize his essay.

Title _____

I. Introduction
   a. Topic: _____

II. Supporting Resources
   a. First paragraph: information about _____
      1. Fact or detail _____
      2. Fact or detail _____
   b. Second paragraph: information about _____
      1. Fact or detail _____
      2. Fact or detail _____
   c. Third paragraph: information about _____
      1. Fact or detail _____
      2. Fact or detail _____

III. Conclusion
   _____
   _____
   _____

TITLE

- Gives readers an interesting clue about the topic

INTRODUCTION

- Introduces the topic, using a formal style
- Gives a preview of what is to come in the essay

INFORMATION ORGANIZED BY IDEA

- Develops the topic by grouping and exploring ideas related to it

Read a Student Model

Alex is a student in Mr. Paulson's seventh-grade Language Arts class. Mr. Paulson gave Alex's class an assignment to write an explanatory essay about a modern technology that has changed our lives on Earth. Mr. Paulson expects the essays to be written clearly and to be well organized. Think about a technology that you might choose when you write your own informative/explanatory essay.

Five-Minute Meals

A technology that has changed our lives is the microwave oven. It offers people a very different way to cook. Before microwave ovens existed, the only way to heat food was with a gas or electric oven. Traditional ovens take time to heat up, time to cook the food, and more time to cool down. Microwave ovens cook food very quickly and stay cool inside after the food is done.

Quick Cooking

The main benefit of this new technology is saving time. You can make dinners and snacks quickly. Meals that used to take 45 minutes or more to heat up now take just a few minutes. However, there are some kinds of cooking you can't do in a microwave oven. You can't grill or fry foods, and you can't brown the outside of foods, either. Still, you can steam vegetables in the microwave oven, you can "bake" a potato, and you can even make a small cake in a mug!

W.7.2.a–d, WHST.7.2.a–d

How Does It Work?

Microwave ovens use electromagnetic waves to cook food. Electromagnetic waves include radio waves, light waves, and X-rays. Food is made up of different types of molecules, including water molecules. When food is heated in a microwave, the water molecules inside the food are displaced by the electromagnetic waves. The waves agitate the water molecules, causing them to rotate at different speeds.

As the water molecules inside the food begin to rotate at increasing speeds, energy is created. The food absorbs the microwave energy, and that energy heats the food inside and out. The particles within the food absorb this energy at the same time. Consequently, unlike food cooked in a traditional oven, all of the food inside a microwave is cooked at the same temperature, at the same time.

Microwave Safety

Microwave ovens are safer than hot ovens as long as you follow a few safety rules. Do not use metal in the microwave because metal can cause dangerous sparks. Use microwave-safe containers only, and if you're not sure, glass or ceramic containers are best. Some kinds of plastic can begin to melt in the microwave, and you don't want plastic to get into your food. Be careful when you remove food from the microwave, especially if it comes in a pouch, as microwave popcorn does. Hot steam rushing out of the pouch can be hot enough to burn you.

FORMATTING

Make ideas clear by using headings to show how your ideas are organized.

TRANSITIONS

Link your ideas, so the reader can follow your logic. Alex uses the word *Consequently* to show a cause-and-effect link.

Circle another transition word or phrase under **Quick Cooking** *on page 102.*

FACTS AND DETAILS

Alex includes many facts and details in this essay.

Underline examples of facts and details in this paragraph.

PRECISE LANGUAGE

Use precise language that names exact things and ideas. Also, use words that describe actions specifically, such as the word *rushing*.

Put an asterisk next to three examples of precise language in paragraph 1.

Chilly or Sore?

Microwave ovens have other uses besides cooking, too! They are great for warming up a heating pad, which you can use to soothe sore muscles or warm up cold toes. If you don't have a heating pad, it's easy to make one. Put some uncooked rice inside a clean cotton tube sock and sew the end closed. If you want a pleasant scent, mix some dried herbs in with the rice. You can also sprinkle the rice with vanilla extract or your favorite scented oil. Your heating pad only takes a minute or two in the microwave to get warm.

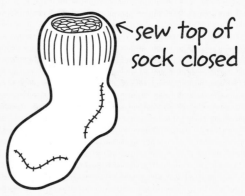

← sew top of sock closed

Some people might say that microwave ovens are not as exciting an invention as computers or the Internet. That may be true, but microwave technology has made it possible for people all over the world to have safe and quick access to hot meals without having to use fire. You can't beat a microwave oven for heating things up without wasting time or energy!

GRAPHICS

Make some information easier to understand by putting it in a chart or showing it in a diagram.

Circle information in the text that is also shown in the diagram.

CONCLUSION

Alex's conclusion sums up the central idea of his essay.

Double underline the statement that summarizes the essay's central idea.

W.7.2.a–b, W.7.2.f, W.7.4, W.7.5, W.7.6, W.7.10, WHST.7.2.a–b, WHST.7.2.f

Use this outline to organize your informative/explanatory essay for the Common Core Review on page 111. Then write your first draft on a separate sheet of paper. Remember to use a formal style and to develop the topic with a variety of facts and details. Also, think about which precise words and transitions will help make your ideas and information clear.

Title _____

I. **Introduction**

   a. Topic: _____

II. **Supporting Resources**

   a. First paragraph: information about _____

     1. Fact or detail _____

     _____

     2. Fact or detail _____

     _____

   b. Second paragraph: information about _____

     1. Fact or detail _____

     _____

     2. Fact or detail _____

     _____

   c. Third paragraph: information about _____

     1. Fact or detail _____

     _____

     2. Fact or detail _____

     _____

III. **Conclusion**

     _____

     _____

L.7.1.c

Phrase and Clause Placement

Guided Instruction A **phrase** is a group of words that functions together as a single part of speech, such as a noun or adjective. A **clause** is a phrase that has a subject and verb. A dependent clause cannot stand alone. When you begin a sentence with a long phrase or a dependent clause, follow it with a comma.

- **Comma needed**

    On Monday evenings after 5:00, the museum is closed. (long introductory phrase)

    Because we're in a hurry, let's heat the soup in the microwave. (dependent clause first)

- **No comma needed**

    After dinner we looked at the stars. (short introductory phrase)

    The star party is at 10:00 P.M. *because the sky will be dark by then.* (dependent clause at end)

Guided Practice Read each sentence carefully. Underline the introductory phrase or dependent clause, and add commas where needed. (Not every sentence has an introductory element or needs a comma.)

1. When my favorite television show comes on I'll watch it eagerly.

2. Alicia Perez gave a speech after she was elected class president.

3. At some time between midnight and dawn an asteroid will pass by Earth.

Independent Practice Write four original sentences, two with a long introductory phrase and two with a dependent clause at the beginning. Add commas where needed.

1. _____

_____

2. _____

_____

3. _____

_____

4. _____

_____

L.7.1.c

Misplaced Modifiers

Guided Instruction A word or phrase often **modifies**, or describes, another word in the same sentence. Make sure, however, that the modifying word or phrase is in a place that makes sense. In the examples below, the modifier has a double underline and the word it modifies has a single underline.

The <u>new</u> <u>children's</u> toys were scattered in the yard. (incorrect)

The children's <u>new</u> <u>toys</u> were scattered in the yard. (correct)

José gave the bicycle to his <u>cousin</u> <u>with silver handlebars</u>. (incorrect)

José gave the <u>bicycle</u> <u>with silver handlebars</u> to his cousin. (correct)

I saw a double <u>rainbow</u> <u>going outside after the storm</u>. (incorrect)

<u>Going outside after the storm</u>, <u>I</u> saw a double rainbow. (correct)

Guided Practice Each modifying word or phrase in the following sentences has a double underline. Study each sentence and then answer the questions.

1. I was sad when I heard about my <u>broken</u> friend's leg.

What does the word seem to modify? _____

What should the word modify? _____

2. Wearing an old shirt, Bryan gave his speech <u>with a big stain on it</u> in class.

What does the phrase seem to modify? _____

What should the phrase modify? _____

3. Rochelle was surprised by her cat <u>trying to do her math homework</u>.

What does the phrase seem to modify? _____

What should the phrase modify? _____

Independent Practice Rewrite the sentences above so that each modifying phrase is placed correctly. Reword sentences if necessary.

1. _____

2. _____

3. _____

Figurative Language: Metaphor and Simile

Guided Instruction **Figurative language** adds interest to writing by inviting readers to imagine things in new ways. Metaphors and similes are types of figurative language that compare two essentially unlike things. A **metaphor** makes the comparison directly, sometimes by using the word *is*, whereas a **simile** uses the words *like* or *as* to show the comparison.

- *The microwave is a dark club where food molecules dance.* (metaphor)

- *Let's explore microwave ovens, those dark clubs where food molecules dance.* (metaphor)

- *Microwave ovens, unlike traditional ovens, cook like race cars.* (simile)

Guided Practice Write whether the figurative language in each sentence is a simile or a metaphor.

1. We still haven't been to Mars, that red stoplight in the sky. _____

2. Music was the vitamin that gave them strength. _____

3. His forehead was as hot as fire. _____

4. My stomach growled like a monster in a horror film. _____

5. The dentist looked into the patient's open cave of a mouth. _____

Independent Practice Turn these comparisons into sentences by using a metaphor or simile, as marked. Then write two original sentences that use these techniques.

1. Space tourism/an amusement park ride (metaphor)

_____

2. A hot sidewalk/frying pan (simile)

_____

3. A day with no chores/a birthday present (metaphor)

_____

4. _____

5. _____

L.7.5

Figurative Language: Hyperbole and Personification

Guided Instruction **Figurative language** stretches the meaning of words in order to entertain readers and make them think. Types of figurative language include **hyperbole** (exaggeration) and **personification** (giving human qualities to an object or animal).

■ *Microwave ovens can cook dinner <u>in a second</u>.* (hyperbole)

■ *A microwave oven <u>can lend you a hand</u> when you want to cook food quickly.* (personification)

Guided Practice Write whether each sentence contains hyperbole or personification.

1. The cat gave me a lecture when his dinner was late. _____

2. We'll be ten years older by the time we get out of this traffic! _____

3. These family photographs tell us stories about the past. _____

4. My handwriting is harder to read than earthworm tracks. _____

5. The skyscraper was so tall that birds couldn't fly over it. _____

6. The spring wind danced through the trees. _____

Independent Practice Complete each sentence with personification or hyperbole, as indicated. Then write two original sentences, using each of these techniques once.

1. The launch pad _____ as the rockets fired. (hyperbole)

2. The meal was so delicious that our taste buds _____. (personification)

3. The prizewinning pumpkin was so large that _____. (hyperbole)

4. The old chair _____ as the boy bounced on it. (personification)

5. _____

6. _____

SL.7.1.a–d, SL.7.3, SL.7.4, SL.7.6

Discuss the Essential Question

How can writers present information effectively?

Prepare for a class discussion about the Essential Question by responding to the questions below. Support your point of view with reasons and examples.

1. How did Alex organize information about his topic?

_____

_____

_____

2. What facts and details did Alex use to develop the essay?

_____

_____

_____

3. What kind of language did Alex use to discuss concepts and connect ideas?

_____

_____

_____

Use your notes above as you discuss the Essential Question with your class or in small groups. Use the organizer below to record your ideas and what you hear in the discussion. Follow the discussion rules on the "Did I?" checklist (page 58).

Ideas I Agree or Disagree With		Questions I Asked
SideText		
SideText		
New Ideas I Had During Discussion		**Questions I Answered**

W.7.2, W.7.2.a–e, L.7.1.c

Read this introductory paragraph from a student informative/ explanatory essay, and answer the questions below.

> (1) A modern technology that has changed our lives is the GPS, or global positioning system. (2) In the old days, people needed paper maps or directions to keep from getting lost. (3) Today, if you are driving in a car to a new place, riding on a boat, or hiking in the woods, an electronic GPS device can guide you on your way. (4) A GPS device can tell you where to find a restaurant or gas station in your car.

1. Which of the following is an example of informal language?

   a. changed our lives

   b. paper maps

   c. in the old days

   d. gas station

2. Which of the following is the best way to correct sentence 4?

   a. A GPS device can tell you, in your car, where to find a restaurant or gas station.

   b. A GPS device in your car can tell you where to find a restaurant or gas station.

   c. A restaurant or gas station can be found in your car by a GPS device.

   d. In your car, a restaurant or gas station can be found by a GPS device.

3. Which is the clearest example of precise language from the text?

   a. modern technology

   b. global positioning system

   c. deep in the woods

   d. can guide you on your way

4. Which of the following details would best help develop this topic?

   a. GPS technology has decreased in cost since its invention.

   b. Some hikers prefer using maps to a GPS.

   c. A detailed GPS map can display a user's current location.

   d. Another technology is the smartphone.

5. Based on this introduction, which heading would you NOT expect to see in this essay?

   a. How a GPS Works

   b. Developments in GPS Technology

   c. How to Use a GPS

   d. Why GPS Technology is Overrated

6. Which transition word or phrase would make sense at the beginning of sentence 4?

   a. Furthermore,

   b. On the other hand,

   c. To begin with,

   d. Nevertheless,

W.7.2.f, W.7.4, W.7.5, W.7.10, L.7.1.c, L.7.5

Read these next two paragraphs from the student informative/explanatory essay, and answer the questions below.

(1) One of the benefits of a GPS device is that it can give directions out loud. (2) When you are driving, you need to keep your eyes glued to the road. (3) Hearing the directions out loud is like having a copilot while you drive. (4) Spoken directions are also helpful when riding a bike or even walking. (5) You can program the address, and the GPS directions can guide you there.

(6) You still may have times when a GPS device gives you wrong directions despite knowing about this technology. (7) However, it usually is the mapping software, not the GPS, that gives you bad advice. (8) GPS signals bounce off of satellites and give coordinates that describe your current location. (9) These coordinates are plugged into the mapping software. (10) If there's a glitch in the software, or the maps are out of date, then the directions can go very wrong.

7. Underline the sentence in the first paragraph that includes a simile.

8. Circle the number of the sentence in the second paragraph that includes an example of personification.

9. Find the misplaced modifier in sentence 6, and write the sentence correctly here.

_____

_____

10. Write a conclusion for this essay.

_____

_____

_____

_____

Assignment: On a separate piece of paper, provide a final draft of the essay you began on page 105. Use what you learned about phrases and clauses, modifiers, and figurative language in the Language section of this unit. Think about how you and your classmates answered the Essential Question. Check your outline to be sure you have organized your ideas well. Be sure to use precise language and transitions. End with a concluding statement.

Introducing UNIT 5

Literary texts almost always involve a conflict of some kind. If you've ever had an argument with a friend, you've experienced conflict. Conflict can also occur between you and an object. Remember the last time your computer crashed? Sometimes you experience conflict with nature, too—for example, when you have to work outdoors on a day so hot that even the thought of going outside makes you sweat. In this unit, you will read stories, poems, and dramas about characters who face conflict as they work toward a goal.

To make stories interesting and exciting, authors use elements of craft and structure. For example, they consider the sounds and connotations of words. They decide if literal language or a figure of speech is the better way to express an idea. Authors also consider a work's structure, or how it is put together. For example, is a poem a better way to tell a particular story than a play or a traditional short story might be? And what about the characters in the story—what are their points of view, and why are their differences important?

Learning about these elements will help you understand and enjoy the stories that you are about to read.

Before Unit 5

Progress Check *Can I?*

After Unit 5

- [ ] Determine the figurative and connotative meanings of words and phrases. [ ]
- [ ] Analyze the impact of rhymes and other repeated sounds on a poem, short story, or play. [ ]
- [ ] Explain how the form or structure of a drama or poem affects its meaning. [ ]
- [ ] Analyze how an author develops the points of view of characters or narrators in a text. [ ]
- [ ] Interpret figures of speech, including allusions, in context. [ ]

HOME◆CONNECT...

IN THIS UNIT, YOUR CHILD WILL...

- Read literary selections, including poems, a drama, a work of historical fiction, and an adventure story.

- Determine the meanings of words and phrases, including figurative and connotative meanings.

- Analyze the effect of rhymes and repeated sounds on a text.

- Analyze how the form or structure of a poem or drama affects the work's meaning.

- Analyze how an author develops and contrasts characters' points of view.

- Interpret figures of speech, including allusions.

- Compare and contrast ideas across four selections on the theme of sources of conflict.

NOTE: All of these learning goals for your child are based on the Grade 7 Common Core State Standards for English Language Arts.

When reading stories, your child needs to remember that many words have **connotative meanings**; that is, the words affect readers' emotions. Read part of a story with your child, and talk about the ways that its words affect your emotions. Discuss how the effect would be different if the author had used more "neutral" words—for example, the word *tasty* instead of the word *scrumptious*, or the word *confidence* instead of the word *arrogance*.

Although dramas and poems can tell stories, they have different structures, and **their structure affects their meaning**. For example, a poem with strong rhythm and rhyme feels very different from a haiku. In a play, the effect of a soliloquy differs from the effect of regular dialogue. Read a short story with your child. Talk about how you would feel if the story were presented as a poem.

At the heart of most stories is a conflict, and that conflict often occurs when characters have **different points of view**. Ask your child to think of a story in which the characters have strongly differing opinions. Why is that difference important to the story?

WAYS TO HELP YOUR CHILD

Listen to the words and phrases your child uses, and identify connotative meanings of which he or she may be unaware. You can also play a game: Say a word and have your child suggest a synonym with a strong positive or negative connotation. Together, explore the connotative meaning of each word.

Conversation Starter: Ask your child to recall a conflict that he or she has experienced—for example, a disagreement with a friend or sibling, a challenge when playing a sport, or a difficult decision. Then recall a conflict that you have experienced. Together, identify the source of each conflict and how the conflict was resolved. Discuss what each of you learned from the experience.

> **ONLINE**
>
> **For more Home Connect activities, continue online at** sadlierconnect.com

Reading Literature: Craft and Structure

Essential Question:
How do authors use language, structure, and characters to create meaning?

RL.7.4

WORDS TO KNOW

amulet

eloquent

luminous

sabre

scintillating

talisman

Poets carefully choose words and phrases for their impact on readers. Look for different kinds of **literary language**, and analyze both their meaning and their impact on the poem.

CITE EVIDENCE

A One type of literary language that poets often use is **rhyme** at the ends of lines. Rhyming words help give a poem its structure and rhythm. Find and underline a word at the end of one of the first four lines that rhymes with *eyes* in line 1.

B Edgar Allan Poe wrote "A Valentine" as a love poem to a woman whose identity he keeps secret. The poem is also a **riddle**—a challenge for readers to find the woman's name hidden in the poem. Double underline any details in lines 1–9 that suggest that readers should search for a name hidden in the poem.

A Valentine

by Edgar Allan Poe

(Genre: Poetry)

For her this rhyme is penned, whose **luminous** eyes,
　Brightly expressive as the twins of Leda,
Shall find her own sweet name, that nestling lies
　Upon the page, enwrapped from every reader.
5　Search narrowly the lines! they hold a treasure
　Divine, a **talisman**, an **amulet**
That must be worn at heart. Search well the measure—
　The words—the syllables. Do not forget
The trivialest point, or you may lose your labor:
10　And yet there is in this no Gordian knot
Which one might not undo without a **sabre**,

If one could merely comprehend the plot.
Enwritten upon the leaf where now are peering
Eyes **scintillating** soul, there lie *perdus*[1]
15 Three **eloquent** words oft uttered in the hearing
Of poets, by poets—as the name is a poet's, too.
Its letters, although naturally lying
Like the knight Pinto, Mendez Ferdinando,
Still form a synonym for Truth.—Cease trying!
20 You will not read the riddle, though you do the
best you can do.

[1]*perdus* French for "lost"

Comprehension Check

How does knowing that the poem is an acrostic affect its meaning as well as your experience when reading it?

CITE EVIDENCE

C "A Valentine" is a special kind of poem called an **acrostic**. The words of an acrostic are written so that certain letters spell out a hidden word or name. Circle the first letter of the first line, the second letter of the second line, the third letter of the third line, and so forth. What name is spelled out?

D Poets use **repetition** of sounds and words to emphasize ideas and create rhythm. In lines 5 and 7 of the poem, the poet repeats the word *search*. Put an asterisk next to a line on page 117 that contains repetition. What effect does the repetition have on the poem?

E The denotation of a word is the word's literal meaning. The **connotation** of a word is the idea or emotional quality that it suggests. Put a box around the word near the end of the poem that literally means "to come to an end" but that has a connotative meaning of "to stop suddenly or abruptly."

RL.7.4

WORDS TO KNOW

bore

coveted

highborn

kinsman

sepulchre

seraph

CITE EVIDENCE

A **Figurative language** has a meaning beyond its literal meaning. One kind of figurative language is **hyperbole**, or exaggeration. Circle two lines in stanza 1 that exaggerate something about Annabel Lee. What does this hyperbole mean?

B Recall that one kind of literary language is the repetition of sounds and words to impact meaning. Underline the words in two lines in stanza 2 that demonstrate repetition.

C A poet who writes a series of words that begin with the same letter or sound creates a kind of repetition called **alliteration**. Put a box around the line in stanza 2 that shows alliteration, and name the consonant sound that is repeated.

Annabel Lee

by Edgar Allan Poe

(Genre: Poetry)

It was many and many a year ago,
　　In a kingdom by the sea,
That a maiden there lived whom you may know
　　By the name of Annabel Lee;
5　And this maiden *she* lived with no other thought
　　Than to love and be loved by me.

I was a child and *she* was a child,
　　In this kingdom by the sea,
But we loved with a love that was more than love—
10　　I and my Annabel Lee—
With a love that the wingèd **seraphs** of Heaven
　　Coveted her and me.

RL.7.4

And this was the reason that, long ago,
  In this kingdom by the sea,
15 A wind blew out of a cloud, chilling
  My beautiful Annabel Lee;
So that her **highborn kinsmen** came
  And **bore** her away from me,
To shut her up in a **sepulchre**
20   In this kingdom by the sea.

Comprehension Check

What effect does the repetition of words and sounds create in stanzas 1 and 2 of the poem?

CITE EVIDENCE

D There are other ways to repeat sounds. In **assonance**, the same vowel sound repeats within or at the end of a series of words. For example, listen for the repeated long-*A* sound in "It's a sh**a**me I didn't get any m**ai**l tod**ay**." In line 15, put a box around the words that demonstrate assonance.

E In **consonance**, the same consonant sound repeats within or at the end of a series of words, as in "The tru**ck** hit a ro**ck** near the thi**ck**et." Circle the words in line 16 that are an example of consonance. Which of those words is repeated in each stanza of the poem, and why?

Guided Practice

Annabel Lee *continued*

RL.7.4

WORDS TO KNOW

demon

dissever

CITE EVIDENCE

A Double underline the words at the end of stanza 4 that create assonance. How is this assonance meant to affect readers?

B Circle the two details in stanza 5 that refer to supernatural beings. How do these details help create hyperbole?

C Underline the word in stanza 5 that literally means "to separate." Discuss the connotative meaning of the word and what it suggests about the speaker's feelings for Annabel Lee.

The angels, not half so happy in Heaven,
    Went envying her and me—
Yes!—that was the reason (as all men know,
    In this kingdom by the sea)
25 That the wind came out of the cloud by night,
    Chilling and killing my Annabel Lee.

But our love it was stronger by far than the love
    Of those who were older than we—
    Of many far wiser than we—
30 And neither the angels in Heaven above,
    Nor the **demons** down under the sea,
Can ever **dissever** my soul from the soul
    Of the beautiful Annabel Lee;

Comprehension Check

1. Which lines create an example of rhyme at the ends of lines?

    a. lines 21 and 30

    b. lines 22, 24, and 26

    c. lines 23, 27, and 32

    d. lines 27, 30, and 32

2. Lines 28–29 are an example of

    a. denotation.

    b. connotative meaning.

    c. repetition of words.

    d. consonance.

3. Which group of words from stanza 5 helps create hyperbole?

    a. our love

    b. stronger by far

    c. those who were older

    d. the beautiful Annabel Lee

4. Which word from stanza 5 has a connotation of "evil and frightful"?

    a. soul

    b. angels

    c. dissever

    d. demons

5. Lines 28 and 29 both end with the word *we*—a combination of rhyme and repetition. Why did the poet make that choice of literary language? With a partner, discuss how that choice helps you understand what the speaker is thinking and feeling in this stanza.

_____

_____

_____

_____

_____

_____

_____

Independent Practice

Annabel Lee *continued*

RL.7.4

WORDS TO KNOW

sounding

tomb

CITE EVIDENCE

A Underline each word in stanza 6 that has a long-*I* sound. Why does the poet use so much assonance here?

B What is the emotional effect of lines 40–41? Circle the words in those lines that create alliteration. Why does the poet not repeat the word *sepulchre* in line 41?

> For the moon never beams, without bringing me dreams
> 35   Of the beautiful Annabel Lee;
> And the stars never rise, but I feel the bright eyes
>   Of the beautiful Annabel Lee;
> And so, all the night-tide, I lie down by the side
>   Of my darling—my darling—my life and my bride,
> 40 In her sepulchre there by the sea—
>   In her **tomb** by the **sounding** sea.

1. In the final stanza (lines 34–39), how does the poet's literary language change?

   a. He does not rhyme any other words with Annabel Lee's name.

   b. He rhymes some words within lines as well as at ends of lines.

   c. He does not include any repetition of words.

   d. His only rhymes come from repeated words.

2. Which group of words in lines 38–39 shows that the poet is using hyperbole?

   a. all the night-tide

   b. I lie down

   c. my darling—my darling

   d. my bride

3. Which set of words from the poem demonstrates consonance?

   a. rise, lie, life, bride

   b. loved, child, cloud

   c. beams, bringing, beautiful

   d. eyes, side, bride

4. Which statement does NOT describe the connotation of the word *tomb*?

   a. *Tomb* suggests the finality of death.

   b. *Tomb* creates a feeling of closure.

   c. *Tomb* reminds readers that everyone will die.

   d. *Tomb* suggests that the person died peacefully.

5. With a partner, discuss different types of repetition and the reasons that a poet might use them. Then analyze how the poet uses repetition in this final stanza. Tell what is repeated and where it occurs. Describe what the repetition means to this stanza and to the poem as a whole.

_____

_____

_____

_____

_____

_____

_____

_____

_____

ANALYZING DRAMATIC STRUCTURE

Guided Instruction

RL.7.5

WORDS TO KNOW

bill

demonstrating

legislator

treaty

A series of connected scenes and acts creates the structure of a play, or drama. A drama's **structure** contributes to its meaning.

CITE EVIDENCE

A The **events** that make up a drama are divided into acts and scenes that provide **structure**. Circle the act and scene number of this section of the play.

B Events in a drama may be expressed in **stage directions**, **dialogue**, or both. Underline the event described in the opening italicized paragraph.

The Longest Walk

(Genre: Drama)

CAST OF CHARACTERS

LILY WILSON, an 18-year-old girl

JAYSON WILSON, her 12-year-old brother

KIM STONEFISH, Lily's best friend

LAURA, a Native American protestor

POLICEMAN

HENRY DAVID THOREAU, American author

MRS. WILSON, mother of Lily and Jayson

ACT I, SCENE 1

1 **SETTING:** *It is 3:00 on a hot, overcast afternoon—July 15, 1978—in Washington, D.C. JAYSON is at home with LILY and KIM, who recently finished their first year at college. They are all watching a live news report on television. The big story of the day is the arrival in the nation's capital of the Longest Walk, a peaceful protest march for Native American rights that began five months and 3,200 miles ago in San Francisco, California.*

KIM *(under her breath, almost whispering):* Wow.

LILY: There must be more than a thousand people marching: Native American activists, African American community leaders, politicians . . . And there's that movie star—what's his name?

JAYSON *(bored):* Who cares? It's just another protest march.

5 **LILY** *(irritated):* Jayson, you have a lot to learn. Those Native Americans have marched on foot to Washington, D.C., from San Francisco! It's taken them months. *(to herself)* Can you imagine walking across the entire country?

JAYSON: What are they protesting, anyway?

LILY *(impatiently):* They're **demonstrating** against the way that Native Americans are being treated by the government.

JAYSON: What's been so terrible for them?

KIM *(with passion):* Where do I begin? First, some members of Congress have introduced **bills** that would close some Native American schools and hospitals. There are also efforts to force Native Americans to pay taxes on reservation land. And to add insult to injury, some **legislators** want to abolish rights established by **treaties**—treaties that were signed years ago by both sides!

10 **LILY** *(impressed):* Wow, Kim, you really care about this!

KIM: Well, I *should* care—I'm half Lenni Lenape.

JAYSON: What does that mean?

KIM: The Lenni Lenape are a Native American group. My people originally lived in what is today New York, New Jersey, Pennsylvania, and Delaware.

LILY: Oh, right! Now I remember from history class: The Lenape were renamed the Delaware by the English.

15 **KIM:** Exactly! And we go back further than that. It was the Lenni Lenape who sold Manhattan to some Dutch settlers!

(They continue to watch the coverage of the march. KIM is especially quiet.)

KIM *(pondering):* You know what? I want to go down there and join the march.

LILY *(aghast):* Are you crazy? There are so many people, not to mention that it's probably 100 degrees outside. And I saw a lot of police there, Kim. You could get in trouble!

Comprehension Check

In what way does Act I, Scene 1, introduce the drama? What details set the scene? Cite specifics from the text.

CITE EVIDENCE

C At the beginning of each scene, the playwright tells you the **setting**, or time and place, of the scene. Double underline the time and place of this scene.

D Structure gives drama meaning, but so do the characters who experience the events. In the Cast of **Characters**, put a box around the names of the three characters introduced in this scene.

E How a character reacts to an event moves a drama's story forward. Underline Kim's reaction to watching the march. What might she do next? Why?

Guided Instruction

The Longest Walk *continued*

RL.7.5

WORDS TO KNOW

civil disobedience

dais

heritage

transcendentalist

trek

CITE EVIDENCE

A When and where does Act I, Scene 2, take place? Double underline details about setting that appear in the text.

B The introduction of a new character is an important structural event in a drama. Circle any details about Laura that appear in stage directions. Then discuss what you learn about Laura from dialogue.

KIM: Lily, remember reading Henry David Thoreau in English class? He was the American **transcendentalist** whose essay *On* **Civil Disobedience** talks about exactly what we're up against! Thoreau said, "A people, as well as an individual, must do justice, cost what it may." *(pointing at the television)* Those marchers are my people, and I'm an individual!

20 **LILY** *(with a sigh):* Then I'm going with you. *(grabbing Jayson's hand):* I promised Mom I'd look after you, Jayson, so you're coming, too!

ACT I, SCENE 2

SETTING: *An hour later, on a path leading to the steps of the United States Capitol, Native American protesters are shouting and holding signs that say, "The Longest Walk, 1978" and "Support Indian Resistance." JAYSON, LILY, and KIM can barely hear each other over the noise.*

JAYSON *(pointing):* What's that flag?

KIM *(shouting):* It's the flag of the American Indian Movement.

*(The marchers begin to turn their attention to a man on a **dais** in front of the steps. Just then, LAURA, an older woman in a wheelchair, approaches them.)*

25 **LAURA** *(suspiciously):* May I ask what you all are doing here?

LILY *(warmly):* Hi! I'm Lily, this is my brother Jayson, and this is my friend Kim. We're here to support the protest.

LAURA *(clearly relieved):* Oh, that's great! I was afraid you might be journalists! My name is Laura.

KIM *(laughing):* Journalists? We're college students! My **heritage** is Lenni Lenape, so I just had to come down and show my support.

LAURA: Lenape? *(brightening)* Well then, as a fellow Lenape, I say to you, *Hohoh!*

30 **JAYSON:** What does that mean?

KIM *(grinning):* In the Lenape language, it's an expression of joy!

LILY *(pointing into the distance):* Laura, who is that speaking?

LAURA: That's one of our leaders. He helped organize the march. I'll introduce you. He and many others have worked for so long to organize this walk. And quite a walk it was—you know, only about twenty Native Americans actually made the entire **trek**. Many of us joined the march along the way in other American cities. *(to KIM)* How did you hear about it?

(KIM is about to reply when she suddenly hears a commotion in front of them. She sees police guiding a group of protestors toward their location.)

35 **POLICEMAN** *(shouting):* All right now—back up, folks! We don't want any trouble today!

(As the group is forced toward KIM and her friends, the protestors become impatient. Other marchers, until now just quietly listening to the speaker, become upset as well. Suddenly, a disturbance breaks out, and KIM is separated from her friends.)

LILY *(calling out while holding tightly to JAYSON):* Kim! KIM!

Comprehension Check

How do the two scenes in Act I fit together? In what way does their structure give meaning to the drama?

CITE EVIDENCE

C A drama may have other structures within its larger form. For example, a **soliloquy** is a speech made to the audience in which a character's thoughts are revealed. A **monologue** is a long speech delivered by one character to another. An **epilogue** is the final section of a play after events have been resolved. Put a box around the monologue in this scene.

D A playwright may build suspense by introducing an event that leaves readers wondering what will happen. Put an asterisk next to the suspenseful event in this scene.

E Underline the stage direction that tells how Lily reacts to being separated from Kim. Is this a good place to end Act I?

Guided Practice

The Longest Walk *continued*

RL.7.5

ACT II, SCENE 1

SETTING: *Twenty minutes later, KIM and the other protestors, fuming with frustration, are standing behind a line of police officers who are* **restricting** *the movement of the group.*

LILY *(to LAURA):* Why are the police holding those people back like that?

40 **LAURA:** They have to make sure no one gets hurt. Some of those folks were getting pretty **agitated**, so I think it was a good idea for the police to separate them from the rest of the crowd. Don't worry—it's only **temporary**.

JAYSON: Temporary? What do you mean? What about Kim?

LILY: We can't stay for the entire **rally**. My mom will be home soon, and we have to get back before she arrives!

(LILY scans the crowd and finally sees KIM standing patiently and helplessly behind the row of police.)

KIM *(her head down, speaking softly to herself):* Me and my bright ideas! How long are they going to keep me here? I could use a Good Samaritan just about now!

45 *(Suddenly, she hears a voice in front of her.)*

HENRY DAVID THOREAU *(Lights come up on him suddenly, as if he were a ghost. His eyes are intelligent and* **intense***, but warm):* A people, as well as an individual, must do justice, cost what it may.

KIM *(looking up, stunned):* Whaaa…? *(hesitatingly and quietly)* M-M-Mr. Thoreau? *(Clearly she is the only person who can see or hear him. She takes a breath, realizing she is about to speak to her mentor.)* I'm scared, Mr. Thoreau, but I think that what the government is doing to Native Americans is unjust.

THOREAU: There will never be a really free and enlightened State until the State comes to recognize the individual as a higher and independent power, from which all its own power and **authority** are derived, and treats him accordingly.

WORDS TO KNOW

agitated

authority

intense

rally

restricting

temporary

CITE EVIDENCE

A Underline the stage directions that tell how Kim reacts to being restricted by the police.

B In this scene, another new character is introduced. Circle the name of the character, and double underline what you learn about him. Do you learn about him from stage directions, dialogue, or both?

KIM *(nodding):* Yes, exactly! That's what you wrote in *On Civil Disobedience.* I love that essay. I want Native Americans to be treated with the respect they deserve, and I know you do, too.

50 **THOREAU:** I please myself with imagining a State at last which can afford to be just to all men, and to treat the individual with respect as a neighbor. *(He steps back out of spotlight, into the darkness.)*

Comprehension Check

1. Which of the following best describes Laura's response to Lily's question?

   a. Laura is angry at the police.

   b. Laura believes the police aren't doing enough to protect people.

   c. Laura feels the police are doing their job.

   d. Laura thinks Lily is overreacting.

2. About how much time has passed since the first scene of the play?

   a. an hour

   b. twenty minutes

   c. an hour and twenty minutes

   d. two days

3. In this scene, we learn about Laura's beliefs from

   a. stage directions only.

   b. dialogue only.

   c. both stage directions and dialogue.

   d. neither stage directions nor dialogue.

4. What is the main event of this scene?

   a. Jayson asks what *temporary* means.

   b. Lily finally finds Kim in the crowd.

   c. Henry David Thoreau appears and speaks to Kim.

   d. Laura expresses her opinion about the police.

5. How is the introduction of the character of Thoreau different from the introduction of Laura in the previous scene? Discuss with a partner how Thoreau impacts the meaning and your understanding of the play. Explain your answer with details from the text.

   _____

   _____

   _____

   _____

   _____

ANALYZING DRAMATIC STRUCTURE

The Longest Walk *continued*

RL.7.5

WORDS TO KNOW

acknowledge

conscientious

perpetuate

philosophy

CITE EVIDENCE

A Reread the definition of the word *soliloquy* on page 127. Circle the name of the character who presents a soliloquy in this scene.

B Underline the dialogue that shows Thoreau's response to Kim's words. What has Kim learned from this experience? Discuss your answer with a partner.

KIM *(to the audience):* America is long overdue to **acknowledge** Native Americans as the original American people. They are entitled to live freely on the land their ancestors lived on, cared for, and loved for thousands of years.

I believe in the **philosophy** that people should take a stand when their government creates bad policies, but I don't believe that it's right to break the law.

For example, I understand the argument that people **perpetuate** bad government when they pay federal taxes while opposing that government's policies. To quote Henry David Thoreau: "Those who, while they disapprove of the character and measures of a government, yield to it their allegiance and support are undoubtedly its most **conscientious** supporters, and so frequently the most serious obstacles to reform."

I appreciate what this means, but I prefer peaceful protest as a way of showing civil disobedience. *(She turns back toward the spot where THOREAU spoke to her.)*

55 **THOREAU** *(reappearing in the light, smiling):* I ask for, not at once no government, but at once a better government.

(With that remark, THOREAU disappears. KIM is brought back to reality by the voice of the POLICEMAN.)

POLICEMAN: All right—rally's over. Everyone can go.

(KIM races toward LILY, JAYSON, and LAURA.)

LILY: Kim, thank goodness you're all right! I don't know how you got through that all by yourself!

60 **KIM** *(smiling to herself):* Well, I wasn't exactly by myself. . . .

EPILOGUE

SETTING: *An hour later, LILY, JAYSON, and KIM are back at the Wilsons' home. Just then, MRS. WILSON enters.*

MRS. WILSON: I'm home! Hello, Kim; it's nice to see you again. So, what did you all do today?

JAYSON *(starting to blurt it out):* We—

LILY *(slapping her hand over his mouth):* We watched the march on television. It's called "The Longest Walk," and it was really impressive. Some Native Americans marched thousands of miles to protest their mistreatment by the government.

65 **MRS. WILSON** *(pausing, and then):* "A people, as well as an individual, must do justice, cost what it may."

JAYSON *(with amazement):* Mom, you just quoted Thoreau!

(THE END)

Comprehension Check

MORE ONLINE sadlierconnect.com

1. Which of the following is NOT true about the soliloquy in this scene?

   a. The speaker is the only character in the scene.

   b. The speaker is expressing personal thoughts and beliefs.

   c. The speaker is addressing the audience.

   d. The speaker's remarks are very brief.

2. Which stage direction could you add before Lily's dialogue in paragraph 59?

   a. *(relieved)*

   b. *(confused)*

   c. *(curious)*

   d. *(upset)*

3. The Epilogue is very short because

   a. Mrs. Wilson is not an important character.

   b. Thoreau has already disappeared.

   c. the play's main events have already been resolved.

   d. it presents a funny moment instead of a serious one.

4. Which is NOT a way that the Epilogue contributes to the play's meaning?

   a. It signals that the play is about to end.

   b. It tells the audience that Lily, Jayson, and Kim reached home safely.

   c. It provides an opportunity for Mrs. Wilson's character to express a belief.

   d. It creates a suspenseful ending.

5. What is the meaning of this play? How does the structure of the play contribute to that meaning? Give evidence for your answer.

   _____

   _____

   _____

   _____

   _____

RL.7.6

WORDS TO KNOW

commencing

construction

entrepreneurship

immigrant

mutually

transform

An author develops different **points of view** for various characters. Comparing these points of view can help the reader undersand a story's events from different perspectives.

CITE EVIDENCE

A The **point of view** of a character refers to that character's feelings about various topics and events. Underline the text that reveals Paul's point of view about Abraham Lincoln.

B The "voice" that tells the story (but often is not an actual character) is the story's narrator. A narrator can also have a point of view. In paragraph 4, circle a phrase that shows the narrator's point of view about the veterans who fought on the Union side in the Civil War.

Race to the Golden Spike
(Genre: Historical Fiction)

1   Paul Kelley looked up at the blazing sun and squinted. Then he looked out across the land and considered his position. He was working on one of the greatest feats of ingenuity, engineering, and **entrepreneurship** in the history of the world!

2   The United States desperately needed a railroad that could cross the continent and, in so doing, **transform** the nation's entire way of life. The late president Abraham Lincoln—how Paul had loved that man—had authorized a transcontinental railroad back in 1862, but it had taken years to get started.

3   Now its **construction** was underway in earnest, and Paul and his fellow workers felt lucky to be a part of it. Nearly all the men on the team he was working with were Irish **immigrants**. They were young men, some still in their teens, others with families back East, and many of them veterans of the War Between the States. Fought for the Union, they did; they fought for the end of slavery, for Mr. Lincoln, and for their own futures in a *United* States. That was the only outcome they would accept.

4   The Union won the war, of course, and now these brave, able-bodied young men were back at work on behalf of their country, building an iron road—a nearly 2,000-mile iron road that would bring the country together in a way never before imagined.

A Transcontinental Race

5   What kept Paul and his co-workers going (other than the pitiful wages they were being paid) was that the construction of the transcontinental railroad was a competition—a race

RL.7.6

between two well-established railroad companies: the Central Pacific Railroad and the Union Pacific Railroad.

6   Each company was responsible for half the line, with the Central Pacific starting in Sacramento, California, and heading east, and the Union Pacific **commencing** in Omaha, Nebraska, and moving west. They were racing toward each other, the plan being to meet at a **mutually** chosen spot in Utah, where the final railroad stake would be pounded into the ground. Then the railroad would be done, and horse-drawn wagons for the journey would be a thing of the past.

Working for the Union Pacific Railroad

7   Although Paul was proud to be a part of this massive American project, his work was not easy. The days were long and hot. He missed his wife and young son back in Massachusetts.

8   But Paul thought back to the months immediately after the war's end, when those who were lucky enough to have survived suddenly found themselves without a purpose. Fighting for the Union had been their job, but now they were civilians again.

9   As soon as the war was over, thousands of men answered the call for workers on the transcontinental railroad. They were truly grateful for the work. It was more than two years since Paul had arrived in Omaha, and he knew he had about that many more still to go. He hadn't seen his family since.

10   Paul also had been hearing rumors that the men who ran the Union Pacific were corrupt. They were getting rich off the manual labor of hard-working veterans! And sometimes wages were late. At least the U.P. was hiring American workers; the Central Pacific was using almost entirely Chinese labor. Paul didn't like that one bit. It was more motivation to win this transcontinental race.

Comprehension Check

What aspects of working on the transcontinental railroad does Paul like? What parts does he not like? Support your answer with text evidence for Paul's point of view on his work.

CITE EVIDENCE

C How does the narrator feel about the amount of money Paul and the men are earning? Put a box around a detail in the text that gives you the answer.

D Double underline the veterans' point of view about having a job on the railroad project.

E Authors will **develop**—or may even change—a character's point of view about a topic as a story unfolds. Place an asterisk beside the sentence that shows Paul's point of view of Chinese workers. What might change his mind about them?

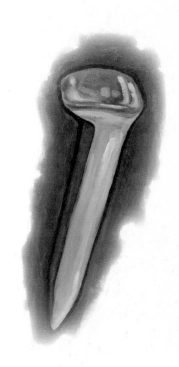

ANALYZING POINT OF VIEW

Race to the Golden Spike *continued*

RL.7.6

WORDS TO KNOW

allocated

arduous

colleague

federal

founded

CITE EVIDENCE

A Double underline the details that show the narrator's point of view about the Sierra Nevada Mountains.

B To make a story more interesting, authors may **contrast the points of view** of various characters (including the narrator). Put a box around a detail that reveals the narrator's point of view about Chinese workers. In what way does this contrast with Paul's point of view?

The Central Pacific Railroad

11   The Central Pacific Railroad began building its side of the transcontinental railroad in Sacramento, California. In fact, the entire project originated there in the mind of a California-based railroad engineer, Theodore Judah. Building a railroad is expensive, however, and Judah had to raise big sums of money for the project. He found in Sacramento five businessmen who saw great potential in the project. In 1861, these people **founded** the Central Pacific Railroad.

12   The idea for a transcontinental railroad had already been receiving attention from politicians in Washington, D.C. (including President Lincoln), and it was not too long before **federal** money was **allocated** to the effort. Armed with this support, Judah and his **colleagues** went to work. Little progress was made during the Civil War, mostly because potential workers were away, fighting as soldiers; but by the war's end in 1865, both the Central Pacific and the Union Pacific were rapidly laying their tracks.

Chinese Immigrant Workers

13   The Central Pacific, however, had a problem that the Union Pacific did not. The Central Pacific's half of the railroad would have to cut through the majestic but massive Sierra Nevada Mountains. The company's owners faced a serious problem: Where could they find workers willing to do such **arduous** labor?

14   The men who ran the Central Pacific found their answer in the Gold Rush; indeed, it turned out to be their salvation. Chinese laborers who had originally been lured to California by the Gold Rush were hired by the thousands to work on the western half of the transcontinental railroad. In 1865, some 7,000 Chinese were working on the project; that number rose to 14,000 by 1867.

RL.7.6

Working in America

15   One such Chinese worker, Shin Lu, had been toiling in the harsh conditions of the Sierra Nevadas all winter. He was excited to be working in America on a project of this scope. He had heard from the other Chinese workers that this was to be the first transcontinental railroad in the entire world.

16   It was exciting to be in a new place, yet Lu missed his family terribly. His mother and father thought he was out of his mind to accept such a project—it was so far away from home—but he needed the work, and many of his friends were also going.

17   The worst part, Lu believed, was how dangerous the work was. First of all, they were using large amounts of explosives. Black gunpowder, homemade liquid nitroglycerin—you name it, they were using it. There was no other way to blast tunnels through the mountains.

18   However, he appreciated how the Chinese workers had shown ingenuity by developing a system by which a worker could be lowered down in a basket alongside a cliff to place an explosive on the wall of rock. After lighting it, the worker would be hauled up. It was the best way to blast through solid rock, but it was dangerous, and sometimes the explosion would go off before the man returned to the top. Some of his friends had been killed in such accidents.

19   Lu wondered if there were Chinese workers laboring for the other company, the Union Pacific. The Central Pacific managers kept saying the Union Pacific was the enemy, but Lu didn't see it that way. To him, they were all working toward a common goal: uniting the coasts of the United States.

Comprehension Check

Compare and contrast Lu's and Paul's points of view about working on the transcontinental railroad. What opinions do they share? On what do they differ? Cite evidence.

CITE EVIDENCE

C Put an asterisk by a detail in paragraph 16 that expresses an opinion that Shin Lu shares with Paul.

D In terms of his work, what is Lu proud of? Circle a key detail in paragraph 18 of the text.

E Underline the two sentences in paragraph 19 that express Lu's point of view about the Union Pacific workers. In what way do Lu and Paul view each other differently?

ANALYZING POINT OF VIEW

Guided Practice

RL.7.6

WORDS TO KNOW

duration

manual

spike

CITE EVIDENCE

A Circle two details that give evidence of Lu's point of view about working in the Sierra Nevada Mountains.

B In Paul's letter, underline any statement that reveals his hope for the future. Has he expressed this hope in the past? Explain.

Race to the Golden Spike *continued*

A Letter from Shin Lu to His Mother

July 22, 1868

Dear Mother,

20   We continue to make our way across the hot, dry desert of a place the Americans call Nevada. The heat is indescribable, and tonight I feel exhausted, but I'm in it for the **duration**.

21   For all its faults, however, the flat expanse of Nevada is much preferred to the mountains of the Sierra Nevadas. I cannot stop thinking about last winter; indeed, I don't know how I survived it. Beyond the cold and the snowstorms, digging icy soil and drilling through cold, black rock was the hardest **manual** labor I have ever done in my life.

22   It was extremely frustrating work, too, because no sooner would we cut a tunnel through a hillside than a mountain's worth of snow would come crashing down on us. Avalanches were a frequent event. I lost count of how many workers died.

I miss you.

Shin Lu

A Letter from Paul Kelley to His Famiy

January 7, 1869

Dearest Catherine and Daniel,

23   I haven't the words to express how much I miss you two.

24   Our work continues here, and they have changed my job: Now I am laying actual track and no longer building culverts, the water pipes that run underneath the railroad. Daniel, my boy, you would have such fun pounding in those railroad **spikes** with me!

25   This job is truly an example of man versus nature. Everyone is anticipating the Wasatch Mountains in Wyoming, which are coming next. The mountains will be very difficult to cut through. So far, we have been lucky with the flatlands of Nebraska, but now we face an entirely new challenge.

26   Just the same, I feel closer to the finish line than ever before—and that means that I will see you soon!

Love, Paul (Daddy)

Comprehension Check

1. Which statement best describes Lu's point of view in his letter?

    a. He is thrilled to be working on the project.

    b. He has become weary of the project.

    c. He is inspired by the places he's seen.

    d. He is tired but is finding the work to be easier.

2. Which of the following does Lu NOT mention in his letter?

    a. the Nevada desert

    b. the Sierra Nevada Mountains

    c. the ingenuity of his fellow workers

    d. the difficult manual labor

3. In their letters, both workers express thoughts about

    a. how flat Nevada is.

    b. how much they miss their families.

    c. how grateful they are to be working.

    d. how dangerous the work is.

4. What is Paul's point of view about working in the Wasatch Mountains?

    a. He wishes he could stay in Nebraska.

    b. He doubts his team will be successful.

    c. He thinks the work will be fun.

    d. He thinks the work will be difficult.

5. With a partner, discuss how Lu's and Paul's opinions regarding their work have changed. How does contrasting "then" and "now" help you understand the story? Give evidence for your answer.

_____

_____

_____

_____

_____

ANALYZING POINT OF VIEW

Independent Practice

Race to the Golden Spike *continued*

RL.7.6

WORDS TO KNOW

considerable

crevasse

promontory

so-called

summit

CITE EVIDENCE

A Circle the term the narrator uses to express a point of view about the two railroad companies.

B Underline Paul's point of view about Chinese workers after he sees the "Big Fill." How does his point of view change?

Toward the Finish Line

27   By the spring of 1869, it was clear that both companies were nearing the finish line. Naturally, there was fierce competition to finish first. These were money-hungry companies, after all, and the one that controlled a greater portion of the transcontinental railroad would have a financial advantage when goods started to travel by train. It took the United States Congress to step in and select a meeting place: a site in Utah Territory called **Promontory Summit**.

The Central Pacific and the "Big Fill"

28   Shin Lu and the other Chinese laborers had worked themselves to the bone, but Lu's spirits had been brighter ever since the finish came into sight. They had one last job to do: the **so-called** "Big Fill." The head of the Central Pacific made a last-minute change to their route, and so a deep **crevasse** had to be filled in with soil. Lu and the others went right to work, and their efforts allowed the Central Pacific to reach Promontory Summit first. Lu was overwhelmed with pride.

The Union Pacific and the "Big Trestle"

29   The Union Pacific had its own final project: the "Big Trestle." Trestles are big metal frames that support railroad tracks that run across valleys or rivers. Paul Kelley and his team raced to erect a temporary structure so the Union Pacific effort wouldn't be delayed. The workers finished on May 5, and the Union Pacific reached Promontory Summit. They came in second, but in the end it didn't matter; it was still a great achievement.

30   Paul had heard about the "Big Fill" and wanted to see it for himself. He couldn't believe his eyes: That job had taken **considerable** effort! When he thought about the thousands of Chinese workers who labored on this and so many other parts of the railroad, Paul decided that they had done well.

The Golden Spike

31   On May 10, 1869, representatives from the two great railroad companies were present when a commemorative golden spike was hammered into the ground. Paul Kelley was there, exhausted but smiling. Shin Lu looked with satisfaction at the railroad he had helped build. It had all been worth it, he thought.

Comprehension Check   MORE ONLINE sadlierconnect.com

1. Shin Lu's point of view grows more positive in this last part of the story because

    a. he finally meets Paul Kelley.

    b. the project comes to a successful end.

    c. he gets to hammer in the golden spike.

    d. he is proud of his work on the "Big Trestle."

2. About which subject does Paul change his point of view at the end of the story?

    a. the Sierra Nevada Mountains

    b. the "Big Fill"

    c. the Chinese laborers

    d. the Central Pacific Railroad

3. In the section "The Golden Spike," which word or phrase is evidence of the narrator's point of view about the two companies?

    a. great

    b. commemorative

    c. golden

    d. worth it

4. About which fact does the narrator feel "in the end it didn't matter"?

    a. The Union Pacific came in first.

    b. The Central Pacific came in first.

    c. The "Big Trestle" was a temporary structure.

    d. The workers received low wages.

5. How can a change in a character's point of view give a story meaning and strengthen its conclusion? Specifically, how does the change in Paul's opinion give this story a satisfying ending?

    _____

    _____

    _____

    _____

    _____

    _____

Toward the Unknown River

(Genre: Adventure—based on actual events)

1   "I've never felt a hotter, more humid day in all my life," young Jack Arthur muttered to himself as he drew his hand across his sweaty brow. He was just 18 years old, trekking through *Mato Grosso*, the "great wilderness" of western Brazil. Jack and his companions had been traveling for weeks but were barely halfway to their destination: the *Dúvida*, or so-called River of Doubt.

2   Jack was a guest of his pal Kermit Roosevelt, himself only 19 and the son of Colonel Theodore Roosevelt, the wildly popular former president of the United States.

3   "Jack, old chum," Kermit had asked him last fall, slapping his hand on Jack's shoulder, "how would you like to go on a journey of a lifetime with my father and me?"

4   Jack, like all Americans, was familiar with Theodore Roosevelt's outdoor adventures and Herculean feats of derring-do. For example, the president's African safari, taken shortly after he left office, was a major event in the newspapers.

5   This trip, a scientific exploration of an unexplored tributary of the Amazon River in Brazil, had received its share of attention, too.

6   Jack loved the outdoors—he and Kermit were both accomplished athletes at Harvard College—so he readily agreed to the invitation. They received permission from their professors to take some time off.

7   Now it was months after their arrival in the South American country of Paraguay, and the past weeks had been unbelievably arduous. Jack thought back to how it began.

Team of Explorers

8   It was a few days after New Year's Day, 1914, when Jack, Kermit, Colonel Roosevelt, and the rest of the team gathered at the Paraguay River to begin the journey to the River of Doubt. There was no simple or direct way to reach the *Dúvida*, but everyone seemed confident about getting there via the Paraguay River, which ran through the wild and dense Brazilian jungle.

9   It was a remarkable team of travelers who would be undertaking this odyssey. Colonel Roosevelt had brought along a secretary as well as his friend Father Zahm, a priest. There were also some American naturalists who wanted to study the plants and animals of the Amazon.

RL.7.4, RL.7.5, RL.7.6, RL.7.10

10   The Brazilian team was headed by Colonel Cândido Rondon, an experienced explorer and traveler. Assisting him was a group of *camaradas*, Brazilian workers who would carry supplies and set up tents.

The Paraguay River

11   It was immediately apparent to Jack that he and the others were not going to simply canoe down the Paraguay to the start of the River of Doubt.

12   For one thing, the river was shallow in some places, making it difficult to negotiate. Barges loaded with five tons of baggage and supplies were so heavy they couldn't move.

13   Quite often the river thinned out and gave way to areas of marsh and jungle. The explorers had to get out and use their long knives to slash their way through the vegetation. The *camaradas* lifted the canoes over their heads and followed close behind.

Mato Grosso

14   They had completed the main stretch of the Paraguay weeks ago, and now they were in the middle of *Mato Grosso*. Jack couldn't believe how hot and humid it was: It was early January, but the sun beat down on them without mercy. But the steamy heat was nothing compared to the insects.

15   Jack had read about the legendary insects of *Mato Grosso*, but he didn't believe until he saw for himself butterflies as big as birds, bumblebees and wasps, and bloodthirsty mosquitoes nipping at any patch of exposed skin. Swatting them was a Sisyphean task; the mosquitoes just kept coming back.

16   But the "great wilderness" was beautiful, too. Jack had never seen a palm tree, much less the tall specimens he spied along the riverbank. There were flowers, too, including orchids of the brightest colors imaginable. Less appealing were the snakes; indeed, an anaconda could squeeze a person to death, people said.

17   Overhead, little monkeys hung from vines, and lime-green parakeets darted by. At one point, Kermit turned back toward Jack and smiled, as if to say, "Enjoy it, pal."

18   Days turned into weeks as they alternately canoed and hiked toward a little Brazilian town that would serve as their launching point for the River of Doubt. The heat and humidity remained unbearable, and fresh water to drink and bathe in was scarce. Food was an issue, as well; there weren't any large animals to hunt. Everyone on the team was hungry, and Jack had eaten enough monkey stew to last him a lifetime.

Approaching the River of Doubt

19   By the end of February, the travelers were exhausted and still had not reached the beginning of the River of Doubt. Jack wondered if it was even worth continuing, but he, like the rest of the team, soldiered on.

20   One of the most treacherous aspects of their river journey was the abundance of waterfalls. They varied in size, but all were dangerous to the men in their fragile, hand-carved wooden canoes.

Toward the Unknown River *continued*

21   The final days approaching the River of Doubt really were the most miserable that Jack had ever endured. A few team members had nearly drowned in the river. The heat and humidity would not abate. Torrents of rain poured down, leading some expedition members to joke that they should start building an ark.

22   Through it all, Jack noted, Colonel Roosevelt and Kermit rarely lost their humor. The rotund ex-president was full of Falstaffian wit and jollity, even in the toughest of conditions. It seemed to Jack that Kermit was totally fed up but hid it from his father, preferring to force a smile in spite of his discomfort.

23   One particularly hot afternoon, with horseflies biting his neck and his shirt soaked with sweat, Jack's mind wandered. He thought of a new song he had heard at school, shortly before leaving for Paraguay. Jack began singing "America the Beautiful" softly to himself:

24   *O beautiful for spacious skies,*
For amber waves of grain,
For purple mountain majesties
Above the fruited plain!

America! America!
God shed His grace on thee,
And crown thy good with brotherhood
From sea to shining sea!

25   Two young *camaradas*, feverish from the heat, looked at him with a smile on their faces. Though they spoke no English, they understood what it meant to be homesick.

Traveling the River of Doubt

26   At long last, on February 27, 1914, the team reached the River of Doubt. Some members of the team refused to go any farther on the journey and begged off. Colonel Roosevelt, Kermit, Jack, Colonel Rondon, and a few *camaradas* continued, however. They had come this far, Jack mused, so they had to finish.

27   The weeks that followed, canoeing down the *Dúvida*, featured more of the same: heat, humidity, insects, and lousy food. The small team would canoe until the rapids became too dangerous; then they would take to the riverbank and hike until the river calmed.

28   There was, however, a new crisis. Colonel Roosevelt had injured his leg, and a bad infection had set in. Even worse, he was showing symptoms of malaria, a serious tropical disease. It became almost impossible for him to walk during those parts of the journey when the river was too rough. Roosevelt repeatedly told his son and Rondon to leave him behind, but they refused to do so.

29 Jack was never more proud of his friend than he was in the weeks that followed. Kermit tended to his father's every need as the group slowly made its way down the River of Doubt.

30 "This river is aptly named," Jack remarked to Kermit one particularly dreary day. "I have my doubts that we are going to make it to the end." Kermit had to nod in agreement.

31 Colonel Roosevelt eventually recovered, however; and one day in late March, Colonel Rondon surprised him with an announcement. On behalf of the Brazilian government, he was naming a section of the River of Doubt *Rio Roosevelt*, or "Roosevelt River." Furthermore, a smaller tributary was declared *Rio Kermit*. Jack stood by as the two Roosevelt men, stunned and proud, accepted the honor.

32 By late April the team of exhausted travelers had reached a small town from which they could travel to the larger town of Manáos. From there, they could arrange for a return to North America.

33 Jack Arthur completed his studies at Harvard University alongside his friend, Kermit Roosevelt. The two young men never forgot their adventure down "the largest unknown river in the world."

Comprehension Check

1A. What does the hyperbole in paragraph 18 exaggerate?

 a. the travelers' hunger

 b. the friendliness of the Brazilians

 c. the amount of time that was passing

 d. the lack of clean water

1B. Which words from the text support the answer to Part A?

 a. "town that would serve as their launching point"

 b. "Days turned into weeks"

 c. "enough monkey stew to last him a lifetime"

 d. "Food was an issue, as well"

2A. What is the denotation of the word *trekking*?

 a. canoeing down a wide river

 b. hiking up a mountain

 c. retreating from a challenge

 d. going on a long, difficult journey

2B. Which word from the text relates to the meaning of the word *trekking* by connoting a sense of duty?

 a. recovered

 b. soldiered

 c. continued

 d. reached

3A. As the journey becomes longer, what is the point of view of the *camaradas*?

   a. They are eager to befriend the natives.

   b. They are ready to revolt against Rondon.

   c. They are excited for the next challenge.

   d. They are very homesick.

3B. What detail from the text supports the answer to Part A?

   a. They choose not to go down the *Dúvida*.

   b. They carry canoes over their heads.

   c. They nurse Colonel Roosevelt back to health.

   d. They smile at Jack when he sings.

4A. The author develops Kermit's point of view over the course of the trip by showing that Kermit

   a. is unhappy throughout the trip.

   b. slowly becomes excited about the trip.

   c. expresses concern near the end of the trip.

   d. never shows doubt about the trip.

4B. Which event in the text supports the answer to Part A?

   a. "Kermit nodded in agreement."

   b. "Kermit . . . slapping his hand on Jack's shoulder."

   c. "Kermit tended to his father's every need."

   d. "The two young men never forgot their adventure."

5A. How does the song relate to what is happening at that moment in the story?

   a. Jack and the *camaradas* become friends.

   b. Jack thinks that the river is beautiful.

   c. Jack feels very homesick.

   d. Jack is suffering in the heat and humidity.

5B. Which word in the song is repeated?

   a. beautiful

   b. America

   c. grace

   d. brotherhood

6. In what way is Jack's point of view different from Kermit's for most of the story? What changes toward the end? Cite evidence from the text.

_____

_____

_____

_____

_____

_____

7. In the section "*Mato Grosso*," where does the author use alliteration? Write the alliterative phrase, and then explain how it impacts that part of the story.

_____

_____

_____

8. How are the lyrics to "America the Beautiful" structured? How do they contribute to the meaning of the song?

_____

_____

_____

_____

9. Write a paragraph analyzing the structure of the story. Use text evidence to show how the story's overall meaning is impacted by its form. Use a separate piece of paper if necessary.

_____

_____

_____

_____

_____

_____

10. Reread the first sentence of the story. Then answer these questions.

A. What does this sentence reveal about Jack's point of view regarding the journey?

_____

_____

B. Explain how the literary language in the sentence leads you to that answer.

_____

_____

_____

_____

Compare and Contrast Texts

RL.9, SL.7.1.a, SL.7.1.c–d

In this unit, you've read texts in which characters face conflict. In "Annabel Lee," "Race to the Golden Spike," and "Toward the Unknown River," humans wrestle with natural forces in some way. Complete the Venn diagram with details from these selections. Then write a brief essay in which you use the details to compare and contrast how the selections explore the conflict of "man vs. nature." Use a separate sheet of paper if you need more room to write. Be prepared to discuss your ideas with the class.

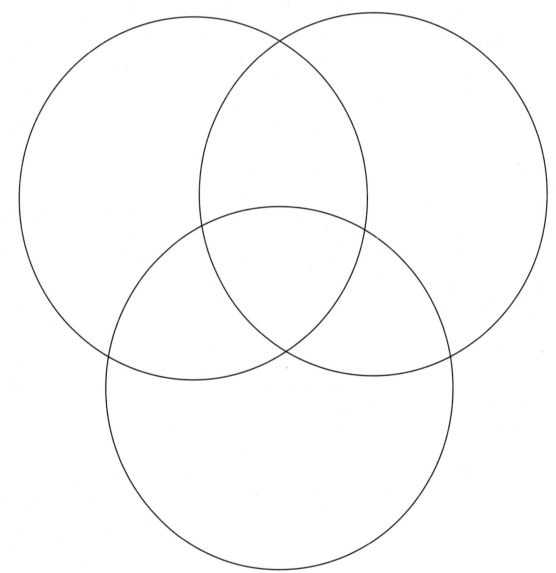

Return to the Essential Question

How do authors use language, structure, and characters to create meaning?

In small groups or as a class, discuss the Essential Question. Think about what you have learned about literary language, dramatic and poetic structure, and point of view. Use evidence from the texts in this unit to answer the question.

Figurative Language

L.7.5.a

Guided Instruction A **figure of speech** is a phrase or expression that uses words in a nonliteral way. Figures of speech can add interest and deeper meaning to a text. Some figures of speech are **allusions**; that is, they refer to a story from literature, mythology, or the Bible. Interpreting allusions will help you better understand and enjoy what you read. Below are some examples of allusions that are used in this unit's selections.

Allusion	Origin	Meaning
Falstaffian	literature (Shakespeare)	jolly, bold, witty, and fat
Gordian knot	Greek mythology	a very difficult problem or puzzle
Good Samaritan	the Bible	someone who unexpectedly helps a person in need

Guided Practice In the following sentences, allusions are underlined and their origins are given. On the lines, write the meaning of each allusion. Use context or a print or online dictionary to help you if necessary.

1. Jack, like all Americans, was familiar with Theodore Roosevelt's . . . <u>Herculean</u> feats of derring-do. (Greek mythology) _____

2. And <u>to add insult to injury</u>, some legislators want to abolish rights established by treaties . . . . (literature [Aesop's fables]) _____

Independent Practice In the following sentences, underline the allusion. Then research its origin, and tell what it means in your own words.

1. It was a remarkable team of travelers who would be undertaking this odyssey.

_____

_____

2. Torrents of rain poured down, leading some expedition members to joke that they should start building an ark. _____

_____

_____

3. Swatting them was a Sisyphean task; the mosquitoes just kept coming back.

_____

RL.7.4, RL.7.5, RL.7.6, L.7.5.a

Read the following texts that include literary language, dramatic and poetic structures, differing points of view, and literary allusions. Then answer the questions on pages 149 and 150.

Rehearsing with a Friend

CAST OF CHARACTERS

JEREMY, a 13-year-old boy
GWEN, a 13-year-old girl

SETTING: *In the present day, JEREMY is at home, practicing his trumpet for a contest the next weekend. The musical piece his teacher, Mr. Green, has selected for him is written for trumpet and piano. Jeremy's friend GWEN will accompany him on the piano. They've been rehearsing for 90 minutes.*

1 **GWEN:** Jeremy, I don't think this section should go quite as fast as you're playing it. It doesn't sound right.

2 **JEREMY** *(irritated):* I'm playing what's printed on the page: "quickly." *(sharply)* I already practiced this part with Mr. Green.

3 **GWEN** *(gently):* Jeremy, I wish you wouldn't disregard my opinion. If we play this section *too* quickly, the music won't make any sense. *(She puts her hands on the piano keys.)* Here, let me show you what I mean—

4 **JEREMY** *(exploding):* Gwen, I haven't got time to argue with you! I like how I'm playing this section, and Mr. Green agrees with me! *(taking a breath)* Look, I've come in second place in this contest for the past three years. If I'm runner-up again, I'll die! I *have* to win this year, and I know how to do it. I've been working on this for months with Mr. Green, and my interpretation of this section stands—quickly, slowly, whatever!

5 **GWEN** *(calmly closing the lid of the piano):* Jeremy, I don't like working like this. It's not creative; it's not fun. I'll talk to you later— after you've calmed down.

(Gwen leaves.)

An Entry from Gwen's Diary

Dear Diary,

Today was a tough day. I was flattered when Jeremy asked me to accompany him on his trumpet for the contest, but rehearsing with him has not been fun. He can be a real Jekyll and Hyde: Some days he's very agreeable and open to my suggestions, and other days he doesn't want to hear from me.

I'm willing to hang in there as long as it takes, but I'm starting to think I'll need the patience of Job to get through this coming week. I wrote a poem—a Japanese *haiku*, in fact—that expresses how I feel.

Friendship can survive:
Even when friends disagree,
Friends can still be friends.

RL.7.4, RL.7.5, RL.7.6, L.7.5.a

Circle the letter next to the best answer choice.

1A. The hyperbole in the drama exaggerates

    a. how quickly Jeremy is playing.

    b. how badly Jeremy wants to win.

    c. how well Jeremy is playing.

    d. how much Gwen dislikes Jeremy.

1B. Which statement supports the answer to Part A?

    a. "I've been working on this for months . . . "

    b. "I don't like working like this."

    c. "Gwen, I haven't got time to argue with you!"

    d. "If I'm runner-up again, I'll die."

2A. How does repetition impact the meaning of "An Entry from Gwen's Diary"?

    a. It reveals how much Jeremy's remarks have hurt her.

    b. It expresses how strong her opinion is about the music.

    c. It emphasizes that she wants to remain friends with Jeremy.

    d. It shows that she does not wish to continue to work with Jeremy.

2B. What part of Gwen's diary entry supports the answer to Part A?

    a. her repetition of "friends" in the *haiku*

    b. her comparison of Jeremy to Jekyll and Hyde

    c. her reference to "the patience of Job"

    d. her statement that she was flattered by Jeremy

3A. What does *exploding* in the stage directions suggest about that moment in the drama?

    a. Jeremy is angry and impatient.

    b. Jeremy is playing too fast.

    c. Jeremy has thought out his position.

    d. Jeremy is not feeling any pressure.

3B. What denotation of the word *exploding* provides evidence for Part A?

    a. explaining

    b. speaking casually, as with a friend

    c. racing ahead

    d. blurting out suddenly

4A. What does the allusion *the patience of Job* in Gwen's diary entry mean for her future?

    a. Gwen doesn't need more patience with Jeremy than she already has.

    b. Gwen will need a lot of patience to deal with Jeremy in the days ahead.

    c. Gwen will have to work hard to keep from losing Jeremy's friendship.

    d. Gwen should schedule two 15-minute rehearsals with Jeremy.

4B. What evidence from Gwen's diary entry supports the answer to Part A?

    a. Gwen wrote a poem to express her feelings.

    b. Gwen was flattered to be asked to accompany Jeremy.

    c. Gwen doesn't like playing with Jeremy.

    d. Gwen says she's "willing to hang in there as long as it takes."

5A. What is Jeremy's point of view about the upcoming contest?

    a. He just wants to perform well, regardless of the outcome.

    b. He wishes that Mr. Green had helped him prepare better.

    c. He cannot bear the thought of losing the contest.

    d. He wishes he weren't playing with Gwen.

RL.7.4, RL.7.5, RL.7.6, L.7.5.a

5B. Which statement from the text provides evidence for the claim above?

   a. "I have to win this year"

   b. "Mr. Green agrees with me!"

   c. "I like how I'm playing this section"

   d. "Gwen, I haven't got time to argue with you!"

6A. Which of the following terms correctly describes paragraph 4 of the drama?

   a. epilogue   **c.** soliloquy

   b. monologue   **d.** stage directions

6B. What evidence from the text supports the answer to Part A?

   a. Jeremy is alone on stage while he speaks.

   b. The text tells what Jeremy does, not what he says.

   c. The drama's conflict has been resolved.

   d. Jeremy is expressing his feelings directly to another character.

7. Find the paragraph in the drama that contains alliteration. Then explain the effect of that alliteration.

_____

_____

_____

8. Gwen's statement *He can be a real Jekyll and Hyde* is an allusion to a story in which the respectable Dr. Jekyll takes a potion that turns him into the evil Mr. Hyde. How does that allusion help you understand what Gwen means?

_____

_____

9. The poem that Gwen writes is a *haiku*—a three-line Japanese poem. What is the impact of the *haiku* on Gwen's diary entry? How might the entry be different if she had written a long poem with rhymed lines?

_____

_____

_____

10. How is Gwen's point of view developed over the course of the drama and the diary entry? As part of your answer, analyze the ways in which her point of view differs from Jeremy's.

_____

_____

_____

_____

Introducing UNIT 6

In this unit about sources of conflict, you will learn how to write an evidence-based text. This type of writing uses evidence—in the form of facts, details, and examples—to inform readers about a topic. In this unit the writing is about an historical conflict, an event in the past that caused an important disagreement between people.

You can write about an historical conflict, too. You will probably start with research so that you can write knowledgeably about the conflict. After creating an introduction in which you identify your topic, you will develop that topic by sharing your information in an organized, interesting way. For example, you may want to start with background information that will help readers understand your topic. Then you will present an explanation that uses facts, details, and examples to support your ideas. Use precise, formal language so that readers will view your essay as a reliable source of information. Finally, wrap up your discussion with a conclusion that explains how the conflict was resolved or how it affected the world we live in today.

Progress Check Can I?

Before Unit 6		After Unit 6
☐	Write an evidence-based text about an historical conflict.	☐
☐	Organize my ideas and information in a way that makes sense for my topic.	☐
☐	Use evidence from informational texts (such as facts, details, and examples) to support my ideas.	☐
☐	Use precise language and a formal writing style.	☐
☐	Write sentences that have different structures.	☐
☐	Use standard English capitalization, punctuation, and spelling in my writing.	☐

HOME◆CONNECT...

IN THIS UNIT, YOUR CHILD WILL...

- Learn how to write an evidence-based text about an historical conflict.

- Use a variety of trustworthy sources to research and gather information.

- Organize ideas effectively, including using a clear introduction and strong conclusion.

- Develop a topic by incorporating various kinds of evidence (such as details, facts, and examples) that support key points.

- Use precise words and a formal writing style.

- Write using a variety of sentence styles: simple, compound, complex, and compound-complex.

- Use standard English capitalization, punctuation, and spelling.

NOTE: All of these learning goals for your child are based on the Grade 7 Common Core State Standards for English Language Arts.

In this unit, your child will learn to **write an evidence-based informative/explanatory text** about an historical conflict. This type of writing uses **researched evidence from trustworthy sources** to explain something to readers. An informative/explanatory text uses a structure that helps readers understand the topic, including an **introduction**; paragraphs that **develop the topic** with **facts, details, examples,** and other supporting evidence; and a **conclusion** that explains the results of the conflict. An evidence-based text uses **precise, formal language** to clearly convey information.

Describe an historical conflict to your child. If possible, show him or her historical photos or visit a museum exhibit about the conflict. Explain what each side wanted and how each side viewed the other. Describe how the conflict played out and what its final outcome was. Point out to your child how you use evidence to support your ideas about the conflict.

WAYS TO HELP YOUR CHILD

Have your child describe a conflict he or she has read about or experienced. Ask your child to think about how each side viewed the issue, what each side wanted to happen, what each side thought about the other, and what each side was willing to do to get its way. Have an informal debate in which you argue one side of a conflict and your child argues the other.

Activity: Explore with your child the unit theme: "Sources of Conflict." Together, research and make a list of important conflicts that people have faced in the past. Remember that some of these conflicts may have taken the form of wars, but many did not. Then choose a conflict to research further. Together, explore why the conflict arose and how it was resolved. Create a three- or four-panel drawing that summarizes the conflict.

> **ONLINE**
> **For more Home Connect activities, continue online at** sadlierconnect.com

Text Types and Purposes: Write Evidence-Based Texts

Essential Question:
How does evidence help writers explain a significant event?

W.7.2, W.7.2.a–b

CREATING AN ORGANIZATIONAL STRUCTURE

Jillian used an outline like the one below to organize her writing so that it explains the causes and outcomes of an historical conflict between factory owners and workers.

```
Title _____
  I. Introduction
     a. Topic: _____
 II. Subtopics and Evidence
     a. First paragraph: information about _____
        1. Fact, detail, or example _____

        2. Fact, detail, or example _____

     b. Second paragraph: information about _____
        1. Fact, detail, or example _____

        2. Fact, detail, or example _____

     c. Third paragraph: information about _____
        1. Fact, detail, or example _____

        2. Fact, detail, or example _____

 III. Conclusion
        _____
```

TITLE

- Gives readers a clue about the nature of the conflict.

INTRODUCTION

- Introduces the topic and previews what Jillian will discuss in the essay.

HEADINGS

- Help show the organization of the text.

BACKGROUND

- Jillian includes information that will help readers better understand the historical issue.

Read a Student Model

Jillian is a student in Mrs. Herrera's seventh-grade Language Arts class. Mrs. Herrera gave the class an assignment: to write an evidence-based text about an historical conflict. For this evidence-based text, Jillian must research to find facts, details, and examples to explain her topic. As you read her writing, think about an historical conflict that you might write about in your own evidence-based text.

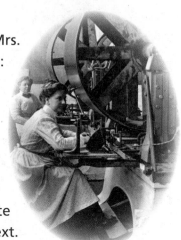

Better Lives for All

Today, most workers in the United States enjoy safe working conditions, weekend time off, and a limit to the numbers of hours in a workday. However, when the United States first became industrialized in the late 1800s, workers faced dangerous conditions and long hours for low pay. By joining together, forming labor unions, and struggling for many years, workers were able to create better lives for themselves and for workers who came after them.

Background: Changing America

In the first half of the nineteenth century, most Americans worked on farms. After the Civil War, industrialization grew rapidly, and more and more people—including women, children, and immigrants—left the farms and went to work in factories in the cities. Factory owners grew eager to profit as much as possible, no matter how poor the working conditions they created. At that time there were few laws to protect workers.

Working Conditions

Workers usually had to work long hours for low pay. For example, teenage girls working in New York City's clothing factories in the early 1900s had to work six days a week, thirteen hours a day, with only a half-hour lunch break. Some workers were locked into their buildings and denied opportunities to go to the bathroom. Most workers were paid only $6.00 a week, but they still had to pay for their own sewing supplies.

Labor Unions

American workers began to form unions in the 1860s. The Knights of Labor was the first national union that accepted all workers in industry. Other unions, such as the American Miners' Association and the National Labor Union, were also formed. Workers began to speak out and to strike, or refuse to work, in order to draw attention to their demand for an eight-hour workday.

The Haymarket Riot

Factory owners disliked strikes, which cost them money and often ended in violence and riots. The worst of these was the Haymarket Riot in Chicago in 1886. During a union strike, several people were injured in clashes with the police. The next day, the strikers held a demonstration. Someone threw a bomb, and the police shot back. Both civilians and police were killed, and although eight men were arrested, the real culprit was never found. This riot led many people to mistrust labor unions, particularly the Knights of Labor, which was blamed for the violence.

EVIDENCE

Use evidence—that is, relevant facts, details, examples, and other information—to support your ideas. The evidence should come from trustworthy sources that you have researched.

Jillian states an important idea in the first sentence of this paragraph. Underline the evidence that supports that idea.

DEFINITIONS

Readers may not be familiar with words that are specific to your subject. Include definitions when needed.

Find and circle the definition of strike.

CAUSE AND EFFECT

There are many strategies that can help explain a topic. The cause-and-effect strategy shows readers why events happened and what the results were.

Put a box around two effects of the Haymarket Riot, as Jillian explains it.

WRITE EVIDENCE-BASED TEXTS

W.7.2.a–c, W.7.2.e–f

TRANSITIONS

Transitional words and phrases can help connect ideas within paragraphs and between paragraphs. These connections can include a change in time or place, a contrast, an additional idea, and more.

Double underline two transitions in this paragraph.

MULTIMEDIA

Multimedia items, such as photographs, help bring the text to life for readers. This image of the Triangle Shirtwaist Factory fire emphasizes the reality of this tragedy.

Box the information in the text that this image helps bring to life.

STYLE/CONCLUSION

Jillian uses a formal style in her writing, using clear language and avoiding personal opinion. The conclusion wraps up the topic by showing some results of the conflict she has described in this text.

Circle the results Jillian describes.

The Garment Workers' Strike

Almost 25 years later, workers were still struggling for their rights. Women working in New York's garment factories—often called "sweatshops"—went on strike in 1909. These women bravely faced arrest and even violence, and they won some victories. However, some women went back to work at the Triangle Shirtwaist Factory without a union agreement. This factory was the scene of a horrible tragedy in 1911, when 129 women, most in their teens and twenties, were killed after a fire broke out. Factory owners had locked the exit doors to keep workers from taking too many breaks.

Conclusion

The horrible events at the Triangle Shirtwaist Factory helped bring attention to the abuse of workers. With this attention, and with further union strikes, more and more safety standards for workers were slowly implemented in the twentieth century. The eight-hour workday was finally instituted for most workers in 1938. The fight for workers' rights that started with the Industrial Revolution continues to benefit workers to this day.

W.7.2.a–f, W.7.4, W.7.5, W.7.9, W.7.10

Use this outline to organize your evidence-based text for the Common Core Review on page 164. Then write your first draft on a separate sheet of paper. Remember to supply relevant information that develops the topic and supports your ideas. In addition, use a formal writing style, precise words, and appropriate transitions.

Title _____

I. Introduction

    a. Topic: _____

II. Subtopics and Evidence

    a. First paragraph: information about _____

        1. Fact, detail, or example _____

        _____

        2. Fact, detail, or example _____

        _____

    b. Second paragraph: information about _____

        1. Fact, detail, or example _____

        _____

        2. Fact, detail, or example _____

        _____

    c. Third paragraph: information about _____

        1. Fact, detail, or example _____

        _____

        2. Fact, detail, or example _____

        _____

III. Conclusion

    _____

    _____

Simple, Compound, Complex, and Compound-Complex Sentences

Guided Instruction There are four basic structures of English sentences. The structures depend on the number of independent and dependent clauses in a sentence. An **independent clause** can stand as a complete sentence on its own. A **dependent clause** needs to be connected to an independent clause in order to make sense.

■ A **simple sentence** is made of one independent clause.

The dog whined for her dinner.   *The storm grew stronger.*

■ A **compound sentence** has more than one independent clause. These clauses are joined by one of the coordinating conjunctions: *and, but, or, nor, for, so,* and *yet.*

The dog whined for her dinner, but she did not scratch at the door.

The storm grew stronger, and it soon became a hurricane.

■ A **complex sentence** has one independent clause and one or more dependent clauses. The clauses are joined by subordinating conjunctions (such as *after, although, because, before, if, since, unless, until, when,* and *while*) or by relative pronouns (such as *that, which,* and *who*). The independent clause does not have to come first in the sentence; sometimes the dependent clause comes first.

The dog whined for her dinner until her owner finally got out the dog food.

When its winds passed 74 miles per hour, the storm was classified as a hurricane.

Our soccer team just played a game that was one for the record books.

■ A **compound-complex sentence** has two or more independent clauses and one or more dependent clauses. This type of sentence may include relative pronouns and both types of conjunctions. The clauses can appear in any order.

The dog whined for her dinner until her owner finally got out the dog food, and then she began to bark excitedly.

When its winds passed 74 miles per hour, the storm was classified as a hurricane, and people prepared for its landfall.

If you haven't heard, our soccer team just played a game that was one for the record books, so we should celebrate the big win.

L.7.1.b

Guided Practice In the sentences below, underline each independent clause. Double underline each dependent clause. Then classify each sentence as simple, compound, complex, or compound-complex.

1. Since we had no sunscreen, we bought some on our way to the beach. _____

2. This yellow house is the largest one on our block. _____

3. My family left the fair at 8:00, so we missed the fireworks display. _____

4. I was really tired on the class trip until we saw the dinosaur bones at the museum. _____

5. Before the car wash, Tanya made signs and Gabe signed up volunteers. _____

Independent Practice Add your own writing to the clauses below to create the kind of sentence described in parentheses.

1. When the lights suddenly went out, (complex) _____

_____

2. Tyler bought that book yesterday, (compound) _____

_____

3. We took a canoe trip down the river, (compound-complex) _____

_____

4. Maria opened another window (complex) _____

_____

5. As the meteorite blazed over our town, (compound-complex)

_____

_____

L.7.2

Standard Capitalization, Punctuation, and Spelling

Guided Instruction When you write, remember to use standard, correct English capitalization, punctuation, and spelling. When you do, you make your writing easier for readers to understand and enjoy.

- **Capitalization**

  It is standard to always capitalize the first word of a sentence. English capitalization also includes the names of people, places, days of the week, and months; the pronoun *I*; and titles, such as book or movie titles. Titles can be either underlined or italicized.

  > **A**lejandra *will visit her cousins in* **H**ouston *in* **J**uly*.*

  > **I** *saw the movie* **A**nnie *for the first time last* **W**ednesday*.*

- **Punctuation**

  The use of punctuation depends on the structure of the sentence, but every sentence needs punctuation at the end. End punctuation includes periods, which identify statements; question marks, which identify questions; and exclamation points, which show emphasis. Within a sentence, commas are used to separate ideas, such as the name of a person being spoken to, long introductory phrases, or dependent clauses. A semicolon can be used to separate closely related independent clauses in the same sentence.

  > *Until Pam hit a home run, our team was facing a certain loss.*

  > *At the end of the recital, give your sister that bouquet of flowers.*

  > *Do you want spaghetti for supper, Evan, or would you rather have lasagna?*

  > *It's very hot out today; how I wish for some cooler weather!*

- **Spelling**

  Be careful to spell correctly, especially with words that sound like other words. Note these examples.

  > *there* (over there) / *they're* (they are) / *their* (belonging to more than one person)

  > *it's* (it is) / *its* (belonging to *it*)

  > *where* (location) / *wear* (put on, as clothes)

  > *whose* (to whom something belongs) / *who's* (who is)

  > *except* (all but this one) / *accept* (agree to do or take)

L.7.2

Guided Practice Rewrite each sentence to correct errors in capitalization, punctuation, and spelling.

1. from the attic to the basement the house was dark and quiet

   _____

2. Who's Hat is this on the chair.

   _____

3. what a great time paul and i had at the lincoln park zoo

   _____

4. because she would leave early friday morning alicia packed for her trip to california on thursday night

   _____

   _____

5. naomi worked at an animal shelter in martinsville in june now she wants a career that will let her work with animals all the time

   _____

   _____

Independent Practice Write a response for each of the directions below. Be sure to use standard capitalization, punctuation, and spelling.

1. Ask your friend if you may borrow her book. Call your friend and the book by name.

   _____

2. Ask the name of the new student across the room.

   _____

3. Explain why you were late to school last week. Name the day of the week you were late, and start the sentence with the word *because*.

   _____

4. Use *there*, *they're*, and *their* in a compound sentence.

   _____

   _____

5. Use two spelling words from page 160 to tell what only one person was willing to do.

   _____

   _____

W.7.9, W.7.9.b, SL.7.1.a–d, SL.7.3, SL.7.4, SL.7.6

Return to the Essential Question

How does evidence help writers explain a significant event?

Prepare for a class discussion about the Essential Question by responding to the questions below. Support your point of view with reasons and examples. Be sure to follow the rules for participating in an effective class discussion.

1. What kind of evidence did Jillian use to show why many people in the early 1900s faced very difficult working conditions?

_____

_____

_____

2. What evidence did Jillian use to support the idea that there was conflict between workers and factory owners?

_____

_____

_____

3. Why is this evidence a necessary part of Jillian's text?

_____

_____

Use your notes above as you discuss the Essential Question with your class or in small groups. Use the organizer below to record your ideas and what you hear in the discussion. Follow the discussion rules on the "Did I?" checklist on page 58.

Ideas I Agree or Disagree With		Questions I Asked
agree		
disagree		
New Ideas I Had During Discussion		Questions I Answered

W.7.2, W.7.2.a–b, W.7.9, L.7.1.b

Read this draft of an introductory paragraph and a background paragraph from a student's evidence-based text, and answer the questions below.

The Salem Witch Trials

(1) One of the most dramatic and strange conflicts in early American history happened when the people of Salem, Massachusetts, executed nineteen people for witchcraft and arrested many more. (2) This witch hysteria was begun by a few girls. (3) Though today we know that this conflict cannot be blamed on witches, there are still many different ideas about why it happened.

How the Witch Hysteria Began

(4) The world of the 1690s was very different from the world we know today. (5) The deeply religious Puritans of this time feared witchcraft and the possible presence of witches. (6) In February 1692, two girls began having mysterious fits, screaming and throwing things. (7) When the doctor diagnosed them as being attacked by witches, hysteria began.

---

1. What is the topic of this text?

a. witches

b. the Salem Witch Trials

c. Puritan New England

d. modern disagreements about history

2. Based on the information in the introduction, what will the text NOT include?

a. a definite cause for the witch hysteria

b. a description of the witch trials conflict

c. ideas about why the trials happened

d. evidence about this conflict

3. Sentence 1 is a

a. simple sentence.

b. compound sentence.

c. complex sentence.

d. compound-complex sentence.

4. Sentence 5 develops the topic by helping readers understand that

a. the Puritans were religious.

b. the Puritans thought witches were real.

c. the people of the time were called Puritans.

d. there were witches in Salem.

W.7.2, W.7.2.b–d, W.7.2.f, W.7.4, W.7.5, W.7.10, L.7.1.b, L.7.2

Read another paragraph from the student evidence-based text and answer the questions below.

> ### Possible Causes
>
> (1) Some scientists today think that the people of Salem were affected by accidentally eating something called ergot. (2) This fungus can cause fits and hallucinations. (3) Perhaps the girls ate it and then imagined seeing witches. (4) Some historians think that there were social causes. (5) These historians note that the first people to be blamed for the witchcraft were poor women who were not accepted by their society.

5. What type of punctuation should be added to sentence 5?

   a. a comma   **c.** a semicolon

   b. a question mark   **d.** none

6. What transitional word or phrase could be added at the beginning of sentence 4?

   a. Furthermore,   **c.** As a result,

   b. In fact,   **d.** However,

7. In sentence 2 above, circle the word that is a more precise replacement for the word *something* in sentence 1.

8. In the paragraph above, underline the effects of eating ergot.

9. Combine and revise sentences 2 and 3 to form a compound-complex sentence.

_____

_____

10. Write a conclusion for this text.

_____

_____

_____

Assignment: On separate paper, provide a final draft of the evidence-based text you began on page 157. Use what you learned about sentence structures and standard English capitalization, punctuation, and spelling in this unit. Think about how you and your classmates answered the Essential Question. Check your outline to be sure you organized your ideas well. Be sure to use precise language and transitions. End with a concluding statement that wraps up the topic well.

Introducing UNIT 7

In this unit about earth and sky, you will see how authors use language and organization to express ideas and information. Nonfiction texts are often meant to inform; that is, authors write nonfiction in order to educate readers about a particular topic. However, authors sometimes write nonfiction to express an opinion about a topic, as well, and to support that opinion with facts.

Nonfiction texts consist of many genres, including web articles, technical texts, scientific texts, and explanatory texts. In this unit, you will read an example of each. Within each text, you will learn ways in which people study the earth and the sky. As you read, consider how each author organizes information and chooses language to make his or her presentation clear and interesting. Ask yourself what the author thinks is important and what point of view he or she is expressing. Finally, explore each text a bit further by thinking about how you can identify those essential features of the text. What do your answers tell you about what makes an effective informational text?

Before Unit 7 ↓

Progress Check *Can I?*

After Unit 7 ↓

☐ Analyze the effect of word choice on a text's tone and meaning. ☐

☐ Analyze how an author organizes information and uses that organization to develop ideas in a text. ☐

☐ Follow and understand a multistep experiment. ☐

☐ Determine an author's point of view and purpose in a text. ☐

☐ Use context clues to help figure out the meanings of unfamiliar words and phrases. ☐

HOME◆CONNECT...

Today's students must learn to analyze a constant flow of information, including analyzing both content and an author's writing choices. As you work through this unit, help your child to look carefully at the writing choices each author has made. Questions like "How does that word affect the meaning of this paragraph?" or "How do you think the author feels about this subject?" can increase understanding of an author's **point of view** and **purpose**.

An author's **word choices** and choice of **organizational structure** can offer insight into the meaning of a text. As you read a scientific or technical text, ask your child to describe how the information is presented (for example, in steps or as a discussion of causes and effects). Discuss why the author might have organized the text that way.

The ability to **follow a multistep procedure** can indicate how well your child is following the structure of some scientific or technical texts. This unit includes an experiment for your child to follow. Work together on the experiment, checking each other's understanding of the procedure.

On the Go: In your travels around the community, find opportunities for you and your child to discuss the ecology of the area or ways in which weather conditions have affected the area. Together, choose a topic from your discussions and draft the text for a feature story that might be part of a local news broadcast. You even may want to refine the text, film the report, and share it with the family.

IN THIS UNIT, YOUR CHILD WILL...

- Read four nonfiction selections, including a web article, a technical text, a scientific text, and an explanatory text.

- Determine word meanings and how word choices affect a text.

- Analyze how an author's way of organizing a text contributes to the effectiveness of the text as a whole.

- Follow a step-by-step procedure related to an experiment or technical task.

- Determine an author's point of view and purpose.

- Use context to figure out the meanings of unfamiliar words and phrases.

- Compare and contrast ideas across four selections on the theme of earth and sky.

NOTE: All of these learning goals for your child are based on the Grade 7 Common Core State Standards for English Language Arts.

WAYS TO HELP YOUR CHILD

Help your child focus on how point of view can be an inherent element of information reporting. See if your child can identify implied points of view, or opinion, while watching different news broadcasts. At the end of a report, ask him or her to identify both the subject of the story and the reporter's opinion on that subject. Discuss how your child came to those conclusions.

ONLINE

For more Home Connect activities, continue online at sadlierconnect.com

Reading Informational Text: Craft and Structure

Essential Question:
How do authors use language and organization to express a point of view?

RI.7.4

WORDS TO KNOW

constellation

encrypted

receiver

sophisticated

To be an effective reader, you must understand the **meanings of words and phrases** that an author chooses. In addition, seeing the effect of an author's word choices will help you understand a text better.

CITE EVIDENCE

A Informational texts often include **technical words**, or words specific to the topic, in order to inform readers. In paragraph 2, underline three examples of technical words.

B Even when presenting scientific facts, an author may choose to use **figurative language** to make an interesting comparison. In paragraph 3, circle a word whose figurative meaning compares GPS satellites to stars.

Satellites and the Global Positioning System

(Genre: Web Article)

By Randolph Sims Magnusson, Editor, *Tech Times Daily*
www.techtimesdaily.net/satellites_and_gps

1   Picture this: You are in a car with your parents, on vacation, and you are close to reaching your destination. You and your parents know you are in the right area. However, you do not know, specifically, how to get to your intended stopping place. Luckily, you realize that there is no need to panic. Your dad turns on a device, types in the address of your destination, and gets detailed directions from an electronic voice. You may not realize it, but you and your parents have just interacted with one of the largest and most **sophisticated** technological operations in use today.

What Is GPS?

2   *GPS* stands for *Global Positioning System*. Typically, we use it to mean both the GPS receivers—or small units that transmit directions, coordinates, and time—and the large network of satellites that orbit Earth and transmit signals to those receivers. The Global Positioning System was originally conceived and operated by the United States military. It used **encrypted** signals to broadcast location. It was employed extensively during the Persian Gulf War in 1991. Then, in 1995, the U.S. government opened up the Global Positioning System for civilian use. This move allowed nonmilitary people the chance to use military satellites to find directions and locations.

3   The United States government owns and operates a **constellation** of 27 satellites that orbit Earth, making up the Global Positioning System. Of this number, 24 satellites are actually in use, while the rest are held as back-up in case a satellite fails.

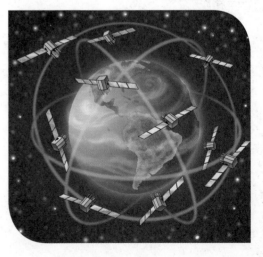

RI.7.4

4   These satellites weigh about 2,000 pounds each. They orbit Earth at a rate of 7,000 miles an hour, which allows each satellite to completely circle the planet twice in a 24-hour period. Each of the 24 satellites moves in a fixed orbit that keeps it from crashing into other satellites and allows its position around Earth to be known at all times.

What Is Trilateration?

5   Think back to your fictional family vacation. This time, imagine that your dad does not have his GPS **receiver** with him. Instead, in order to isolate your location, you must ask the people around you to tell you where you are.

6   When you ask the first person to tell you where you are, she answers, "You are 1,400 miles from Fargo, North Dakota." You get out your map and draw a circle, with Fargo at the center. The circle covers every place that lies within 1,400 miles of Fargo. This leaves a lot of possibilities!

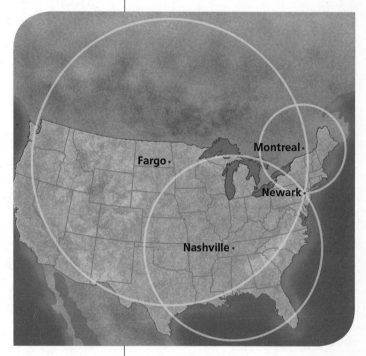

7   You decide to ask another person for help. This time, the gentleman answers, "You are 874 miles away from Nashville, Tennessee." You draw a second circle on your map, this time with Nashville at the center, extending out 874 miles. Now you are starting to refine your search. You notice the two places where the two circles intersect. These are the only two possibilities for your location.

8   You then ask one more person for help. The teenager answers, "You are 366 miles from Montreal, Canada." You draw one more circle, with Montreal at the center. Now, instead of multiple points of intersection, you see only one, at Newark, New Jersey. You have just identified your location.

Comprehension Check

The author of this text chooses words that help create a formal tone. Look again at the words or phrases you put a box around in paragraphs 7 and 8. What are some words you could replace these with in order to create a more informal tone?

CITE EVIDENCE

C   Word meanings can affect the **tone** of a text. Look closely at the last sentence in paragraph 5. Put a box around the two words that create a more formal, educational tone for the sentence.

D   In paragraph 7, the author uses a technical term meaning "to meet." Put an asterisk next to the word that means "to meet."

E   Think about the tone of paragraphs 7 and 8. Put a box around three words or phrases that help create a more formal tone in these paragraphs.

ANALYZING WORD MEANINGS

Guided Instruction

RI.7.4

WORDS TO KNOW

atomic

electromagnetic

nanosecond

sphere

trilateration

CITE EVIDENCE

A You can sometimes figure out meanings of technical words based on processes described in the text. Paragraph 9 introduces a technical term for the process of drawing intersecting circles, described earlier in the section. Circle that term.

B Paragraph 11 uses technical words to describe satellite positioning. Underline the two sentences that explain the requirements for 3-D trilateration.

9   This method of identification, known as **trilateration**, is very similar to the way that GPS maps locations—although the satellite system works much more quickly! The biggest difference between the map method and the way GPS works is that the map method is 2-D, or two-dimensional, trilateration. This means that you are working with flat surfaces rather than three-dimensional objects. GPS receivers use 3-D, or three-dimensional, trilateration to find people or objects.

How Does 3-D Trilateration Work?

10   Three-dimensional trilateration works very similarly to two-dimensional trilateration. Instead of circles, however, the mapping process involves **spheres**. Picture the circles you drew on your imaginary map. This time, instead of circles, visualize spheres; instead of a flat map, visualize the spheres in space, with the possible locations touching many different points on Earth.

11   When these spheres intersect, locations on Earth's surface can be identified. Unlike 2-D trilateration, it takes four spheres to truly pinpoint an exact position. In fact, Earth itself could act as the fourth sphere: You could eliminate any points in space and just use those that intersect on Earth's surface. GPS typically uses four satellites, however, in order to identify the location more accurately. For any given location on Earth there are always four satellites in Earth's orbit that are in the correct position to use for GPS navigation.

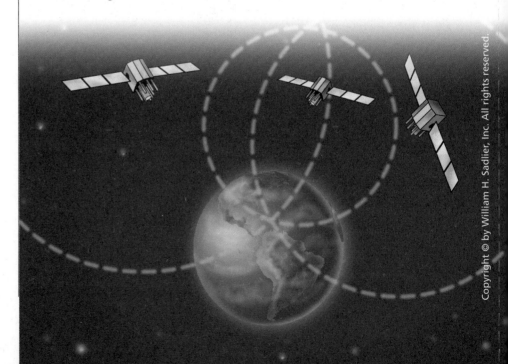

RI.7.4

How Does a GPS Determine Location?

12   As we have seen, a GPS receiver works by finding its location in relation to four orbiting satellites. To determine its location, the GPS needs two important pieces of information: where each satellite is and its distance away from the GPS receiver. The GPS receiver gets this information from the satellites themselves.

13   GPS satellites regularly send signals as high-frequency **electromagnetic** radio waves—fancy language for waves that travel at the speed of light. A signal includes information about the satellite's position and the exact time that the signal is sent. The GPS receiver picks up the signal and then calculates how long the signal took to travel from the transmitting satellite to the GPS receiver. Given that the speed of light is 186,000 miles per second, you can see that it does not take long for the signal to reach the GPS receiver. This means that GPS receivers need access to measurements of time reported in tiny units.

14   The **atomic** clock is the most precise tool in existence for keeping time. It notes time to the nearest **nanosecond**. The time on each satellite's atomic clock is sent in each signal transmission. Ideally, a GPS receiver would also have an atomic clock for determining the time difference from when the signal was sent to when it was received. Unfortunately, an atomic clock costs $50,000–$100,000. This means that a GPS receiver must use a plain quartz clock such as you might have at home.

15   To solve the problem of the differences in precision between the atomic clock and its quartz clock, the GPS receiver analyzes the time signals from each of the four GPS satellites. This tells the receiver how far off the "true time" its clock is and allows the receiver to compensate when it does its calculations.

Comprehension Check

How can understanding technical words help you read the rest of this article?

CITE EVIDENCE

C In this web article, the author occasionally makes some word choices to create a less formal tone. In paragraph 13, put a box around the words that create a less formal tone.

D In paragraph 14, a unit of measurement for extremely small periods of time is mentioned. Put an asterisk next to this technical term.

E In paragraph 14, the author uses the technical term for the type of clock that would be used in a typical home setting. Double underline this word. Why does the author offer an explanation of the types of clocks used by GPS units?

ANALYZING WORD MEANINGS

Guided Practice

RI.7.4

WORDS TO KNOW

aviation

environmental

pertinent

preservation

CITE EVIDENCE

A In paragraph 16, the author uses a technical word meaning "speed." Put a box around the word.

B With a partner, underline examples of technical language that appear in paragraph 18. Discuss the effect these word choices have on the tone of the text.

Why Does Time Matter So Much?

16   Remember the information a GPS receiver needs in order to pinpoint its location: the position of at least three satellites and the distance between the receiver and each of those satellites. Since satellites send radio signals with the velocity of the speed of light, the GPS receiver can determine the distance to each satellite by calculating the time it takes each signal to reach Earth.

17   The receiver is able to get and analyze signals from all the GPS satellites at the same time, then use trilateration to determine its position. And assuming the GPS receiver is in your hand or mounted on your car dashboard, you then know your position, too!

So, How Does GPS Help Me?

18   Besides giving you directions and telling you where you are, GPS technology has many other applications. These include aviation, public safety, disaster aid, and **environmental preservation**.

19   The use of GPS in **aviation** may be one of the most important applications of the technology. Pilots track their routes using the Global Positioning System, leading to greater accuracy in flight patterns and landing times and increased safety and efficiency in the air. Not only do the people flying and directing the planes benefit, but the passengers do as well.

20   In a disaster, whether natural (such as a tornado) or man-made (such as a building collapse), time is of the essence. Relief officials must be able to get to potential victims quickly and safely. GPS tracking gives emergency service providers an accurate representation of all **pertinent** landmarks, roadways, and bodies of water.

21   In 2005, GPS became a key member of the rescue team after Hurricane Katrina and Hurricane Rita attacked the Gulf Coast. In both cases, emergency services personnel were able to enter the affected areas with complete knowledge of the landmarks they would encounter. GPS technology saved valuable minutes, so that emergency workers could focus on the victims instead of their surroundings.

Comprehension Check

1. Throughout the selection, the author mentions important applications of GPS technology. Based on your reading, what does *applications* mean?

a. requests for employment

b. medical treatments

c. hard work

d. uses for something

2. In paragraphs 19–21, the author gives evidence for the idea that GPS technology has several applications by discussing all of the following EXCEPT

a. tourism.

b. disaster aid.

c. aviation.

d. public safety.

3. Which of the following passages contains figurative language?

a. "Since satellites send radio signals with the velocity of the speed of light . . . "

b. "The use of GPS in aviation may be one of the most important applications of the technology."

c. "In 2005, GPS became a key member of the rescue team after Hurricane Katrina and Hurricane Rita attacked the Gulf Coast."

d. ". . . so that emergency workers could focus on the victims instead of their surroundings."

4. In paragraph 20, the word *representation* refers to

a. a lawyer.

b. a map.

c. a demonstration.

d. a satellite.

5. With a partner, discuss why the author may have chosen to use both technical and casual language in this web article. What effect does this mix have on the tone of the article? What does this mix suggest about the author's intended audience?

_____

_____

_____

_____

_____

_____

ANALYZING WORD MEANINGS

Independent Practice

Satellites and the Global Positioning System *continued*

RI.7.4

WORDS TO KNOW

cellular

innovation

measure

smartphone

timely

CITE EVIDENCE

A In paragraph 22, the author uses two technical terms that mean "natural" or "biological." Put a box around each of those terms.

B In paragraph 23, circle the terms the author uses for "members of the armed forces" and "people who do not work in a certain profession." Why does the author choose these terms rather than using more informal language?

22 A third application of GPS technology lies in its usefulness in maintaining the environment. One of the greatest obstacles in environmental preservation has always been the lack of **timely** information. GPS allows environmentalists to identify and observe patterns, including those that can have devastating ecological consequences. Furthermore, GPS allows for accurate tracking of man-made environmental disasters, like oil spills and fires. Scientists can track the long-term consequences of these disasters and, ideally, put preventative **measures** into place.

What Is the Future of the Global Positioning System?

23 If you have ever used a **smartphone** to find your location or get directions, you are already a part of the future of GPS. What once was used only for military purposes has now become a common technology used by civilians as well as by military personnel. However, these are not the only applications that GPS may hold for the future.

24 One of the anticipated innovations in GPS is the invention of a GPS technology that works indoors. Right now, if you are using the map on your smart phone inside a building, you are not actually tapping into the global satellite system. Instead, your phone is using the positions of the **cellular** towers around you to make an approximation. In the future, we can expect to see GPS technology applied to both indoor and outdoor systems.

25 A more creative application for the future is the possibility of self-driving cars. Someday you may be the passenger while sitting in the driver's seat of your own car! By using GPS to navigate self-driven vehicles, scientists hope to eliminate human error on the roadways. Doing so could lead to a significant decrease in both traffic and accidents, especially in major metropolitan areas.

26 The Global Positioning System is a technological **innovation** that many people today take for granted. It allows for the kinds of precise location services, directional mapping, and

environmental tracking that were not possible 100 years ago. Now we can see not only where we are but also where we are going, in clear, exact images. Through GPS, the possibilities of satellite-directed technologies are as endless as human imagination!

Comprehension Check

(MORE ONLINE) **sadlierconnect.com**

1. Define the phrase *ecological consequences* (paragraph 22).

   a. financial difficulties

   b. effects on nature

   c. personal concerns

   d. atmospheric changes

2. Which word in paragraph 25 means "to plan and travel on a given course"?

   a. self-driven

   b. metropolitan

   c. eliminate

   d. navigate

3. In the final section of this web article, which of the following is NOT one of the "anticipated innovations in GPS"?

   a. improved transportation safety

   b. improved national defense

   c. more widespread use of GPS

   d. an "indoor" GPS system

4. In the conclusion to this article, the author uses figurative language to compare the possibilities of GPS to

   a. the interior of a building.

   b. a cleaned-up environment.

   c. people's creativity.

   d. an automobile.

5. In this web article, the author uses technical language in very specific places. When does the author use technical language, and why? What impact does word choice have on the overall tone of this article?

   _____

   _____

   _____

   _____

   _____

   _____

RI.7.5

WORDS TO KNOW

atmospheric

evaporation

eye

hurricane

Authors of technical texts use **text structure** to present material in an organized way. Common structures include **sequential**, **comparative**, and **causal**.

CITE EVIDENCE

A Authors who use a **sequential structure** describe steps in the order in which they occur. Put a box around the block of text that illustrates sequential organization.

B A **causal structure** shows how one event causes another. In paragraph 4, underline the sentence that shows a causal relationship between paragraphs 3 and 4.

Hurricanes
Earth's Most Violent Storms
(Genre: Technical Text)

1   **Hurricanes** are among the greatest weather phenomena on our planet. They can be as large as 600 miles across and can reach wind speeds of up to 200 miles per hour. The strength and force of a hurricane can have devastating consequences for those in its path. Furthermore, the aftereffects of a powerful hurricane can linger for years.

2   One of the earliest written records of a hurricane came from Christopher Columbus in 1494, and people have been documenting hurricane movements ever since. Today, scientists have moved beyond tracking hurricanes to studying the complex processes that lead to the development of hurricanes. In this way, scientists hope to be better able to predict both the occurrence of hurricanes and the intensity that a particular hurricane will achieve.

Understanding Hurricane Conditions

3   Three basic **atmospheric** and environmental conditions must be present in order for a hurricane to develop:

a. First, warm oceanic temperatures cause sufficient heat and moisture to develop in the atmosphere.

b. Next, seawater **evaporation** combines with heat and energy to propel the movements of the hurricane.

c. Then, a strong wind pattern near the surface of the ocean causes the air to turn inward upon itself.

4   When all three requirements are met, conditions are ripe for the presence of a hurricane. Both the Atlantic and eastern Pacific Oceans see these conditions most frequently in late summer. In the Atlantic Ocean, the peak hurricane season runs from June 1 until November 30. In the eastern Pacific, it runs from May 15 until November 30.

RI.7.5

5 Simply having the presence of these conditions is not enough, however, to guarantee the development of a hurricane. The atmospheric conditions must first undergo a variety of processes before the intense power of a hurricane can be fully generated.

The Stages of Hurricane Development

Stage 1: Evaporation

6 During the first stage of development, warm water rises upward from near the surface of the ocean. The water temperature must be greater than 80 degrees Fahrenheit for this to occur. The rising water causes evaporation, creating an area of low pressure below and leading to higher levels of humidity. This provides energy for the hurricane to develop.

Stage 2: Wind Force

7 Once the warm air has risen, air begins to circulate and spiral. Air with higher pressure collides with air with lower pressure. Moisture is forced upward. As the "old" air is pushed upward, "new" air continues to swirl into the area of evaporation, creating a constant cycle of air pressure.

Stage 3: Cloud Formation

8 As the warm, moist air rises, it cools. The water in the air then begins to form clouds. The clouds shift with the movement of the air above the surface. As the system spins and builds, the clouds begin to spin and build, as well. The storm system grows, gaining more and more power as warm air and moisture are forced upward from the surface of the ocean.

Stage 4: Wind Rotation

9 The combination of strong winds and evaporation causes the air to spiral. The air begins to spin faster, resulting in the development of an **eye** in the center of the growing storm. Inside the eye, the air pressure is very low. Conditions are calm and clear. Outwardly, however, the storm becomes ever more powerful, as higher air pressure rotates around and into the eye of the storm.

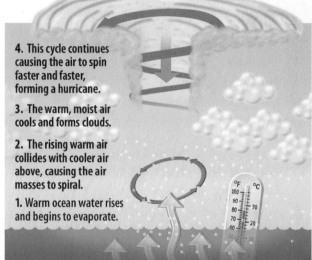

4. This cycle continues causing the air to spin faster and faster, forming a hurricane.

3. The warm, moist air cools and forms clouds.

2. The rising warm air collides with cooler air above, causing the air masses to spiral.

1. Warm ocean water rises and begins to evaporate.

CITE EVIDENCE

C On this page, the author clearly details a sequential structure. Put an asterisk by each step in the sequence.

D In paragraph 7, the author notes the importance of "a constant cycle of air pressure." Double underline the cause of this cycle.

E In paragraph 9, double underline two sentences that show a causal relationship. How do a sequential structure and a causal structure work together in this part of the text?

Comprehension Check

How does the illustration of the steps in the development of a hurricane contribute to your understanding of the text?

Guided Instruction

Hurricanes Earth's Most Violent Storms *continued*

WORDS TO KNOW

apprised

classified

infrared

storm surge

CITE EVIDENCE

A Information that has a **comparative structure** shows how details are similar to or different from each other. Put a box around the block of information on this page that focuses on technical differences among hurricanes.

B Throughout this technical text, the author has provided clear direction as to how each subsection will be organized. Circle the two lines of text that help readers recognize the structure of this page.

The Stages of Hurricane Development (continued)

Stage 5: Dissipation

10   As the hurricane reaches land, it begins to weaken. Without the evaporation cycles of the ocean waters, hurricanes lose the conditions needed to build force, and the system dissipates. However, it is often days before the hurricane completely dies out. It will typically move farther inland, leaving extensive rain and wind damage in its wake.

Hurricane Classification

11   The intensity and strength of the storm determines its official title. As the winds spiral, reaching speeds of up to 38 miles per hour (mph), the storm is officially **classified** as a "tropical depression." When the strength of the winds in the storm reaches 39 mph, the storm is called a "tropical storm." Once the winds hit 74 mph, the tropical storm officially becomes a hurricane. Scientists refer to all hurricane-like events as "tropical cyclones." This term includes hurricanes, typhoons, and cyclones.

12   Scientists also classify hurricanes according to their size and strength. The storm classification also indicates how much damage the storm can be expected to cause once it reaches land. This damage is assessed according to the height of the **storm surge**—that is, the rise of the ocean water onto the shoreline. The classifications are as follows:

- Category 1: wind speeds of 74–95 mph; storm surge heights of 4–5 feet
- Category 2: wind speeds of 96–110 mph; storm surges of 6–8 feet
- Category 3: wind speeds of 111–130 mph; storm surges of 9–12 feet
- Category 4: wind speeds of 131–155 mph; storm surges of 13–18 feet
- Category 5: wind speeds greater than 155 mph; storm surges greater than 19 feet in height

13   Although Category 4 and 5 hurricanes are comparatively rare, they cause considerable destruction whenever they reach land. Hurricane Katrina, a Category 4 hurricane, hit the Gulf Coast of the United States in 2005, leaving behind it communities shattered by its sheer force. Katrina reached 400 miles across and hit wind speeds of more than 125 mph. Storm surges from Katrina reached 14 feet high in some coastal areas and more than 28 feet high in New Orleans, Louisiana. More than 1,800 people died, either during the storm or as neighborhoods attempted to recover in the weeks following Katrina's arrival. It is estimated that Katrina caused some $81 billion in property damage.

Studying Hurricanes

14   In an effort to better understand and predict the movements of hurricanes, scientists study the creation, life cycle, and intensity of the storms. Meteorologists, or scientists who study atmospheric processes, use satellite technology to gather remote data on hurricanes. Additionally, scientists look at surface data gathered by specially equipped aircraft. Weather centers track and monitor hurricanes and other extreme weather events in order to keep the public **apprised** of developing concerns.

15   One of the most important methods of gathering data on hurricanes is through the use of weather satellites. These satellites track the movements of hurricanes, as well as atmospheric changes that occur within the storms. The satellites monitor cloud movements and air circulation patterns. They also track the rainfall, air speed, and precipitation generated by the storm. Typically, weather satellites are equipped with **infrared** sensors. These sensors allow meteorologists to monitor temperatures in the hurricane. Within the last 15 years, scientists have been able to use these data to identify important patterns in hurricane intensity and relative humidity.

CITE EVIDENCE

C In paragraph 13, the author adds more specific details to the comparison of wind speeds and storm surges in the previous paragraph. Underline the details that further illustrate this comparison.

D In paragraphs 14 and 15, the author changes the structure of the text. Circle the text that specifies you are reading a new section of the piece. What purpose do these two paragraphs serve in the overall structure of the text?

Comprehension Check

So far, how has the structure of the text helped you understand the topic of hurricanes?

Guided Practice

Hurricanes Earth's Most Violent Storms *continued*

RI.7.5, RST.7.3, RST.7.6

WORDS TO KNOW

bulb

condensation

hygrometer

relative humidity

saturation

CITE EVIDENCE

A This page is organized with one main heading, one subheading, and one title. Identify and underline each of these items.

B Circle the sentence that introduces the step-by-step procedure on this page. Discuss with a partner how you would complete the experiment and why the author included the experiment in the text.

Relative Humidity

16 The term **relative humidity** refers to the amount of water that is actually in the air. The rate of evaporation of water into the atmosphere is not consistent. As evaporation speeds up or slows down, the percentage of water in the air changes. This percentage is called relative humidity.

17 When meteorologists calculate relative humidity, they look at the rate of evaporation in the atmosphere. They then compare this rate of evaporation to the maximum, or **saturation**, rate for the existing temperature. They make this calculation using a special device called a **hygrometer**. When the relative humidity is at 100%, the air is full of water. As more water evaporates, an equal amount of water condenses, or collects. You can see evidence of **condensation** in the presence of clouds and fog.

18 Conversely, a lower percentage of relative humidity indicates that water is evaporating more quickly than it is condensing. Desert climates experience very low percentages of relative humidity and very high speeds of evaporation.

19 **Learn About Relative Humidity** Relative humidity can be better understood through a simple, at-home experiment:

Temperature and Relative Humidity

Materials Needed:

- two household thermometers
- paper towels or pieces of cloth
- water at room temperature
- paper and pen for recording results

Procedures

a. Place one of the thermometers on the work surface. This is the dry **bulb** thermometer.

b. Thoroughly wet the piece of cloth or paper towel in the water.

c. Wrap the wet cloth around the bulb end of the other thermometer. This is the wet bulb thermometer.

d. Place the wet bulb thermometer near the dry bulb thermometer.

e. Record the temperatures indicated on each thermometer.

f. Wait 5 minutes.

g. Record the temperature on each thermometer again.

h. Continue to record the temperatures in 5-minute intervals. Do this for a total of 20 minutes or until the wet bulb temperature holds steady.

Comprehension Check

1. Which organizational structure has appeared in this article so far?

   a. comparative

   b. sequential

   c. causal

   d. all of the above

2. What is the author's purpose in including the subsection "Learn About Relative Humidity"?

   a. to encourage young readers to pursue a career in meteorology

   b. to provide a hands-on representation of a scientific concept

   c. to demonstrate advanced scientific theories through experimentation

   d. to indicate a change in the overall structure of the text

3. What is the purpose of the illustration on page 180?

   a. to show what the experiment should look like when performed correctly

   b. to reveal to readers the results of the experiment

   c. to emphasize that many tools that meteorologists use are quite simple

   d. none of the above

4. The experiment on pages 180–181 has a structure that is primarily

   a. comparative.

   b. sequential.

   c. causal.

   d. all of the above

5. Suppose you did not perform the experiment on these pages. Would merely reading about the experiments be as effective as conducting the experiments yourself? What do the experiments contribute to the text? Compare answers with a partner and explain your thoughts.

   _____

   _____

   _____

   _____

Independent Practice

Hurricanes Earth's Most Violent Storms *continued*

RI.7.5, RST.7.6

WORDS TO KNOW

awe

propulsion

theorized

ventured

CITE EVIDENCE

A Paragraphs 22 and 23 relate to the relative humidity experiment. Circle the text that indicates this relationship.

B Double underline a causal relationship in paragraph 24. What purpose do paragraphs 24 and 25 serve in the overall structure of this text?

Interpreting the Data

20   Look at the differences between the temperatures recorded for the wet bulb thermometer and the dry bulb thermometer. A large difference between the temperatures means that evaporation is occurring quickly. Consequently, the relative humidity in the air is low.

21   A small difference between the temperatures means that the water around the wet bulb is not evaporating quickly. The air is already heavy with moisture. Any new water attempting to enter the atmosphere must become condensation. The percentage of relative humidity is high.

Hurricanes and Relative Humidity

22   Since hurricanes develop through the evaporation of warm moisture into the air, scientists have **theorized** that hurricane intensity may be related to relative humidity. In 2012, scientists from NASA's Jet **Propulsion** Laboratory in Pasadena, California, published the results of an eight-year study. The study analyzed the relationship between hurricane intensity and relative humidity.

23   After studying data gathered between 2002 and 2010, scientists determined that hurricanes that intensify quickly exist in environments with higher levels of relative humidity. In contrast, hurricanes that were weakening did so in environments with lower levels of relative humidity. These data represent one of the first times scientists have **ventured** to study the intensity of hurricane systems rather than just the storms' development and life cycle.

24   Hurricanes present one of the most awesome displays of nature's fury on Earth. From their initial stages of development, through their slow movement across the ocean, they are studied by scientists so that we might have a better understanding of these amazing storms.

15°C

25% Relative humidity

10°C

50% Relative humidity

5°C

100% Relative humidity

25   The better we understand hurricanes, the more we can predict their behaviors and, therefore, provide sufficient warning to those in their path. With continued study and greater understanding, perhaps someday we can find ways to avoid the destruction of a hurricane without lessening our **awe** of its power.

Comprehension Check

MORE ONLINE **sadlierconnect.com**

1. Overall, how is the information in this technical text presented?

   a. sequentially

   b. comparatively

   c. causally

   d. none of the above

2. What is the author's purpose for summarizing the experiment in paragraphs 20 and 21?

   a. to encourage readers to complete the experiment

   b. to relate the results of the experiment to the overall topic of the article

   c. to present theories that could be explored through an additional experiment

   d. to give an opinion about ideas related to the experiment

3. Throughout the text, the author indicates changes in topic through the use of

   a. large section headings.

   b. subsection headings.

   c. titles for special elements.

   d. all of the above

4. What is the main purpose of the diagrams and photographs included in the text?

   a. to keep readers interested in the subject matter

   b. to provide visual support for the concepts being discussed

   c. to introduce readers to new and unfamiliar ideas

   d. to change the structure of the text

5. How did the overall structure of this text contribute to your understanding of the material? Cite evidence to support your answer.

   _____

   _____

   _____

   _____

   _____

Guided Instruction

RI.7.6, RST.7.8

WORDS TO KNOW

aqueous

contiguous

ecosystem

estuary

watershed

Some scientific texts include statements of the author's **point of view**, or **position**, regarding the topic. Critical readers must determine whether a given statement is a **fact**, an **opinion**, or a **reasoned judgment**.

CITE EVIDENCE

A Authors use **facts**—details that can be proven—to support their personal **points of view,** or **positions**. Underline two facts in paragraph 1 that support this author's point of view.

B Authors who want to express an **opinion**—a statement that can be supported but with which people can disagree—often do so early in a text. Put an asterisk next to the sentence in paragraph 2 that expresses this author's opinion about what people should think.

Our Fragile Ecosystem
The Importance of Preserving the Wetlands
(Genre: Scientific Text)

1   It is estimated that before the coming of European colonists in the 1600s, more than 220 million acres in what is now the United States were wetlands. Since then, it has lost over 50% of these wetlands. In 2009, there were only 110 million acres of wetlands in the **contiguous** United States (the lower 48 states).

2   An area of 110 million acres may seem like a great deal of space devoted to wetlands. However, quite the opposite is true. Consider how your life would change if you were to lose 53% of the space in your house, or if you had to sleep on only 53% of your bed every night. The way you now live would be vastly altered, and not for the better. In the same way, the widespread destruction of the wetlands in the United States is, even now, having painful effects on our environment. If we do not continue to work toward preservation, those effects will worsen with time. The wetlands represent a unique and important element in Earth's ecosystems. If we want to maintain the delicate balance that exists among natural areas, then preservation of the wetlands should be at the top of our environmental priorities.

What Is a Wetland?

3   The definition of a wetland environment would appear to be quite simple: an **ecosystem** that is neither dry land, nor water, but a combination of both. However, the political battle

surrounding the preservation of the wetlands has blurred the meaning. To date, more than 50 different definitions have been assigned to the wetland ecosystems in the United States.

4   A widely accepted definition comes from the United States Army Corps of Engineers. This group is responsible for maintaining the provisions of the Clean Water Act that apply to the wetlands. The Corps definition states, "Wetlands are inundated or saturated by surface or groundwater at a frequency and duration sufficient to support . . . a prevalence of vegetation typically adapted for life in saturated soil conditions." In simpler terms, a wetland is an ecosystem that balances both **aqueous** and dry conditions. This balance results in plant and animal life that is specifically adapted for the unique wetland environment.

5   Wetlands are located in almost every one of the lower 48 states. California and Kentucky, however, have seen a much greater decrease in their wetland areas. Both of those states now have less than 20% of their original wetland regions. Similarly, the Florida Everglades, the largest wetland environment in the world, has lost more than 60% of its functional area.

6   It is estimated that the United States continues to lose between 70,000 and 90,000 acres of wetlands every year. As more people settle in coastal areas, the increased need for development threatens natural resources. We move nearer to unique environments because we want to be a part of the natural phenomena that produce such beauty. However, if we are not careful, we may forget to preserve the very thing we love.

Types of Wetlands

Coastal Wetlands

7   There are two main types of wetlands: coastal and inland. Coastal wetlands are located on the eastern and western coasts of the United States. They include both saltwater and freshwater **estuaries** that are located along a coastal **watershed**. About 40% of the wetlands in the United States are coastal wetlands, and 81% of those are located in the southeastern United States.

Comprehension Check

In this scientific text, what point of view does the author express? Why does the author take this position?

CITE EVIDENCE

C Authors use statements of fact in an argument meant to show a **reasoned judgment**—a carefully thought-out position about the topic. Circle two such statements of fact in paragraph 5.

D Authors may attempt to show that they are making a reasoned judgment by presenting facts and opinions together. In paragraph 6, underline the two statements of fact. Then put a box around the opinion that is based upon these facts.

ANALYZING POINTS OF VIEW

Guided Instruction

WORDS TO KNOW

filtration

integral

prolific

safeguard

toxin

waterfowl

CITE EVIDENCE

A Authors use **loaded language** to evoke strong emotions in their readers. In the last two sentences of paragraph 10, underline four examples of loaded language.

B The structure of this scientific text intersperses the author's point of view with factual information about wetlands. Put an asterisk next to two paragraphs on these pages that include factual information but not opinions.

Our Fragile Ecosystem The Importance of Preserving the Wetlands *continued*

8   Coastal wetlands are one of the most beautiful and **prolific** ecosystems on Earth. Much of the seafood served in American restaurants originates in a coastal wetland. More than half of the commercially harvested fish in the United States spend at least some portion of their lives living and feeding in a coastal wetland.

9   Coastal wetlands also play a role in other major industries. Some 24% of the natural gas produced in the United States travels through the coastal wetlands of Louisiana. Whenever you use commercial gas for heat, for cooking, or even for driving, you should appreciate the importance of the coastal wetlands.

10   Of course, the coastal wetlands are a wonderful ecosystem in their own right. The coastal wetlands are home to 85% of the country's migrating **waterfowl**. They are also home to more than 45% of the threatened and endangered species in the United States. Wetlands serve to filter impurities from water sources before they are deposited into the ocean. Additionally, they **safeguard** the coastline from the devastating effects of major weather events. In every way possible, the coastal wetlands are a vital and irreplaceable part of the ecosystem.

Inland Wetlands

11   The second type of wetlands found in the United States are inland wetlands. Inland wetlands are not located along ocean coasts. Instead, inland wetlands can be found along freshwater lakes and marshes, on the banks of rivers, and around ponds and other bodies of water native to forest environments.

RI.7.6, RH.7.6, RST.7.8

12   Inland wetlands also differ from coastal wetlands in their general nature. Unlike coastal wetlands, inland wetlands do not move with the tides. Instead, they maintain a more stable environment. This stability allows for the growth of different types of vegetation than are found in a coastal environment.

13   Similar to coastal wetlands, inland wetlands are also home to many different species of waterfowl, marine life, and plants. Inland wetlands play a large role in the development of trout populations. They are also home to small mammals, like muskrats and beavers, and amphibious species, like frogs and salamanders. Without the wetlands, these species would be in serious danger of extinction.

The Importance of Preserving the Wetlands

14   Although wetlands cover less than 10% of Earth's surface, they are responsible for 25% of the world's productivity. Wetlands provide flood protection and water **filtration**. The thick vegetation in the wetlands serves to filter out impurities that are trapped as water moves through the ecosystem. Unfortunately, if the groundwater becomes too contaminated, the pollutants filtered by the wetland vegetation can act as a **toxin** to the environment. In other words, the natural processes of the wetland vegetation can actually cause problems for the ecosystem. However, the inherent bacteria that are an **integral** part of wetland environments neutralize some of the contaminants that can be found in waterways.

15   The same vegetation that cleanses water can also keep it away from the coastal shorelines. The plant life in the wetlands deflects storm surges that can cause erosion damage to the shoreline. In 2005, Hurricane Katrina caused significant damage to the Gulf Coast. Current studies theorize that a healthy wetland ecosystem could have minimized this damage.

CITE EVIDENCE

C Explanations provide facts that can support an author's position. In paragraph 14, circle the facts that help explain the idea that wetlands have important functions.

D Authors also use **inclusion** (the addition of specific details that support an opinion) and **avoidance** (the omission of details that seem contrary to an opinion) to help their point of view gain acceptance. Put a box around the two sentences in paragraph 15 that illustrate an example of inclusion.

Comprehension Check

How can determining the author's point of view help you understand the author's purpose in writing this scientific text?

Guided Practice

RI.7.6, RH.7.6, RST.7.8

WORDS TO KNOW

depleted

equilibrium

mandated

viable

wholesale

CITE EVIDENCE

A Underline the sentence in paragraph 16 that is not a statement of fact.

B Put an asterisk next to the names of the two federal agencies the author includes to show a reasoned judgment. Discuss with a partner the effect of the inclusion of these agencies on your opinion of the topic.

Our Fragile Ecosystem The Importance of Preserving the Wetlands *continued*

Current Efforts in Preservation

16   From the 1950s until the 1970s, the United States experienced record losses in wetland acreage. During that period, the United States lost, on average, 458,000 acres of **viable** wetland each year. The realization that the country could be headed for the **wholesale** elimination of an entire ecosystem led to increased efforts to protect and preserve our country's wetlands. And those efforts have had some success. By 2009, wetland loss had gone from 458,000 acres each year to approximately 14,000 acres each year. While these numbers represent significant improvement, more should be done, for the wetlands are still being **depleted**.

17   Currently, the Environmental Protection Agency (EPA) and the Army Corps of Engineers are leading federal efforts to preserve this valuable environment. In 1948, an early version of what came to be known as the Clean Water Act was passed. It **mandated** that the federal government enact procedures dedicated to preserving and maintaining our nation's water resources. Today, the EPA and the Army Corps of Engineers work together to ensure that **equilibrium** in the wetlands is maintained. In addition, both groups focus on balancing the desires of commercial interests against the still-diminishing wetlands.

18   State and local governments also play a significant role in helping to preserve the wetlands. In order to assist local governments in this mission, the EPA awards Wetland Program Development Grants to local community groups dedicated to the preservation of wetlands. The EPA's Five Star Restoration Challenge Grant Program provides funding to groups looking to restore already damaged wetland ecosystems.

19   To date, these programs have supported nearly 600 wetland preservation and restoration projects and have awarded more than $30 million in funds for wetland improvement. In total, almost 9,000 acres of wetland have been restored or improved through these federal grant programs.

Comprehension Check

1. Which of the following techniques helps support the author's point of view?

   a. loaded language

   b. inclusion of helpful details

   c. use of reasoned judgment

   d. all of the above

2. The author's position is supported by a text structure in which

   a. only statements of opinion are included.

   b. only statements of fact are included.

   c. facts and opinions are both presented.

   d. opposing opinions are presented.

3. In paragraph 16, the phrase *the wholesale elimination of an entire ecosystem* is best described as an example of

   a. avoidance.

   b. inclusion.

   c. loaded language.

   d. reasoned judgment.

4. What is the best explanation of the purpose for paragraphs 17–19?

   a. They show readers that the problem of wetland preservation is now under control.

   b. They inform readers that some help for the problem has come from the government.

   c. They help readers understand that the problem is best handled by the government.

   d. They encourage readers to apply for federal grants and solve the problem themselves.

5. Work with a partner to list some facts or questions that the author may have avoided in order to keep the focus on his or her point of view.

_____

_____

_____

_____

_____

_____

Independent Practice

Our Fragile Ecosystem The Importance of Preserving the Wetlands *continued*

RI.7.6, RH.7.6, RST.7.5

WORDS TO KNOW

contaminant

invaluable

native

urban sprawl

CITE EVIDENCE

A Put a box around the change in organizational structure on this page.

B Circle examples of loaded language in paragraph 21. What does this language tell you about the author's point of view?

20   However, it will take more than just federal monies to help preserve the integrity of the country's inland and coastal wetlands. Private citizens must also work to protect these **invaluable** resources. Individuals can help by taking some of the following actions:

- Plant **native** vegetation in order to avoid introducing any potentially harmful species of plant into the environment.

- Avoid using fertilizer and pesticides in personal gardening and landscaping. Work to avoid adding chemical **contaminants** to the water supply.

- Volunteer with a local conservation group to help preserve a wetland, stream, or other body of water.

- Work with a community group to help restore a local endangered wetland. Look into getting funding through the federal programs already mentioned, as well as state and local agencies.

- Find out if your local government sponsors an adopt-a-wetland program, and then get involved!

21   The wetlands are one of our most important ecosystems. They house essential elements of the environment that cannot be found elsewhere. They serve to protect and preserve other natural surroundings through flood control and filtering. They provide necessary lifelines for hundreds of unique and vital plant and animal species. And they play important roles in commercial industries worldwide.

22   As a country, we cannot afford to lose such a critical resource. Since the European settlement of the United States in the 1600s, the wetlands have been a target for the negative consequences of **urban sprawl**, leading to the elimination of over a hundred million acres. We cannot let this happen again.

Comprehension Check

MORE ONLINE **sadlierconnect.com**

1. In what way does paragraph 20 present a contrast to paragraphs 17–19?

   a. It suggests that the government has secret reasons for not doing more for the environment.

   b. It reveals ways in which the Clean Water Act has failed to solve the problem.

   c. It encourages readers not to think that only the government can solve the problem.

   d. none of the above

2. For what main purpose does the author include a bulleted list in paragraph 20?

   a. to show readers that they, too, can help solve the wetlands problem

   b. to show readers that there are other opinions on the central issue

   c. to remind readers that many wetlands remain threatened or endangered

   d. to blame readers for not helping solve the problem in the past

3. Which statement best represents the author's overall point of view on the preservation of the wetlands?

   a. There are enough wetland ecosystems to support future generations.

   b. The wetlands are an essential ecosystem that must be preserved.

   c. The wetlands have been in danger for so long that they cannot be saved.

   d. Private citizens must rely on government entities to preserve wetlands.

4. Which statement best describes the purpose of paragraph 21?

   a. It condemns industry for polluting wetlands.

   b. It challenges readers to get involved in wetland preservation.

   c. It repeats information from the author's introduction.

   d. It summarizes the reasons that wetlands are valuable.

5. Is the use of loaded language appropriate for a scientific text? Defend your position.

   _____

   _____

   _____

   _____

   _____

Satellites
Bridging the Gap from Earth to Sky
(Genre: Technical Text)

1   In 1957, the Soviet government (the government that ruled Russia and several other countries in Asia and Eastern Europe at that time) launched *Sputnik I*, the first satellite to orbit Earth. Although the Soviet government kept the launch under tight secrecy, we now know that *Sputnik I* was a metal sphere, 23 inches around and 184 pounds in weight. Onboard, the satellite carried a thermometer, a battery, a radio transmitter, and nitrogen gas. The satellite orbited for 92 days, until it was pulled into Earth's gravity and destroyed upon reentry.

2   The Soviet accomplishment was incredible, and the launch of *Sputnik I* was the impetus for a competition with the United States for leadership in space exploration. By today's standards, however, *Sputnik I* was a highly simplistic craft, with very little utility in space. Today, satellites are a vital, if often unrecognized, presence in our daily lives. Without the presence of satellites orbiting above us, some of our common amenities—weather reports, news and information distribution, and even cable television—would cease to exist.

Anatomy of a Satellite

3   A satellite is any object that orbits, or circles, Earth or another astronomical body. The term *satellite*, however, is typically taken to mean a man-made object placed into orbit for a specific purpose. Building and launching satellites can cost anywhere from $50 million to $400 million, and they are usually custom-made devices. The exception is the series of satellites that make up the Global Positioning System. These 27 satellites are almost exact copies of each other, in order to better facilitate consistent function.

4   A typical satellite is composed of six fundamental elements:

   a. Satellite Housing—the outside container of the satellite. The housing is either square or cylindrical, depending on the type of stabilizing system employed to keep the satellite in orbit. Solar cells, used to power the satellite, are mounted to the housing, as is the communications antenna.
   b. Power System—solar-powered, battery-powered, or both. Satellites must maintain a constant source of electricity in order to function properly.
   c. Antenna System—to provide for tracking and communications. The antenna system receives electronic signals necessary for positioning.
   d. Control System—the command center of the satellite. The control system monitors all of the satellite functions and receives and transmits data signals from Earth.
   e. Station Keeping—keeps the satellite in orbit. The station keeping uses thrusters to maintain the correct orbit. When the thrusters run out of fuel, the satellite stops working.
   f. Transponders—help maintain strong signals between Earth and the satellite.

RI.7.4, RI.7.5, RI.7.6

5   The main function of a satellite is to transmit and receive signals. A signal, called an uplink, is sent from Earth's surface to the satellite. The signal frequency is called a gigahertz (GHz) range signal. The satellite transmits this signal to the appropriate receiving stations back on Earth. This type of transmission is called a downlink. Only those receiving stations within the satellite's functional area can accept and transmit the downlink.

Types of Satellites

6   Although most satellites are made of the same elements, arising from the same basic functionalities, a wide variety of satellites orbit Earth. They are classified according to their intended function, the type of orbit they maintain, and their altitude above Earth.

Satellite Function

7   Satellites maintain a variety of roles and allow for a large number of practical applications on Earth. These include the following:

- Weather satellites: aid in identifying and forecasting weather patterns

- Military satellites: used for military purposes—use is typically secret, not disclosed to the general public

- Rescue satellites: receive and transmit distress calls

- Scientific satellites: aid in scientific research (One of the best known of these is the Hubble Space Telescope.)

- Communications satellites: facilitate voice and data transmission

- Navigational satellites: pinpoint locations and guide directions (The Global Positioning System includes a series of navigational satellites.)

- Broadcast satellites: transmit television signals

- Earth observation satellites: track changes in Earth's systems

Satellite Orbit

8   Besides differing in function, satellites can differ in the type of orbit they maintain in space. The orbit of a satellite is the pattern by which the satellite circles Earth. The two orbital patterns are either circular or elliptical (egg-shaped). The point on the orbital path that is closest to Earth is called the perigee; the point that is farthest away is called the apogee.

9   There are three basic types of satellite orbits:

a. Geostationary orbits: Geostationary orbits, also known as geosynchronous or synchronous orbits, are orbital patterns in which the satellite maintains a stable position above a spot on Earth's surface. In order to maintain consistent functionality, broadcast satellites follow geostationary orbits.

b. Asynchronous orbits: Satellites in asynchronous orbits pass a spot on Earth's surface at different times during the day. Observation satellites usually follow asynchronous orbit patterns.

c. Polar orbits: During a polar orbit, the satellite flies low in the atmosphere and passes over each pole (North and South) in the course of one revolution. Polar orbiting satellites include those used for photography and mapping.

Satellites: Bridging the Gap from Earth to Sky *continued*

Satellite Altitude

10 The height of the satellite above Earth's surface is its altitude. Different orbiting altitudes are needed for different types of satellites. Satellite altitudes are generally divided into the following three categories:

a. Low altitude orbit: 0 to 1,200 miles above Earth: Observation satellites usually orbit at this altitude band. These satellites are used for capturing images, from mapping to geologic movements. This classification also includes search-and-rescue satellites, used for relaying emergency distress signals from aircraft and ships.

b. Medium altitude orbit: about 1,200 to 22,000 miles above Earth: This altitude is used by the Global Positioning System, or GPS. The GPS is a series of 27 satellites maintained by the United States government. These satellites are used to determine exact locations.

c. High altitude (geostationary) orbit: 22,236 miles above Earth's equator. Weather satellites that aid in both the tracking and the forecasting of weather patterns use a high geosynchronous orbit. Communications satellites also orbit Earth at this altitude.

Getting into Orbit

11 Satellites get into space, and into orbit, through a two-step process: the launch phase and the injection phase. Each phase has a very specific role in introducing the satellite into Earth's gravitational pull.

Launch Phase

12 During the launch phase, the satellite is attached to either an expendable rocket or to a space shuttle. Expendable rockets shoot straight up into Earth's atmosphere. When the correct altitude and orbital speed are reached, the rocket releases the satellite into a temporary elliptical orbit.

13 Shuttle launches used to be one of the most common methods of getting a satellite into orbit. During a space shuttle launch, the satellite is attached to the space shuttle. When the shuttle reaches the correct altitude, the satellite and shuttle detach from each other, and the satellite goes into temporary orbit.

Injection Phase

14 The object injection phase places the satellite into a permanent orbital pattern. During the injection phase, the satellite apogee kick motors fire, moving the object into its intended circular orbital pattern.

15 Satellites are able to stay in orbit due to the balance between velocity and gravitational force. Velocity is the speed the satellite would travel if it were moving in a straight line. Without gravity, the velocity of the satellite would cause it to travel straight into space. Without velocity, gravity would cause the satellite to fall back to Earth. The combination of the two keeps the satellite in orbit.

16   Once used only for military purposes, satellites have become an integral part of life on Earth. Satellites play a role in practically everything—from communications to emergency services to television signals. Without satellites, we would miss many of the applications we consider essential to our daily lives. Understanding satellites—their operation and use—allows us a greater insight into the ways in which Earth and sky are becoming ever more connected in today's world.

Comprehension Check

1A. The technical meaning of the word *orbit* is

    a. a path in space.

    b. to compass an area.

    c. the scope of an event.

    d. a sphere of influence.

1B. Which sentence from the text does NOT provide a clue to the answer for Part A?

    a. "The term *satellite*, however, is typically taken to mean a man-made object placed into orbit for a specific purpose."

    b. "The station keeping uses thrusters to maintain the correct orbit."

    c. " . . . satellites can differ in the type of orbit they maintain in space."

    d. "Different orbiting altitudes are needed for different types of satellites."

2A. Which statement represents the author's point of view?

    a. Humans should attempt to lessen their use of satellite technology.

    b. Satellites serve no viable purpose in today's society.

    c. Satellites are a crucial element in life on Earth today.

    d. Satellite technology is an invasion of personal privacy.

2B. Which sentence from the text best supports the answer to Part A?

    a. "Today, satellites are a vital . . . presence in our daily lives."

    b. "By today's standards, however, *Sputnik I* was a highly simplistic craft . . ."

    c. "A satellite is any object that orbits, or circles, Earth."

    d. "These satellites are used to determine exact locations."

3A. What is the purpose of the list in paragraph 4?

   a. to make a comparative analysis of different types of satellites

   b. to explain the components of a satellite

   c. to indicate that the other text is of lesser importance

   d. to show how satellites are built according to a series of steps

3B. Which element of text structure supports the answer to Part A?

   a. the organization of paragraphs 1 and 2

   b. the use of subsections on page 193

   c. the topic heading **Anatomy of a Satellite**

   d. the comparison between *Sputnik I* and modern satellites

4A. The technical term *uplink* refers to

   a. a signal transmission from a satellite to Earth's surface.

   b. a connection maintained between similar types of satellites.

   c. a way of providing a satellite with information.

   d. an element of the orbital pattern of a satellite.

4B. Which sentence from the text best supports the answer to Part A?

   a. "The signal frequency is called a gigahertz (GHz) range signal."

   b. "A signal, called an uplink, is sent from Earth's surface to the satellite."

   c. "The main function of a satellite is to transmit and receive signals."

   d. "Besides differing in function, satellites can differ in the type of orbit they maintain in space."

5A. The text that appears under the heading **Getting into Orbit** has a structure that is primarily

   a. sequential.

   b. comparative.

   c. causal.

   d. none of the above

5B. Which sentence from the text best supports the answer to Part A?

   a. "Shuttle launches used to be one of the most common methods of getting a satellite into orbit."

   b. "Satellites get into space, and into orbit, through a two-step process: the launch phase and the injection phase."

   c. "Each phase has a very specific role in introducing the satellite into Earth's gravitational pull."

   d. "Expendable rockets shoot straight up into Earth's atmosphere."

6. Describe the organizational structure of the list of satellite functions in paragraph 7.

_____

_____

_____

7. Based on your reading, define the technical term _synchronous orbit_.

_____

_____

8. Think about the effect of word meanings and structure. How would you describe the tone of this text?

_____

_____

_____

9. Based on your reading, define the technical terms _apogee_ and _perigee_.

_____

_____

_____

10. Below are three statements from the text.

- Without satellites, we would miss many of the applications we consider essential to our daily lives.

- Without velocity, gravity would cause the satellite to fall back to Earth.

- The object injection phase places the satellite into a permanent orbital pattern.

A. Underline the statement that represents the author's point of view.

B. Find two more statements in the text that illustrate a point of view that the author holds. Write them here.

_____

_____

_____

Support a Claim

RI.7.9, SL.7.1.a, SL.7.1.c–d, SL.7.3

In this unit you've read a web article about the use of satellites in GPS technology, a technical text detailing the development of hurricanes, an opinion-based scientific text on the preservation of the wetlands, and another technical text on how satellites work. Think about how the authors were able to incorporate their own points of view into each of these texts. In the chart, list details that help you understand the author's point of view in each selection. Then write a brief essay comparing the addition of point of view in each of the selections. Use a separate sheet of paper if you need more room to write. Be prepared to discuss your ideas with the class.

Satellites and the Global Positioning System	Our Fragile Ecosystem

To help present their point of view within a text, authors make specific language choices and choices about what facts to include or omit.

Hurricanes: Earth's Most Violent Storms	Satellites: Bridging the Gap from Earth to Sky

Return to the Essential Question

How do authors use language and organization to express a point of view?

In small groups or as a class, discuss the Essential Question. Think about what you have learned about the power of word meanings, text structure, and point of view in a text. Use evidence from the four texts in this unit to answer the question.

Context Clues

L.7.4.a

Guided Instruction When you come across an unfamiliar word or phrase, look for context clues that may help you figure out the meaning. **Context clues** are bits of helpful information that appear near the word or phrase in question. There are four types of context clues:

- **Definition:** The unfamiliar word is defined in the sentence in which it appears. *The teacher expected complete* deference, *or respect, from her students.* (*Respect* is the definition of *deference.*)

- **Antonym:** The opposite meaning of the unfamiliar word is given. *Jeffrey's room was* immaculate, *but his sister Allison's room was* messy. (*Messy* is an antonym of *immaculate.*)

- **Synonym:** A word similar in meaning to the unfamiliar word is given. *That* mammoth *dog was so* large *that his head reached up to my waist.* (*Mammoth* and *large* have very similar meanings.)

- **Inference:** The meaning of the unfamiliar word is not stated explicitly. *Diego's* tenacity *helped him win the debate.* (You can infer that *tenacity* means *stubbornness.*)

Guided Practice In each of the sentences below, study the word in **bold** type. Identify the type of context clue being used and then define the word.

1. Typically, we use it to mean both the GPS **receivers**—or small units that transmit directions, coordinates, and time—and the large network of satellites . . .

   _____

2. Once the warm air has risen, air begins to **circulate** and spiral.

   _____

3. Similar to coastal wetlands, inland wetlands are also home to many different **species** of waterfowl, marine life, and plants.

   _____

Independent Practice Find these words in the Close Reading selection (pages 192–195). Use context clues from the selection to help define each word.

1. impetus (page 192, paragraph 2) _____

2. applications (page 193, paragraph 7) _____

3. detach (page 194, paragraph 13) _____

4. insight (page 195, paragraph 16) _____

RI.7.4, RI.7.5, RI.7.6, L.7.4.a

Read the following texts that include word meanings and text structures that help define an author's point of view. Then answer the questions on pages 201 and 202.

The Hurricane Hunters

1   Meteorologists predict hurricanes using various tools, such as satellites, infrared sensors, and on-ground monitoring systems. However, a special government group, known as the Hurricane Hunters, does more: It undertakes the dangerous job of flying into violent storms to gather vital, current information about hurricanes.

2   Hurricane Hunters fly directly into the eye of the hurricane. There, the atmosphere is calm and clear. However, the winds on the outer shell of the hurricane can reach speeds of 200 mph. Before Hurricane Hunters can reach the eye of the storm, they must first brave those violent outer winds.

3   Once inside the storm, Hurricane Hunters gather data through their planes' onboard instruments. They also use a specialized piece of equipment called a dropsonde. A dropsonde is a small tube containing data-collecting instruments and a radio transmitter. The tube is attached to a parachute. Hurricane Hunters then release the dropsonde into the exact center of the eye of the hurricane. Just before the dropsonde reaches the water below, it sends all of the information gathered to the computer systems on the aircraft. In this way, Hurricane Hunters are able to gather data about the intensity of the storm.

The Science of "Space Weather"

1   Monitoring and predicting weather patterns is about more than weather systems seen on Earth. In fact, "space weather" is becoming an increasingly important area of scientific research.

2   "Space weather" refers to weather effects created by the interaction of the sun and Earth, in space. These interactions create geomagnetic "storms." Geomagnetic storms impact Earth's systems in a number of ways, including the following:

• Satellite disruption: When a satellite hits a geomagnetic storm, the solar particles in the storm can damage the apparatus. As a result, satellite services can be disrupted, both in space and on Earth.

• Electric power disturbances: Entire power grids can be downed by a geomagnetic storm. By monitoring space weather, scientists are able to warn power companies of impending storms. The power companies can then take action to minimize or avoid service outages.

3   In today's world, many of our vital systems are run by electronic, computer-based technologies. With this in mind, the research being done by space weather scientists is of ever-increasing importance. Through their work, we someday may be able to avoid the potential for a complete shutdown of our most vital systems.

RI.7.4, RI.7.5, RI.7.6, L.7.4.a

Circle the letter next to the best answer choice.

1A. Which statement best expresses the author's point of view about the Hurricane Hunters?

   a. They are the best meteorologists.

   b. They are brave people doing necessary work.

   c. They could do a better job if they had better equipment.

   d. They are gathering data that may turn out to be unimportant.

1B. Which loaded language from "The Hurricane Hunters" supports the answer to Part A?

   a. "Meteorologists predict hurricanes"

   b. "gather data through their planes' onboard instruments"

   c. "undertakes the dangerous job of flying into violent storms"

   d. "satellites, infrared sensors, and on-ground monitoring systems"

2A. The information in paragraphs 2 and 3 of "The Hurricane Hunters" is structured

   a. causally.

   b. sequentially.

   c. comparatively.

   d. none of the above

2B. Which word or group of words from those paragraphs does NOT support the answer in Part A?

   a. Just before

   b. they must first brave

   c. However

   d. Once inside the storm

3A. What is the meaning of *geomagnetic*?

   a. pertaining to the sun and the oceans

   b. pertaining to Earth and the sun

   c. pertaining to Earth and the solar system

   d. pertaining to the sky and the sun

3B. In which paragraph from "The Science of 'Space Weather'" is the meaning of the term defined?

   a. paragraph 1

   b. paragraph 2

   c. paragraph 3

   d. It is not defined in the text.

4A. What is the author's point of view on the study of "space weather"?

   a. It does little to help weather forecasters on Earth.

   b. It was not important until the latter part of the twentieth century.

   c. It is an essential new field of research.

   d. It is based on flawed science.

4B. Which phrase from "The Science of 'Space Weather'" supports the answer to Part A?

   a. "predicting weather patterns is about more than weather systems seen on Earth"

   b. "scientists are able to warn power companies of impending storms"

   c. "solar particles in the storm can damage the craft"

   d. "'space weather' is becoming an increasingly important area of scientific research"

5A. According to paragraph 2 of "The Science of 'Space Weather,'" an *apparatus* is

   a. a mechanical device.

   b. a spacecraft.

   c. a vehicle.

   d. an electronic disruption.

5B. Which word in paragraph 2 best helps define the term?

   a. geomagnetic

   b. satellite

   c. space

   d. power

RI.7.4, RI.7.5, RI.7.6, L.7.4.a

6A. What is the meaning of the technical term *transmitter* in paragraph 3 of "The Hurricane Hunters"?

    a. part of a hurricane

    b. an atmospheric instrument

    c. a signaling device

    d. part of a plane

6B. Which context clue from the text helped you determine the answer to Part A?

    a. "their planes' onboard instruments"

    b. "reaches the water below"

    c. "sends all of the information"

    d. "computer systems on the aircraft"

7. Based on what you have read, why does the author believe that research into "space weather" is important?

_____

_____

_____

8. Given what you know about word meanings and structure, which of the two texts would you call more formal in tone? Why?

_____

_____

_____

_____

9. What is one type of organizational or structural element that could be added to "The Science of 'Space Weather'" to help show the concepts more clearly?

_____

_____

10. How does the scientific research described in "The Hurricane Hunters" differ from that described in "The Science of 'Space Weather'"? How is it the same?

_____

_____

_____

_____

Introducing UNIT 8

In this unit about earth and sky, you will learn how to write a research report. When you write a research report, your primary goal is to search multiple places for information that answers your question about a particular subject, and then to put your findings together in a clear and organized way.

Your research report should be thorough and well developed. Research your subject and take note of the information that answers your specific research question. Record the sources where you found the information so you can share them with your readers. Break your subject down in a way that will help readers understand it better. Explain each important point clearly, and include facts, details, and examples to support your ideas. Make sure to use formal language and to pay attention to writing conventions. At the end of your report, cite your sources so your reader knows your information is reliable.

Before Unit 8

After Unit 8

Progress Check *Can I?*

☐ Conduct research to answer a question. ☐

☐ Gather relevant information from outside sources. ☐

☐ Introduce a topic clearly. ☐

☐ Use an appropriate strategy to organize ideas and information. ☐

☐ Develop a topic with facts, details, and examples. ☐

☐ Maintain a formal style. ☐

☐ Write a strong conclusion. ☐

☐ Understand and use verbal phrases correctly. ☐

☐ Recognize and correct dangling modifiers. ☐

IN THIS UNIT, YOUR CHILD WILL...

- Learn to write an informative or explanatory text that introduces a topic, organizes information logically, and ends with a conclusion.

- Conduct a short research project to answer a question, drawing on several sources, both in print and online.

- Draw evidence from informational texts to support analysis, reflection, and research.

- Produce clear and coherent writing.

- Use formal language as appropriate.

- Use verbal phrases correctly.

- Recognize and correct dangling modifiers.

NOTE: All of these learning goals for your child are based on the Grade 7 Common Core State Standards for English Language Arts.

In this unit, your child will learn to **research and present knowledge** in a well-developed **research report**. Your child will **gather** relevant facts and details and clearly **organize** them in a structured report. Help your child with these skills by working together to find reliable **sources** of information, both in print and online. Together, discuss what makes each source credible and how it can be used in a research report.

Help your child find a topic that will spark his or her interest. For example, you might brainstorm ideas about how environmental and geological changes can have unforeseen consequences. Ask questions to prompt a more comprehensive explanation; for example, ask your child what he or she learns from **quotations**, **examples**, and **graphics** in each source. Encourage your child to use **formal language** when crafting written responses, and to follow appropriate conventions while writing a report.

WAYS TO HELP YOUR CHILD

Have your child practice finding reliable sources of information. For example, you might compare an article from an online encyclopedia with an opinion piece from the local paper. Talk about what makes the encyclopedia article a more credible source of facts, and how your child can identify those sources that are appropriate for research purposes.

Activity: Explore with your child the unit theme, "earth and sky." Together, research and discuss how changes in Earth's environmental structures can have long-reaching, and often unexpected, consequences. You and your child might choose one area of change or concern in your local community and discuss the causes and effects of the event. Make a cause-and-effect chart with your child, and complete the activity by discussing how human impact on the environment can have both positive and negative effects on future generations.

ONLINE
For more Home Connect activities, continue online at sadlierconnect.com

Research to Build and Present Knowledge: Write Research Reports

Essential Question:
How do writers present information as the result of their research?

W.7.2, W.7.2.a–c,
WHST.7.2, WHST.7.2.a–c

CREATING AN ORGANIZATIONAL STRUCTURE

Eliza used an outline to organize the information in her research report. It shows what main ideas and supporting information will be in each paragraph.

Title _____

I. **Introduction**
   a. Topic: _____
   b. Preview information: _____

II. **Supporting Resources**
   a. First paragraph: information about _____
      1. Fact or detail _____
      2. Example _____
   b. Second paragraph: information about _____
      1. Fact or detail _____
      2. Example _____
   c. Third paragraph: information about _____
      1. Fact or detail _____
      2. Example _____

III. **Conclusion**
   _____

INTRODUCTION

- Introduces the topic clearly
- Previews the information to come

TRANSITIONS

The transition word "Therefore" shows a cause-and-effect link.

ORGANIZATION OF INFORMATION

Eliza develops the topic by presenting information chronologically, or according to a timeline of the topic.

Read a Student Model

Eliza is a student in Mrs. Mariel's seventh-grade Language Arts class. Mrs. Mariel gave Eliza's class an assignment: to write a research report about an environmental or geological change on Earth. Mrs. Mariel expects the reports to be written clearly and to be well organized. Think about an environmental change that you might choose when you write your own research report.

The Dust Bowl

In the United States, the period from 1931 until 1940 was known as the Great Depression. This economic collapse forced millions of Americans to leave their homes to look for work. The Great Plains region was particularly devastated. Years of poor farming practices led to what is now known as the Dust Bowl, which seriously affected both the land and the people. Therefore, understanding the causes and effects of the Dust Bowl, and how the land eventually recovered from it, is essential to avoiding a repeat of this catastrophe.

History of the Dust Bowl

In 1862, Congress passed the Homestead Act, encouraging Americans to settle in the Great Plains. The act gave a parcel of land to anyone who could make it productive. By 1890, almost six million people had signed up. Wheat was one of the major crops of the farming community.

W.7.2, W.7.2.b, W.7.2.d–e, WHST.7.2, WHST.7.2.b, WHST.7.2.d–e

Poor Soil Management

Unfortunately, these lands were being tilled and ploughed without any attention to the potential harm to the enormous grasslands of the Great Plains. The new crops, like wheat, that were being introduced into the soil had shallow root systems, making them particularly vulnerable to climate changes. The soil was overworked and began to erode. Then, in 1931, a drought struck the region. An area already experiencing the overwhelming financial consequences of the Great Depression was now faced with the loss of its only source of economic stability.

Devastating Consequences

The lack of water caused the soil, already loose from overuse, to turn into dust, which was then blown by the wind into raging dust storms. The worst storms brought dust that covered the area like snow. People had trouble breathing, and railway travel was stopped until workers could shovel the dust off of the tracks. Houses were boarded up, and every opening to the outside was sealed. People described the conditions as blizzard-like, with streetlights so covered by the dust that it looked like dusk in the middle of the day.

Many farming families were forced to leave the area because of the dust. With failed crops, lost homes, and rampant sickness brought on by the blowing dust, people moved either further west or back to their families in the east. The areas most affected by the Dust Bowl lost up to 60 percent of their population as farming communities were destroyed.

PRECISE LANGUAGE

Eliza uses precise language—nouns and verbs that give her readers a clear and specific idea of the information she wants to communicate.

Circle at least two examples of precise language in the first paragraph on this page.

GIVE RELEVANT INFORMATION

Eliza thoroughly researched her subject, so she was able to give important facts about the causes and effects of the Dust Bowl.

FACTS, DETAILS, AND EXAMPLES

Eliza includes key facts and concrete details necessary to explain her topic. Then she supports them with examples.

Underline three examples that support the fact that dust "covered the area like snow."

FORMAL STYLE

Research reports should use a formal, academic style, avoiding slang, contractions, and personal statements by the writer.

GRAPHICS

In an historical research report, images can help the reader better understand the topic.

CONCLUSION

Eliza's conclusion summarizes the central idea of her report.

Place an asterisk next to the statement that summarizes the report's central idea.

INCLUDE A LIST OF SOURCES

Citing sources shows the reader that your information is both credible and reliable—that is, that your information comes from trustworthy, expert sources.

Rehabilitation

In 1935, the federal government established the Soil Conservation Service, which showed farmers how to use better farming techniques. At the same time, the Shelterbelt Project began. Areas of trees were planted on farms to help stop erosion and to block the blowing dust. As farmers came back into the Dust Bowl region, new techniques and more environmentally friendly practices were put into place, and the soil began to return to its pre-drought conditions.

By 1938, the drought had begun to diminish. In 1935, almost 50 million acres of land in the Great Plains were covered in eroded soil. By 1939, fewer than 10 million acres were still seeing severe conditions. During the 1940s, normal rainfall returned, and crops and grasslands once again covered the Great Plains. However, those affected by the Dust Bowl would be forever changed. That disaster illustrated how people must not abuse the land but instead work responsibly to preserve it for future generations.

Sources

"Dust Bowl During the Great Depression." American Memory Timeline. Classroom Presentation Teacher Resources. Library of Congress Home. Web. 13 Aug. 2013.

Gibson, Arrell M. "Dust Bowl." Encyclopedia Americana. Grolier Online. Web. 8 Aug. 2013.

Hurt, R. Douglas. "Dust Bowl." The New Book of Knowledge. Grolier Online. Web. 12 Aug. 2013.

Worster, Donald. Dust Bowl: The Southern Plains in the 1930s. New York: Oxford University Press, 1979. Print.

W.7.2.b, W.7.5, W.7.7, WHST.7.2.b

Use index cards like the ones below to take notes for your research report on an environmental or geological change on Earth. You may use print or digital sources to find information. You will then use these notes to create your outline on page 210.

Environmental or geologic change: _____

Source 1
Summarize or paraphrase information:

Source 2
Summarize or paraphrase information:

Source 3
Summarize or paraphrase information:

WRITE RESEARCH REPORTS

W.7.2.a–b, W.7.2.f, W.7.4, W.7.5, W.7.6, W.7.7, W.7.10, WHST.7.2.a–b, WHST.7.2.f

Use an outline like the one below to organize your research report on an environmental or geological change on Earth. Then write a first draft of your research report on a separate sheet of paper. You will use this draft to write your final research report in the Common Core Review section on page 216.

Title _____

I. **Introduction**

    a. Topic: _____

    b. Preview information: _____

II. **Supporting Resources**

    a. First paragraph: information about _____

        1. Fact or detail _____

        _____

        2. Example _____

        _____

    b. Second paragraph: information about _____

        1. Fact or detail _____

        _____

        2. Example _____

        _____

    c. Third paragraph: information about _____

        1. Fact or detail _____

        _____

        2. Example _____

        _____

III. **Conclusion**

    _____

    _____

Verbals and Verbal Phrases

Guided Instruction A **verbal** is a verb form that is used as a noun, adjective, or adverb. For example, in the sentence *Jogging is good exercise*, you can see that "jogging" is formed from the verb "to jog." It is not the verb of this sentence, however; it is a noun functioning as the subject of the sentence. There are three kinds of verbals in English: gerunds, infinitives, and participles. A **verbal phrase** is made up of a verbal and the words (modifiers and complements) that go with it.

- A **gerund** is a verb form that ends in *–ing* and functions as a noun. A **gerund phrase** is made up of a gerund and the words that go with it. A gerund or gerund phrase can do anything in a sentence that a noun can do.

  Gardening is an enjoyable way to spend time outdoors. (gerund as subject)

  I enjoy skiing more than any other sport. (gerund as direct object)

  Walking to school can be faster than riding the bus. (gerund phrase as subject)

  Fear kept me from crossing the rope bridge. (gerund phrase as object of preposition)

- An **infinitive** is the *to* form of a verb, such as *to see*, *to laugh*, and *to sleep*. An **infinitive phrase** is made up of an infinitive and the words that go with it. An infinitive or infinitive phrase can function as a noun and can do anything in a sentence that a noun can do. An infinitive or infinitive phrase can also function as an adjective or an adverb in a sentence.

  To laugh brings great joy. (infinitive as noun/subject)

  He wants to win a motocross championship. (infinitive phrase as noun/direct object)

  That was an effort to be proud of. (infinitive phrase as adjective modifying *effort*)

  I'll try to show I can do a good job. (infinitive phrase as adverb modifying *try*)

- A **participle** is a verb form that functions as an adjective. Most participles end in *-ing* or *-ed*. A **participial phrase** is made up of the participle and the words that go with it.

  Grinning, Heather accepted the award. (participle modifying *Heather*)

  Spattered with mud, Grant walked slowly back to the locker room. (participial phrase modifying *Grant*)

  The birds flying overhead are seagulls. (participial phrase modifying *birds*)

Guided Practice For each sentence below, identify the words in italics as a *gerund, gerund phrase, infinitive, infinitive phrase, participle,* or *participial phrase.*

1. Josh left school early *to go to his dental appointment.* _____

2. *Hang gliding* is the next best thing to flying like a bird. _____

3. *Grunting*, the football player fumbled the ball as he was tackled. _____

4. Marion couldn't imagine *reading another book like the scary one she had just finished.* _____

5. My former home, *seeming smaller than it had when I was young*, stood across the street. _____

6. After this tiring weekend I just want *to rest.* _____

7. *Amazed by the performance*, the crowd cheered and applauded the singer. _____

Independent Practice Tell whether the italicized verbal phrase in each sentence is a gerund phrase, an infinitive phrase, or a participial phrase. Then tell the phrase's part of speech (*noun, adjective,* or *adverb*). If the verbal phrase is a noun, tell its function in the sentence (*subject, direct object, object of a preposition*). If the verbal phrase is an adjective or adverb, tell what word the phrase modifies.

1. I can't stand *going to bed early on weekends!* _____
_____

2. For Jackie, housework was a chore *to be avoided.* _____
_____

3. The blue vase, *bumped by the careless shopper*, crashed to the floor. _____
_____

4. The last bus left *to go to the stadium.* _____
_____

5. *Being first in line at lunch* is always my goal. _____
_____

6. *Gliding silently beneath the water's surface*, the shark approached the swimmers.
_____

Dangling Modifiers

Guided Instruction Phrases and clauses should be placed in a sentence so that they relate directly to the words they modify. You have already learned about **misplaced modifiers**. Now you will learn about **dangling modifiers**. A **dangling modifier** is a phrase that modifies a word not clearly stated in the sentence.

- **Dangling Modifier**

  Turning the corner, _the house came into view_. (Incorrect: Who or what was turning the corner?)

  Turning the corner, _I caught sight of the house_. (Correct: Now you can tell who or what the phrase is modifying.)

  After seeing the movie, _the book is sure to be great_. (Incorrect: Who saw the movie?)

  After seeing the movie, _I can't wait to read the book_, _which is sure to be great_. (Correct: Now you can tell who or what the phrase is modifying.)

Guided Practice Read each sentence below and underline the dangling modifier.

1. Being excused from soccer practice, home is a good place to relax.

2. The test score was terrible, not having studied the chapter.

3. While writing my essay for class, the dog sat in my lap.

4. When riding my bike down the street, a tree branch fell onto a car.

Independent Practice Correct each of the sentences above. Make sure the modifying phrase is correctly placed next to the word that it modifies.

1. _____

   _____

2. _____

   _____

3. _____

   _____

4. _____

   _____

SL.7.1.a–d, SL.7.3, SL.7.4, SL.7.6

Discuss the Essential Question

How do writers present information as the result of their research?

Prepare for a class discussion about the Essential Question by responding to the questions below. Support your point of view with reasons and examples, and follow the discussion rules you learned earlier in this book.

1. How did Eliza organize information about her topic?

_____

_____

_____

_____

2. What facts and details did Eliza use to develop the report?

_____

_____

_____

3. What kind of language did Eliza use to discuss concepts and connect ideas?

_____

_____

_____

Use your notes above as you discuss the Essential Question with your class or in small groups. Use the organizer below to record your ideas and what you hear in the discussion. Follow the discussion rules on the "Did I?" checklist (page 58).

Ideas I Agree or Disagree With		Questions I Asked
agree		
disagree		
New Ideas I Had During Discussion		**Questions I Answered**

W.7.2, W.7.2.a–b, W.7.2.d–e, L.7.1.c

Read this draft paragraph from a student research report and answer the questions below.

> (1) Glacier National Park encompasses over 1,000,000 acres in northwest Montana. (2) Under pressure from influential leaders of the time, the area was established as a national park on May 11, 1910. (3) At the time, there were almost 150 glaciers present within the park. (4) However, the glaciers are going away far more rapidly than scientists had once predicted. (5) Today, there are only twenty-five glaciers larger than twenty-five acres left in the park.

1. Which of the following does this introduction NOT accomplish?

   a. establishing the topic to be examined

   b. using specific details to support claims

   c. explaining the cause of the main problem

   d. placing the analysis in an historical period

2. Which of the following is the dangling modifier in sentence 2 meant to modify?

   a. the area of the park

   b. the government

   c. the influential leaders

   d. the park's glaciers

3. Which is the clearest example of a concrete detail from the text?

   a. "the glaciers are going away"

   b. "encompasses over 1,000,000 acres"

   c. "established as a national park"

   d. none of the above

4. Which of the following details would best help develop this topic?

   a. The park is a famous hiking destination.

   b. Many visitors take aerial tours of the park.

   c. The largest glaciers will vanish by 2030.

   d. Some European parks feature glaciers.

5. Based on this introduction, which of the following is NOT a heading that you might expect to see in this essay?

   a. Climate Change in Glacier National Park

   b. Glacier Recession in Glacier National Park

   c. The Changing Face of Glacier National Park

   d. Visitor Activities in Glacier National Park

6. How would you change sentence 4 to achieve a more precise, formal style?

   a. correct the dangling modifier

   b. replace *going away* with *disappearing*

   c. replace *rapidly* with *fast*

   d. remove the comma after *However*

W.7.2.c, W.7.2.f, W.7.4, W.7.5, W.7.6, W.7.10, L.7.1.a

Read these next two paragraphs from the student research report and answer the questions below.

(1) A glacier is a large mass of snow and ice that moves over land. (2) Glaciers form when fallen snow stays in one place long enough to form ice. (3) The ice then compacts into a slowly moving mass. (4) The largest glaciers can reach up to 62 miles in width. (5) Moving like slowly flowing rivers, glaciers usually advance only a few inches each day, if at all.

(6) In Glacier National Park, the largest glaciers are melting more quickly than would naturally be expected. (7) Glaciers are a good measure of climate changes. (8) Colder average temperatures lead to glacier growth, while warmer temperatures result in a decrease in glacier size. (9) Currently, long-term measurements in Glacier National Park show an increase in average summer temperatures. (10) Many scientists believe that these changes are a direct effect of global climate change, and that the consequences of melting glaciers could be significant for life on Earth.

7. What sentence in paragraph 1 includes a participial phrase? _____

8. What sentence in paragraph 2 contains a transition word? _____

9. Which sentence on this page contains an infinitive? _____

10. Write a conclusion for this report. Use a separate sheet of paper if necessary.

_____

_____

_____

Assignment: On separate paper, provide a final draft of the research report you began on page 209. Use what you learned about verbal phrases and dangling modifiers in the Language section of this unit. Think about how you and your classmates answered the Essential Question. Check your outline to be sure you organized your ideas well. Be sure to use relevant facts and concrete details and correct writing conventions. Cite your sources. End with a strong conclusion.

Introducing UNIT 9

Do you like to read stories that take place in the past? Many stories about people who lived in the past are based on actual historical events. In this unit, you will read not only fictional stories based on historical events but also historical accounts of those events.

It is fun to read historical fiction, and it is even more enlightening to watch the movie version of an historical story and compare it to the original text. Did the filmmaker follow the text very closely, or is the film quite different? This skill of comparing and contrasting is also useful for analyzing historical fiction and first-person nonfiction accounts of events. Like a filmmaker, an author may decide to alter history in order to make the story more dramatic. The words that an author uses are also an important part of enjoying and understanding historical fiction. An author may use words associated with a certain period of history. He or she also may choose words for their connotation, or emotional meaning, to make a story exciting.

Exploring various elements of craft and structure makes reading fictional texts more enjoyable. Let's see what we find as we explore these tales of the past!

Before Unit 9   **Progress Check** *Can I?*   **After Unit 9**

☐ ☐ Compare and contrast a written story with a film that is based on the same story.

☐ ☐ Determine the meanings of words and phrases that are related to social studies and history.

☐ ☐ Compare and contrast a piece of historical fiction with an historical account of the same time period.

☐ ☐ Compare and contrast primary and secondary sources that are about the same topic.

☐ ☐ Understand the different connotations of words that have similar meanings.

Unit 9 ■ Reading Literature: Integration of Knowledge and Ideas   **217**

HOME◆CONNECT...

Your child undoubtedly has some favorite movies, so ask whether any of those movies were **based on a written story**. Go over a list of his or her favorite movies, looking for examples. Talk about how the movies are different from the original texts.

It can be a fascinating exercise to take a story that is based on an historical event and compare it to an actual **first-person historical account** of the same event. Encourage your child to talk about how he or she includes or leaves out details when telling stories about events in which he or she has had a part.

Your child probably knows the definitions of most of the words he or she uses, but those words' **connotative meanings** may be less familiar. Explain to your child that words have cultural and emotional meanings as well as literal, "dictionary" definitions. With your child, think of words that have particularly potent connotative meanings. (Adjectives are a great place to start.) Talk about the situations in which these words would be used.

Conversation Starter: Ask your child to share a personal story about something that happened to him or her in the past. Then ask your child to imagine making a movie based on that story. Would your child change the story to make the movie more exciting? If so, how, and how much? Discuss the events of the story. You may even want to create an outline storyboard for key moments in this imaginary movie.

IN THIS UNIT, YOUR CHILD WILL...

- Compare a written story to a movie version of the story.

- Read and comprehend domain-specific terms having to do with social studies and history.

- Compare a work of historical fiction to an historical account of the same time period.

- Compare a primary source and a secondary source that deal with the same topic.

- Understand the connotations of multiple words that have the same definition.

NOTE: All of these learning goals for your child are based on the Grade 7 Common Core State Standards for English Language Arts.

WAYS TO HELP YOUR CHILD

Play a game with your child in which you take turns thinking of words with strong connotative meanings but similar definitions. Start with a "mild" word like *big*, for example, and encourage your child to work up toward words like *huge* or *colossal*. Pause as you play to discuss how the connotative meanings would affect the way readers would interpret a description of a story.

ONLINE

For more Home Connect activities, continue online at sadlierconnect.com

Reading Literature: Integration of Knowledge and Ideas

Essential Question:
How can different media and forms of a text affect our understanding?

Guided Instruction

RL.7.7, RH.7.4

WORDS TO KNOW

diverges

expanse

repose

stoicism

wary

You can **compare a written story to its film version** and analyze the techniques the filmmakers used in creating the adaptation. Also, when reading historical fiction, look for **terms that relate to history and social studies.**

CITE EVIDENCE

A The word *ally* often is a **word related to history**. In the introduction, circle a form of this word and draw boxes around details that offer clues to its meaning. What does the word *ally* mean?

B Find and underline the history term *tomahawk*. Then, using context clues, give a simple definition of the word *tomahawk*.

The Last of the Mohicans
(Genre: Historical Fiction)

*In 1757, a war was raging in North America between Britain and France over who would control the vast **expanses** of the continent. The name "French and Indian War" identifies the two groups allied against the British.*

James Fenimore Cooper's novel The Last of the Mohicans *was published in 1826. It begins with a threat to Fort William Henry, under the command of Colonel Munro. Munro's daughters, Cora and Alice, demand to go to him despite what will be a dangerous journey through a forest populated with native tribes allied with the French.*

Cora and Alice are escorted by Major Duncan Heyward and a native scout named Magua. In this excerpt, Heyward is introduced to Magua.

1   His eyes fell on the still, upright, and rigid form of the "Indian runner" . . . Although in a state of perfect **repose**, and apparently disregarding, with characteristic **stoicism**, the excitement and bustle around him, there was a sullen fierceness mingled with the quiet of the savage that was likely to arrest the attention of much more experienced eyes than those which now scanned him, in unconcealed amazement.

2   The native bore both the tomahawk and knife of his tribe; and yet his appearance was not altogether that of a warrior. On the contrary, there was an air of neglect about his person, like that which might have proceeded from great and recent exertion, which he had not yet found leisure to repair.

3   His eye, alone, which glistened like a fiery star amid lowering clouds, was to be seen in its state of native wildness. For a single instant his searching and yet **wary** glance met the wondering look of the other, and then changing its direction, partly in cunning, and partly in disdain, it remained fixed, as if penetrating the distant air.

Exciting *Mohicans* Diverges from the Novel

(Genre: Movie Review)

1   Director Michael Mann has delivered an exciting film adaptation of James Fenimore Cooper's novel *The Last of the Mohicans*, but it takes liberties with the story's plot and characters.

2   The film **diverges** from the novel right from the start. A key early scene in which Major Duncan Heyward is introduced to his scout, Magua, is much more developed in the book. Cooper offers a thorough description of Magua as seen through the eyes of Heyward. Embedded in the major's description are stereotypes typical of Cooper's time, and they add to the racial tension that pervades the novel.

3   In the corresponding scene in Mann's film, Magua steps out of the dark shadows and reveals himself to Heyward. The costume and makeup team have matched Cooper's description of Magua well. Actor Wes Studi communicates the character's stillness and apparent lack of feeling. The most effective moment in this scene is the look Magua gives Heyward at the end: a perfect mix of curiosity and disdain.

Comprehension Check

Which filmmaking techniques does the movie reviewer explicitly mention? What aspects of filmmaking are implied? Cite specifics.

Guided Instruction

RL.7.7, RH.7.4

CITE EVIDENCE

C Find the words *repose* and *stoicism* in paragraph 1 on page 220, and double underline them. Then find the sentence in the movie review on this page that describes how the film captured these words, and double underline that sentence.

D When a **written story is adapted into a film**, the **screenwriter** may not follow the story exactly. In paragraph 2 of the movie review on this page, underline one way in which the film and the novel—the written story—are different.

E A film's **costume and makeup designers** are responsible for representing the characters visually. In the movie review, put an asterisk by the reviewer's statement about how the character of Magua appears in the film in comparison to his description in the novel. What does the **actor** playing Magua add to the character?

Guided Instruction

RL.7.7, RH.7.4

WORDS TO KNOW

animated

exuberance

meager

soldiery

steed

CITE EVIDENCE

A The word *outpost* is a social studies term. Find the word in the introduction on this page and then, in the same paragraph, put an asterisk next to a term that refers to the same thing. What is an outpost?

B The movie review mentions the importance of **casting**, or selecting actors. In paragraphs 5 and 6 of the movie review on page 223, underline the ways that the actresses playing Cora and Alice differ from the characters' descriptions in the novel.

C The use of **sound** is a critical technique in moviemaking. In paragraph 8 of the movie review on page 223, put a box around a word that describes the sound of this scene. How does the sound of this scene compare to its description in the novel?

The Last of the Mohicans *continued*

Cora, Alice, Heyward, and other British soldiers begin their long journey on horseback through the forest to Fort William Henry. Accompanying them to that outpost is Magua, who rides up ahead.

4   A young man . . . conducted to their **steeds** two females, who, as it was apparent by their dresses, were prepared to encounter the fatigues of a journey in the woods.

5   `[Alice] . . . and she was the more juvenile in her appearance, though both were young, permitted glimpses of her dazzling complexion, fair golden hair, and bright blue eyes . . . The flush which still lingered above the pines in the western sky was not more bright nor delicate than the bloom on her cheek; nor was the opening day more cheering than the **animated** smile which she bestowed on the youth, as he assisted her into the saddle.

6   [Cora] . . . concealed her charms from the gaze of the **soldiery** with a care that seemed better fitted to the experience of four or five additional years. It could be seen, however, that her person, though molded with the same exquisite proportions, of which none of the graces were lost by the traveling dress she wore, was rather fuller and more mature than that of her companion.

7   . . . [Alice] was the first to dash aside the slight branches of the bushes, and to follow the runner along the dark and tangled pathway . . . after which they emerged from the broad border of underbrush which grew along the line of the highway, and entered under the high but dark arches of the forest.

8   In a few moments a colt was seen gliding, like a fallow deer, among the straight trunks of the pines; and, in another instant, [Magua] came into view, with as much rapidity as he could excite his **meager** beast to endure . . . Until now this personage had escaped the observation of the travelers.

Exciting *Mohicans* Diverges from the Novel *continued*

RL.7.7

4   One of the many responsibilities of a film director is casting the right actors. The scene in which Colonel Munro's two daughters, Cora and Alice, prepare for their journey proves this point. The actors offer a strong sense of who these two young women are.

5   The role of the younger sister, Alice, is particularly well cast. The luminous young actress Jodhi May does not have Alice's blue eyes (as described in the novel), but she brings a childlike **exuberance** to the role. When she expresses to Heyward her naïve hope that they shall see some "red men" during their journey in "the wilderness," we understand her character at once.

6   Cora, as played by Madeleine Stowe, is another example of how the film varies from the book. Cora is supposed to be an older, darker-skinned half sister to Alice. In the film, Stowe is all fair skin and youthful loveliness.

7   Compliments must be paid to the exquisite period costumes the women wear. The tension between their riding dresses—still elegant, despite their practicality—and the rawness of the forest is tangible.

8   A sense of danger pervades the scene that follows in which the traveling party finally gets underway, accompanied by Magua on foot. They move through the thick, barely lit forest silently, with Cora throwing nervous glances at a cougar she spies in the brush.

Comprehension Check

How does the reviewer's description of the film version affect your understanding of the excerpts from the novel? Give an example to support your answer.

CITE EVIDENCE

D **Lighting** is an important filmmaking technique. Even in an outdoor scene lit by the sun, the **cinematographer** is responsible for how light or dark the scene is. In paragraph 7 of the novel on page 222, double underline two descriptions of the light. Then, in paragraph 8 of the movie review, double underline how that aspect of the film has been handled.

E Circle the movie review's description of Cora's and Alice's dresses, which are part of the film's costume design. Then circle any details about the dresses in the novel excerpt on page 222. Are the movie costumes similar to or different from the novel's descriptions?

223

COMPARING AND CONTRASTING VERSIONS

Guided Practice

The Last of the Mohicans *continued*

RL.7.7

WORDS TO KNOW

accouterment

emblem

hue

musket

sage

sultriness

CITE EVIDENCE

A In the movie review on page 225, put an asterisk by a phrase that describes the sound of the scene. How is the sound of this scene different in the written story on this page?

B The cinematographer determines not only what is light and dark but also the **colors** in the film. Double underline any detail in the novel excerpt that mentions color. Then double underline in the movie review on page 225 any phrases that describe colors. Discuss with a partner how these decisions shape this scene.

Soon Cora, Alice, Heyward, and Magua will encounter three men: an older man named Chingachgook, his son Uncas, and a white hunter named Hawkeye. Chingachgook and Uncas are Mohican, a native tribe, and they are the last Mohicans known to survive. This excerpt describes both the forest and Chingachgook; the following page describes Hawkeye.

9   On that day, two men were lingering on the banks of a small but rapid stream . . . the vast canopy of woods spread itself to the margin of the river, overhanging the water, and shadowing its dark current with a deeper **hue**. The rays of the sun were beginning to grow less fierce . . . Still that breathing silence, which marks the drowsy **sultriness** of an American landscape in July, pervaded the secluded spot, interrupted only by the low voices of the men, the occasional and lazy tap of a woodpecker, the discordant cry of some gaudy jay, or a swelling on the ear, from the dull roar of a distant waterfall.

10   . . . One of these loiterers showed the red skin and wild **accouterments** of a native of the woods. [Chingachgook's] body . . . presented a terrific **emblem** of death, drawn in intermingled colors of white and black. His closely shaved head . . . was without ornament of any kind . . . A tomahawk and scalping knife, of English manufacture, were in his girdle. . . .

Exciting *Mohicans* Diverges from the Novel *continued*

9   There is an early chapter in the novel that the film version does not include in which the characters of Hawkeye, Chingachgook, and Uncas are described in detail. In its place, the film shows a brief scene with no dialogue in which the men discover that a group of rival natives are on their way to ambush Heyward and the other travelers. The scene is breathtaking. It recreates a forest so dense that direct sunlight cannot break through. The vegetation is colored in darker, not lighter, shades of green.

10   Chingachgook is instantly recognizable as an Indian of the period. He is clothed from head to toe (we therefore have no idea if his chest bears a black-and-white "emblem of death," as the novel describes), and the full hair on his head ends in a long black ponytail. For weapons, he carries a long **musket** and a tomahawk. He appears older than his companions but does not suggest the old **sage** from the book.

Comprehension Check

1. One detail about Chingachgook that both the novel and film mention is his

   a. ponytail.　　**c.** musket.

   b. tomahawk.　　**d.** shaved head.

2. Which detail from the novel, if filmed, would be the responsibility of the cinematographer?

   a. "his closely shaved head was without ornament of any kind"

   b. "that breathing silence . . . pervaded the secluded spot"

   c. "the dull roar of a distant waterfall"

   d. "the rays of the sun were beginning to grow less fierce"

3. Paragraph 9 mentions a chapter from the novel not included in the movie. Who would be responsible for such a decision?

   a. the actors

   b. the cinematographer

   c. the screenwriter

   d. the casting director

4. Which of the following words is a term from history or social studies?

   a. hue

   b. landscape

   c. vegetation

   d. musket

5. Discuss with a partner which technique of filmmaking was the most crucial in adapting this section of the novel. Cite specifics in your argument.

_____

_____

_____

Independent Practice

The Last of the Mohicans *continued*

RL.7.7, RH.7.4

WORDS TO KNOW

agile

buckskin

garb

rude

sinew

CITE EVIDENCE

A Underline in the novel excerpt and in the review any words or phrases that describe Hawkeye's eyes. How are these descriptions similar and different? Cite evidence from the text.

B The word *wampum* is a social studies term. Circle any words in paragraph 12 on page 227 that offer a clue as to its meaning. Then give a meaning in your own words, and check it in a print or online dictionary.

11 . . . the other [man] exhibited, through the mask of his **rude** and nearly savage equipments, the brighter, though sun-burned and long-faced complexion of one who might claim descent from a European parentage.

12 The frame of the white man, judging by such parts as were not concealed by his clothes, was like that of one who had known hardships and exertion from his earliest youth.

13 He wore a hunting shirt of forest green, fringed with faded yellow, and a summer cap of skins which had been shorn of their fur. He also bore a knife in a girdle of wampum, like that which confined the scanty garments of [Chingachgook], but no tomahawk.

14 His moccasins were ornamented . . . while the only part of his under dress which appeared below the hunting frock was a pair of **buckskin** leggings, that laced at the sides, and which were gartered above the knees, with the **sinews** of a deer. A pouch and horn completed his personal accouterments. . . .

15 The eye of [Hawkeye] was small, quick, keen, and restless, roving while he spoke, on every side of him, as if in quest of game, or distrusting the sudden approach of some lurking enemy.

Independent Practice

Exciting *Mohicans* Diverges from the Novel *continued*

11   The great British actor Daniel Day-Lewis is well cast as Hawkeye. His lean frame and long face support his portrayal of a white man raised by Indians who is stern and steady yet physically **agile**. In this scene with Chingachgook and Uncas in the forest, he practically dances over the moss-covered rocks in the stream as he looks for clues left by the rival group. His eyes carry an expression of calm alertness.

12   Hawkeye presents more fine work from the film's costume designer. He wears traditional native **garb**, including a long, pale deerskin garment similar to a smock. He keeps a knife tied to his belt and carries a musket over his shoulder. He wears buckskin leggings and wampum beads in his hair.

13   Uncas, the son of Chingachgook, is played by Canadian actor Eric Schweig. Schweig portrays him as every bit the eager, "youthful warrior" of the novel.

Comprehension Check

(MORE ONLINE) **sadlierconnect.com**

1. Which two items of Hawkeye's costume appear in both the novel and the film?

   a. a knife and buckskin leggings

   b. a green shirt and animal skin cap

   c. a musket and moccasins

   d. a pouch and wampum beads

2. Which technique of filmmaking is NOT mentioned in the movie review?

   a. costume design

   b. casting

   c. sound

   d. acting

3. All of the following terms from the novel come from social studies EXCEPT

   a. buckskin leggings.

   b. complexion.

   c. moccasins.

   d. wampum.

4. Which of the following characteristics of Hawkeye is mentioned only in the novel?

   a. his long face

   b. his being a white man

   c. his alertness

   d. his sun-burned skin

5. Choose any two film techniques and analyze what effect they have on the film.

   _____

   _____

   _____

Guided Instruction

RL.7.9, RH.7.9

WORDS TO KNOW

aspect

colony

confirm

enabled

A fictional account of an historical event can be compared to a nonfiction historical account of the same event.

CITE EVIDENCE

A A **primary source** is a firsthand account or other document created at the time of an historical event, such as a letter, journal, or official record. A **secondary source,** such as a textbook or magazine article, uses primary source material to interpret and analyze an event. This selection is not a real primary source, but it mirrors the type of source James Fenimore Cooper might have used. Circle the word on this page that suggests it is a type of primary source.

B Authors of historical fiction research **historical accounts** of events to make their stories believable. In this way, an author adapts and "uses" history to tell a story. Underline in paragraph 5 an historical detail that this work shares with *The Last of the Mohicans*.

Journal of a British Officer

(Genre: Historical Account)

1   **July 22, 1757** Today, after months of fighting on the western front of the **colony** of Pennsylvania, I arrived at my present location of Fort Edward in New York, where I have entered into the service of General Daniel Webb as an officer of the British army.

2   It is an extremely tense time. The war with the French and their native allies has been going on for more than three years. The British have suffered several recent failures, and many noble lives have been lost. The other soldiers and I are perplexed, for we know the French are fewer in number; we suspect it is their alliance with the various native groups that has **enabled** them to pressure us so.

3   Tomorrow General Webb will travel to Fort William Henry to **confirm** what has been rumored: groups of Frenchmen and natives are waiting on Lake George to attack the fort. He will meet with Lieutenant Colonel George Munro, who is in charge there.

4   **July 29, 1757** General Webb returned today with confirmation of the worst: the French are indeed gathering near Fort William Henry and have every intention of attacking. I fear another devastating loss for our side, and so I imagine General Webb will be asked by Munro to send support.

5   **July 30, 1757** Today brought an unusual turn of events. I was summoned to the office of General Webb wherein I witnessed the arrival of an officer whose name I could not discern. General Webb has ordered this officer to Fort William Henry as part of an official party for the purpose of accompanying the sister and niece of a Major Drummond, who serves with Colonel Munro at the fort. The sister insists on being with her brother at the fort. General Webb ordered me to go along.

6   General Webb also asked a local native—a Huron—to accompany us. This native is responsible for intercepting the message that contained the plot to attack Fort William Henry. He is to be our runner, scout, and guide through the forest, which is no doubt full of enemy natives. The Huron are supposedly allied with the French, but this man is loyal to the British crown, I am told.

7   I watched the native scout very closely as he stood before my commanding officer: he hardly moved, which was odd, especially for a fleet-footed runner. Of course all the natives claim to be runners, it's some sort of privilege, though I admit it is one of many **aspects** of natives I have yet to understand.

8   My concern grew as I gazed at him, for the scout had an evil look to him. He's dangerous, capable of unexpected behavior, I thought. I watched the officer's face, too; he looked as suspicious as I was. At one point General Webb addressed the native directly, and the native replied in English. I was astonished; it was inflected with a strong accent, but English it was.

9   His countenance was alert, as if ready for battle. He had piercing dark brown eyes that stared straight ahead and moved only when General Webb addressed him. The look he gave my commander upon their introduction seemed to express confidence.

10   The native's overall appearance was sharp and neat, and his manner of dress made a strong impression. His chest was partially bare, covered on the left side by a woven blanket. The skin on his face was smooth, dark, and unmarked; I had expected to see evidence of war paint, yet I did not. He carried a musket, a knife, and a tomahawk.

Comprehension Check

How does what you learn about the native scout's appearance and behavior compare to what you learn about Magua in James Fenimore Cooper's novel?

CITE EVIDENCE

C A primary source can help establish the time and place of an event. Box in paragraph 1 the date of the journal entry and where the author is located on that date.

D What detail about the native in paragraph 6 is not the same as the one in the excerpt from Cooper's novel on page 220? Put an asterisk next to it.

E Double underline details the author gives about the native scout's physical appearance. How does this description compare to the description of Magua in Cooper's novel?

Guided Instruction

Journal of a British Officer *continued*

WORDS TO KNOW

altered

estimation

incident

league

portion

prospect

CITE EVIDENCE

A Underline any words or phrases that describe the author's opinion of young Anna's behavior as she mounts her horse. Are any of these details similar to those used in Cooper's novel? Explain.

B Primary sources often reveal the personal opinions of their authors. Secondary sources, like biographies, often try to be unbiased. Circle the journal author's personal opinion of the native scout in paragraph 17.

11   **July 31, 1757** I write this at the end of the first day of our journey through the forest accompanying the woman and her daughter. We marched a number of **leagues**—so many I cannot remember now—and at last reached an area that was suitable for camping. At the moment I can hear the buzzing of insects all around me.

12   In the privacy of this journal I can report how totally insufferable both of these women are. The daughter, Anna, is the worse of the two: she is very young, 15 years old at my **estimation**, and her behavior reveals someone who is totally naïve in the ways of the world. I overheard her expressing to another soldier her excitement at the **prospect** of going through the "wilderness," as she called it, and she said she also hoped to meet "red men." How the soldier kept from rolling his eyes I'll never know. She would do better to hope *against* meeting any natives; they are dangerous savages.

13   As I lifted her into her saddle, she smiled at me with a false, forced charm. She has bright blue eyes which she no doubt employs to charm young men, but I am not that young. I did nothing more than my duty.

14   Her mother is about thirty-five years old and carries a world-weariness of more years than that. She made no effort to connect with me—friendly or otherwise—as I helped her

into her saddle. Indeed, she seemed to resent my attempt, and I must confess this actually endeared her to me.

15   I'm curious to meet Major Drummond after meeting his sister. Mrs. Hill (for that is her name) is heavy of form, with dark hair and a complexion more olive than fair. She has on her face the lines of one who has not always had an easy life, but she carries herself with dignity.

16   The older woman rode ahead of young Anna, following our commander and the scout, who rode a powerful steed. I followed them in the rear at some distance; my duty being to keep the marching officers in their lines. If Anna's mother felt any trepidation at venturing further into the forest her face did not betray it, though I admit to noticing her glance from time to time into the thick brush—no doubt in response to the sudden movement of a wild animal.

17   The native scout never left my sight at any time, and I must admit that this impressed me and I felt some admiration for him. Though I suppose it could be argued that the scout's job is to stay far enough ahead of the group to be an effective protector, it comforted me that I could keep our entire travelling party in sight. At times the path became very narrow and the arrangement of the soldiers had to be **altered**, but the men did so at my direction without complaint.

18   The **portion** of the journey that we accomplished today was uneventful, I'm pleased to report. Not a single native person was sighted, although there was a startling moment when a young horse cut across our path. The men were alert after that **incident**, to be sure.

CITE EVIDENCE

C Place an asterisk by the sentence in the journal that tells who rides in front. Is this detail the same in Cooper's novel? If so, explain whether Cooper might have altered such a detail to serve his purposes in his novel.

D Double underline in paragraph 17 the detail about the native scout that differs from the description of Magua in Cooper's novel.

E A secondary source like Cooper's novel uses and interprets facts from a primary source. In the novel, Cooper describes a colt "gliding" among the trees. Box the sentence in paragraph 18 of the journal that this detail might have been based on.

Comprehension Check

How does the information about the woman and her daughter in this journal entry differ from the information in the section of Cooper's novel that begins on page 222? What conclusion can you draw about why Cooper's details are different? What might he be trying to achieve?

Guided Practice

RL.7.9, RH.7.9

WORDS TO KNOW

canopy

evidence

occurred

physical

sentry

CITE EVIDENCE

A Circle a phrase in paragraph 21 that suggests that this journal is a primary source.

B Underline in paragraph 23 a detail about the colors of the forest that is similar to the one that Cooper uses in his novel. What is the effect in Cooper's novel of describing these colors? Is the effect similar or different here?

Journal of a British Officer *continued*

19   **August 1, 1757** Our second day through the forest is complete, another large sum of leagues travelled. Today there was concern that we would run into hostile natives—that was the idea delivered by our scout, for at one point he rode ahead and returned a short while later with a look of concern on his face.

20   He is trained, as all runners are, to look for telltale signs of native activity, including rocks that have been overturned in a stream, or disturbance of the surrounding vegetation. I also know that he looks closely at the moss that grows on the top of rocks to see if it has been trampled upon.

21   He claimed to have seen such **evidence**, so we were on high alert the entire day. I sensed concern among the two women, but by nightfall no event had **occurred** and we decided to take our chances and set up camp in a clearing; there is, of course, always the chance of a nighttime attack, but our **sentries** stand guard all night.

22   I would be remiss if I did not include here an account of the forest itself; not that I think I shall ever forget it. It has astonishing **physical** beauty; to begin with, the trees are so tall one can barely see their tops, and the branches that grow closer to the ground arc out at such an angle as to create a **canopy**. It creates a sensation of having a roof over one's head despite the obvious fact that one is out of doors.

23   Sunlight barely reaches the forest's floor, which is covered in leaves and pine needles. At the end of the day, the colors of the forest become darker hued, with greens appearing almost blue, and blues becoming purple.

24   The sounds of the forest are almost entirely created by its animal and insect residents; birds are calling, bees are buzzing, squirrels jump from branch to branch and shuffle leaves underfoot. Sometimes one can even hear the rush of a river or waterfall in the distance, but other than that, the forest is a silent place.

Comprehension Check

1. Which of the following would be an example of a secondary source?

   a. letters from Anna to her uncle

   b. a biography of General Webb

   c. Major Drummond's birth certificate

   d. the aunt's diary

2. Which detail described in the journal is similar to one Cooper uses in his novel?

   a. Sometimes the native scout rides ahead.

   b. The journey took more than a day.

   c. The native scout checks rocks to see if they have been overturned.

   d. Squirrels jump from branch to branch.

3. Which statement about the relationship between the journal and the novel is true?

   a. The novel gives more detail about how Magua scouts for natives.

   b. Both texts contain vivid descriptions of the forest.

   c. Neither text is concerned with the women's feelings about the journey.

   d. Only the journal describes the sounds of the forest.

4. Which elements of paragraph 22 suggest that the text is a primary source?

   a. It has a first-person point of view.

   b. The author speaks of his own role as a writer.

   c. The author includes his reaction to what he sees.

   d. All of the above.

5. Which details from this section of the primary source are similar to those Cooper used? Which are different? Work with a partner and discuss why this might be so and how it affects your understanding of the story.

   _____

   _____

   _____

   _____

   _____

Independent Practice

RL.7.9, RH.7.9

WORDS TO KNOW

corded

hide

intricate

provocation

CITE EVIDENCE

A Review paragraphs 12–15 in Cooper's novel. Then underline in paragraphs 27 and 28 of the journal details about the white man's physical appearance that are different for the character of Hawkeye in the novel.

B Recall that primary sources give specific dates for events. Circle the date on which the travelling party encountered the white man and the native man.

25   **August 2, 1757** We were nearly finished with our journey today when we suddenly came upon two men in the woods. One was a native, and one was white. To say our travelling party was stunned at the sight of them would be an understatement. Immediately my men raised their muskets in defense, but the white man called out in clear English that he was not our enemy.

26   Only later did I learn the legend of the white man: he was apparently raised by natives. Under what circumstances he found himself in such a position I do not know, but I must admit hearing this explanation explained much about his appearance.

27   This man is the most peculiar blend of white European and native I have ever seen. His face was long and narrow and his skin a light color, yet red with sunburn. It was evident from his sunburn that he lived most of his life outdoors. His long black hair was tied neatly in a ponytail.

28   His clothing was the strongest evidence of his native roots; he wore garments made from animal **hides**. He wore a long shirt of a dark brown color. He had buckskin leggings on his long legs, laced along their sides. There were animal skin moccasins on his feet as well.

29   He was clearly a man of considerable physical strength; he was lean and broad shouldered, and his bare forearms were **corded** with muscle and veins.

30   The other man was native, as I have said. I am not certain of his association; one soldier said Mohican, another said Huron, but I sensed no connection between him and our scout.

31 His appearance was most remarkable; his front was without a garment, and visible was a large black-and-white tattoo so **intricate** I cannot describe it. He carried a hand-woven basket that he handled nervously. In fact, his energy was very active; his eyes moved as if he were ready to strike us at the smallest **provocation**.

Comprehension Check

MORE ONLINE **sadlierconnect.com**

1. Which of the following details does the journal offer that the novel does not?

    a. the meaning of the native man's tattoo

    b. the fact that one of the men is of white European descent

    c. the fact that the native man carries a hand-woven basket

    d. the color of the white man's hunting shirt

2. Which statement correctly compares the descriptions of Hawkeye in the novel and the white man in the journal?

    a. The descriptions are totally identical.

    b. Only the journal's description treats Hawkeye as a comical character.

    c. Only the novel's description mentions clothing details.

    d. Both descriptions suggest that Hawkeye knows how to live off the land.

3. The character of Hawkeye is probably based on a man like the white man in the journal. In which text do we learn that Hawkeye can speak English?

    a. only in the journal

    b. only in the novel

    c. in both the journal and the novel

    d. in neither the journal nor the novel

4. What detail about Chingachgook's tattoo in the novel is different from that in the journal?

    a. that it is an emblem of death

    b. that it is black and white

    c. that it is on Chingachgook's chest

    d. that it is so small it can hardly be seen

5. How might the sections of James Fenimore Cooper's novel be different if he had used the same details provided in the journal? Cite specifics.

    _____

    _____

    _____

    _____

    _____

A Plains Family Moves West

By Peter McMann-Farningsworth

(Genre: Historical Fiction)

1   Norma pulled her hat down over her head to the tip of her slender nose and tried to fall asleep. She was exhausted, and the setting sun beaming in through the rear opening of the covered wagon was keeping her awake. She and her four sisters and three brothers were squeezed into the wagon bed, four on each side, and they had to sleep sitting up. She was thirteen years old—not old by any means, but the oldest of the eight children.

2   It was August 1, 1844, and Norma and her family were relocating to Oregon from their home in Missouri. Her mother, Sarah, had weak lungs, and doctors had suggested that the cool forest air of the Pacific Northwest would alleviate her suffering, which included violent fits of coughing. Norma saw how gaunt her mother's face was, however, and sadly suspected that something much worse was ailing her. Upon hearing the doctors' recommendations, Ronald, Norma's loyal and loving father, set in motion plans to move the family from Platte County, Missouri, to Oregon.

Departure

3   Norma thought back to the day their family packed up two wagons and bade their friends and neighbors goodbye. The occasion had an air of a celebration to it, but Norma could not say why. She knew well that the journey promised to be unbelievably difficult; for one thing, they would have to brave the elements of summer, including an unrelenting sun as well as violent July thunderstorms. Even less predictable than the weather were the Indians, who did not favor white people traversing their lands.

4   They would not be alone, however, as theirs was not the only family desiring to relocate from the dry plains of Missouri to somewhere greener. Other families, packed into their own wagons, came together in one long wagon train, divided into companies.

Journey

5   The first few weeks, Norma admitted, were rather fun. They stopped every night and set up a camp where they would eat and sleep. The other families' children were friendly and fun; the adults played instruments and sang. One of the boys, Jed, a lanky lad of sixteen, asked Norma to dance one evening. She looked to her mother for permission, and Sarah gave it with a wink.

Challenges

6   One particularly hot day, the cattle were pulling the wagon by their yokes when one of the bulls collapsed. Norma's father called out to Captain Shaw, a slim young army

RL.7.7, RL.7.9

officer taking his own family to Oregon, who was leading their company.

7   Captain Shaw led the company toward a river where the cattle could drink and rest. When they were refreshed, the beasts did not want to resume the trip—in fact, they appeared not to want to move at all. Captain Shaw had to prod the steers until they began ambling back up to the main road.

8   A worse incident involved poor, sick Sarah. One afternoon, the caravan was traveling by a river when the cattle pulling the first wagon suddenly took off down the riverbank and overturned the wagon. It so happened that day that Sarah was riding up front with Captain Shaw, who was driving.

9   The force of the crash threw Sarah into the air, and she landed hard on her right side. Ronald rushed to her in a panic. He and Captain Shaw carried her thin frame to the second wagon, from which Norma and her siblings were watching anxiously.

10   The company would have to stop and wait for a doctor; luckily enough, there was a surgeon farther up in the train.

11   This surgeon set Sarah's broken arm in a splint and ordered her to remain in the wagon bed for the remainder of the trip. Ronald looked at his wife and then looked west toward the sun. He was determined to deliver his family to their new home.

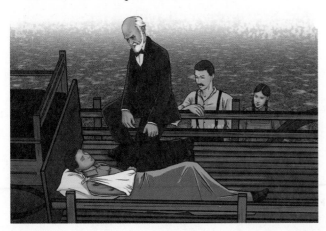

Great *Plains*

(Genre: Movie Review)

1   The new film *Plains Family* is a stunningly realistic look at the difficult journey American pioneer families took in the mid-nineteenth century. Its director, Annabel Nancy Jackson, deserves praise for her full-blooded yet restrained interpretation of Q. Wayne Sumner's magnificently straightforward screenplay, which is based on Peter McMann-Farningsworth's historical novel *A Plains Family Moves West*.

2   Jackson and her cinematographer, Paul Weymouth Daniels, have clearly worked hard to create the gorgeous images of the American West that permeate the film.

3   The opening shot shows young Norma peering out the back of her family's covered wagon early one evening. Jackson cuts to what the character is looking at, namely an incredible sunset rich in reds, oranges, and even purples.

4   Perhaps more impressive is how Daniels has lit the nighttime camp scenes. Most of the time, the characters are lit only by the flickering embers of the dying campfire. The lighting successfully heightens the drama of the scene.

Across the Plains in 1844

by Catherine Sager Pringle

(Genre: Historical Account)

1   My father was one of the restless ones who are not content to remain in one place for long. Late in the fall of 1838, we emigrated from Ohio to Missouri. Our first halting place was on Green River, but the next year we took a farm in Platte County. Father engaged in farming and blacksmithing, and he had a wide reputation for ingenuity. Anyone who needed to have something made or mended sought his shop.

2   The promise of a more healthful climate induced my mother to favor a further move to Oregon. Immigration was the theme all autumn, and we decided to start for Oregon. Late in 1843 Father sold his property and moved us near St. Joseph, and in April 1844 we started across the plains. The first encampments were a great pleasure to us children. We were three girls and two boys, ranging from the baby girl to be born on the way to the older boy, hardly old enough to be much help.

Starting on the Plains

3   We waited several days at the Missouri River. Many friends came that far to see the emigrants start on their long journey; there was much sadness at the parting, and it was a sorrowful company that crossed the Missouri that bright spring morning.

4   The motion of the wagon made us all sick, and weeks passed before we got used to it all. Rain came down and required us to tie down the wagon covers, and that increased our sickness by confining the air we breathed.

5   Our cattle recrossed in the night and went back to their winter quarters. This caused delay in recovering them and a weary, forced march to rejoin the train. This was divided into companies, and we were in the company commanded by William Shaw. Soon after starting, Indians raided our camp one night and drove off several cattle. The animals were pursued but never recovered.

6   Soon everything went more smoothly, and our train made steady headway. The weather was fine, and we enjoyed the journey pleasantly. There were several musical instruments among the emigrants, and these sounded clearly on the evening air when camp was made and merry talk and laughter resounded from almost every campfire.

Incidents of Travel

7   We had one wagon, two steady yoke of old cattle, and several of young and not well-broken ones. Father, who was no ox driver, had trouble with these until one day he called on Captain Shaw for assistance. It was furnished by the good captain's prodding the refractory steer until they were glad to come to terms. Reaching buffalo

country, Father got someone to drive his team and then joined the hunt, for he knew the importance of supplying our company with meat. He not only killed the great bison but often also brought home an antelope that had fallen at his unerring aim—something not often acquired by ordinary marksmen.

8   Soon after crossing South Platte, the unwieldy oxen ran on a bank and overturned the wagon, greatly injuring our mother. She lay long insensible in the tent put up for the occasion.

9   On August 1 we nooned in a beautiful grove on the north side of the Platte. We had by this time gotten used to climbing in and out of the wagon when in motion. When performing this feat that afternoon, however, my dress caught on an axle helve, and I was thrown under the wagon wheel, which passed over and badly crushed my leg before Father could stop the team.

10   He picked me up and saw the extent of the injury when the injured limb hung dangling in the air.

11   In a broken voice he exclaimed, "My dear child, your leg is broken all to pieces!" The news soon spread along the train, and a halt was called. A surgeon was found and the limb set; then we pushed on the same night to Laramie, where we arrived soon after dark. This accident confined me to the wagon the remainder of the long journey.

Comprehension Check

1A. What does *yoke* mean in paragraph 6 of "A Plains Family Moves West"?

   a. a wooden bar attached to the necks of cattle

   b. a shade that shields cattle from the sun

   c. a brace that supports the legs of cattle when they get tired

   d. a large wooden wheel

1B. Which detail from the historical fiction selection supports the answer to Part A?

   a. "when one of the bulls collapsed"

   b. "one particularly hot day"

   c. "the cattle were pulling the wagon"

   d. "Norma's father called out to Captain Shaw"

2A. The text by Catherine Sager Pringle is

   a. a primary source.

   b. a secondary source.

   c. both a primary and secondary source—a mix of the two.

   d. neither a primary nor a secondary source.

2B. Which of the following supports the answer to Part A?

   a. The story is written in the third person.

   b. The story is written in the first person.

   c. The story does not establish a time or place.

   d. The story analyzes a primary source.

3A. Which selection reveals that Sarah approves of Norma's dancing?

    a. "A Plains Family Moves West"

    b. "Across the Plains in 1844"

    c. both selections

    d. neither selection

3B. Which detail from the text supports the answer to Part A?

    a. "merry talk and laughter resounded"

    b. "She lay long insensible in the tent"

    c. "There were several musical instruments among the emigrants"

    d. "gave it with a wink"

4A. Which statement about the relationship between the historical fiction selection and the historical account is accurate?

    a. The main character in both selections is named Norma.

    b. Only the fiction selection identifies the mother's specific illness.

    c. Only the fictional account deals with the dangers posed by Indians.

    d. Only the historical account establishes the year of the family's move.

4B. What evidence supports the answer to Part A?

    a. "The promise of a more healthful climate induced my mother to favor a further move"

    b. "Her mother, Sarah, had weak lungs"

    c. "did not favor white people traversing"

    d. "Late in the fall of 1838, we emigrated from Ohio to Missouri"

5A. Which of these filmmaking jobs does the movie reviewer mention?

    a. acting

    b. sound

    c. lighting

    d. costumes

5B. Every paragraph from the movie review gives evidence for the answer to Part A EXCEPT

    a. paragraph 1.

    b. paragraph 2.

    c. paragraph 3.

    d. paragraph 4.

6. Why are terms such as *wagon train* (paragraph 4 of the historical fiction), and *Missouri River* (paragraph 3 of the historical account) important to these selections?

_____

_____

_____

_____

7. How does the reviewer's description of the film affect your understanding of the historical fiction selection? Cite specifics in your explanation.

_____

_____

_____

_____

8. Imagine another primary source related to Catherine Sager Pringle's historical account. Suggest how it might impact the story if the author of the fiction selection were to use it.

_____

_____

_____

_____

9. Analyze the effect that the cinematographer's work had on the film _Plains Family_. Support your answer with examples from the movie review.

_____

_____

_____

_____

10. Identify two details from Pringle's story that Peter McMann-Farningsworth, the author of "A Plains Family Moves West," either altered or left out. Write a paragraph discussing the effect of these omissions. Cite specifics in your answer.

_____

_____

_____

_____

Support a Claim

R.9, SL.7.1.a, SL.7.1.c–d

In this unit you've read two works of historical fiction, two journals, and two movie reviews. Think about the claim below and how these selections might support that claim. In the chart list key details that serve as evidence. Then write a brief essay in which you use the information in the chart to support the claim. Be prepared to discuss your ideas with the class.

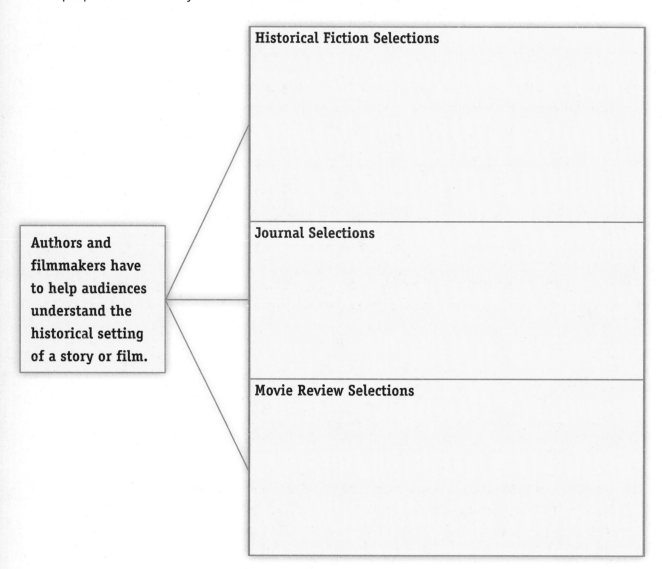

Authors and filmmakers have to help audiences understand the historical setting of a story or film.

Historical Fiction Selections

Journal Selections

Movie Review Selections

Return to the Essential Question

How can different media and forms of a text affect our understanding?

In small groups or as a class, discuss the Essential Question. Think about what you have learned about how written stories compare to their film versions, about history and social studies terms, and about the way that historical fiction can use and alter historical facts provided by primary sources and nonfiction accounts. Use evidence from the texts in this unit to answer the question.

Word Meanings

Guided Instruction Many words have both a **denotation** and a **connotation**. A word's denotation is its literal definition, the definition found in a dictionary. A word's connotation refers to the emotions and ideas readers associate with the word. The chart below shows the connotations of different words from "A Plains Family Moves West," all of which have a similar denotation.

Word	Connotation	Use in the Text
slender	elegant and graceful	"the tip of her slender nose . . . "
gaunt	sickly	"Norma saw how gaunt her mother's face was . . . "
lanky	long-limbed; awkward	"Jed, a lanky lad of sixteen . . . "
slim	attractive and fit	"Captain Shaw, a slim young army officer . . . "
thin	perhaps unwell; not full enough	"Captain Shaw carried her thin frame to the second wagon . . . "

Guided Practice Complete each sentence with a word from the chart. Think about the word's connotation when choosing the word.

1. Will may not be eating enough; he's too _____.

2. She must be working out; she looks _____ and healthy.

3. I have a basketball player's build; I'm tall and _____.

Independent Practice Replace the underlined word in the sentence with a synonym with a different connotation. Tell how the meaning of the sentence changes.

"Today brought an <u>unusual</u> turn of events."

_____

_____

"My concern grew as I gazed at him, for the scout had an <u>evil</u> look to him."

_____

_____

_____

RL.7.7, RL.7.9, RL.7.10, L.7.5.c

Reread "A Plains Family Moves West." Then read the continuation of the "Great *Plains*" movie review and the letter below. Think about the differences between a written story and its filmed version and between primary sources and secondary sources. Answer the questions on pages 245 and 246.

Great *Plains* (continued)

1   Director Annabel Nancy Jackson has assembled a fine ensemble of actors to play the principal roles in *Plains Family*, but she misses the mark in a few places.

2   Paige Carlsberg, in her feature film debut, is an interesting choice for the main character of Norma. Carlsberg is too old for the role; Norma is supposed to be 12 years old, and the actress looks at least 18. Yet the age difference does the film a favor, for Carlsberg infuses Norma with a toughness and grit that the original novel frankly misses.

3   Completely miscast, however, is Aaron Richards as Captain Shaw. The character is supposed to be a tall, handsome young farm-hand who helps save the life of Sarah. Instead Jackson has cast a short, middle-aged veteran actor who comes off as much too gruff. Shaw is supposed to be a sympathetic character, but the casting spoils any chance of that.

4   Brief mention must go to the marvelous young actors playing Norma's siblings. Tate Myers is a standout as young Joe.

Joe's Letter to His Grandmother

August 3, 1844

Dear Grandmother,

1   I don't want you to worry too much, but Mother has been injured on our journey to Oregon. The day before yesterday, the two cattle pulling one of our wagons broke loose of the yoke and ran off down a steep embankment toward the South Platte River.

2   With the yoke loose, the falling tongue up front broke as the wagon tumbled down the bank, which in turn caused the entire wagon to flip over. The force of the event caused the jockey box to come loose as well, throwing bolts, nails, and tools all over the place.

3   Mother was thrown from the driver's seat where she was sitting with Father. She fell hard on her right side and screamed. Father leapt down heroically at once, lifted her up, and carefully carried her to a nearby wagon. Luckily, a surgeon from farther up the train came to help. He set Mother's arm in a splint and told her to rest.

4   Please know that other than this unfortunate accident, the trip has been fine—even fun, sometimes. I love going to the trading posts, where Father buys supplies and hears the news. In fact, I'm at a trading post now, and I'll mail this letter to you from here.

Love, Joe

RL.7.7, RL.7.9

Circle the letter next to the best answer choice.

1A. In which selection do we learn that Sarah was in pain after she was thrown from the wagon?

a. "A Plains Family Moves West"

b. "Joe's Letter to His Grandmother"

c. the movie review "Great *Plains*"

d. No selection tells this detail.

1B. Which statement supports the answer to Part A?

a. "fell hard on her right side and screamed"

b. "she misses the mark in a few places"

c. "she was sitting with Father"

d. "the crash threw her into the air"

2A. Which of the following statements about primary and secondary sources is true?

a. Authors of primary sources often reveal personal opinions.

b. Encyclopedia articles often contain their author's opinion.

c. A newspaper article, if written well, will express an opinion.

d. Opinions in primary sources are useless to authors of secondary sources.

2B. Which choice is a personal opinion that indicates that "Joe's Letter" is a primary source?

a. "Mother was thrown from the driver's seat"

b. "two cattle . . . broke loose"

c. "He set Mother's arm in a splint"

d. "the trip has been fine—even fun, sometimes"

3A. The social studies term *jockey box* refers to

a. a box containing food.

b. a box upon which the driver sits.

c. a box containing tools.

d. a box containing money.

3B. Which detail from Joe's letter is a clue to the answer to Part A?

a. Mother was thrown from the driver's seat.

b. Bolts, nails, and tools flew everywhere.

c. Two cattle broke loose of the yoke.

d. The falling tongue broke.

4A. A primary source may do all of the following EXCEPT

a. establish the time of an event.

b. establish where an event took place.

c. offer a first-person account of an event.

d. gather facts from multiple sources.

4B. What detail does NOT help establish the time and place of "Joe's Letter"?

a. He is on a journey to Oregon.

b. A surgeon set Mother's arm.

c. Father buys supplies at the trading posts.

d. The date of the letter is August 3, 1844.

5A. According to the film reviewer, the actress playing Norma was

a. simply superb.

b. older than the role indicated.

c. an example of perfect casting.

d. wearing the wrong costume.

5B. What evidence supports the answer to Part A?

a. "Paige Carlsberg . . . is an interesting choice"

b. "Norma is supposed to be 12 years old"

c. "Carlsberg infuses Norma . . . with a toughness and grit"

d. "Carlsberg is too old for the role"

RL.7.7, RL.7.9, L.7.5.c

6A. In Joe's letter, what social studies term means "a long piece of wood that connects a covered wagon to a yoke"?

    a. yoke

    b. embankment

    c. tongue

    d. splint

6B. What text supports the answer to Part A?

    a. "toward the South Platte River"

    b. "the event caused the jockey box to come loose"

    c. "the falling tongue up front broke as the wagon tumbled"

    d. "I'm at a trading post now"

7. How would readers have a different understanding of the following sentence if the word *tender* were used instead of the word *sympathetic*?

Shaw is supposed to be a sympathetic character, but the casting spoils any chance of that.

_____

_____

_____

8. How does the film reviewer's analysis of the actors and their performances help you understand the characters in the original story?

_____

_____

_____

9. How does the author of "A Plains Family Moves West" use details from the historical event described in "Joe's Letter to His Grandmother"? Does he alter any details from Joe's letter? Explain and give details.

_____

_____

_____

10. Read this line from "Joe's Letter to His Grandmother":

. . . other than this <u>unfortunate</u> *accident, the trip has been fine—even fun . . .*

Consider the following synonyms for *unfortunate*, and tell how the meaning of the sentence would change in each instance: *disastrous, hopeless, inappropriate*.

_____

_____

_____

_____

Introducing UNIT 10

In this unit about tales of the past, you will learn how to write an opinion piece, also called an argument. In this piece, you will thoroughly research an event from the past that you find interesting. Then you will shape and support an opinion about this event to inform and persuade your readers.

In your first paragraph, introduce your topic and explain your claim, or your position on the topic, to readers. Next, make sure readers understand the topic by giving background information. In the body of the essay, support your claim with logical reasoning and evidence from informational texts found in reliable sources. Use language that clarifies the relationships among your claims, reasons, and evidence, and that maintains a formal style. Acknowledge opposing claims, and argue against them. Finally, write a conclusion that follows from and supports your argument.

Progress Check *Can I?*

Before Unit 10 / **After Unit 10**

☐	Write an opinion piece about an event from the past.	☐
☐	Acknowledge and argue against opposing claims.	☐
☐	Make a claim and support it with logical reasoning and evidence.	☐
☐	Draw evidence from trustworthy informational sources.	☐
☐	Correctly punctuate coordinate and cumulative adjectives.	☐
☐	Use language to express ideas precisely and concisely.	☐

HOME ✦ CONNECT...

I n this unit, your child will learn about **writing an opinion piece** about an event from the past. Explain that this type of writing **includes a claim** based on the writer's opinion and must back up that claim with **relevant evidence and logical reasoning**. Your child must use trustworthy **sources** to find evidence to support the claim he or she writes about. Additionally, your child will be asked to acknowledge and **address opposing claims** about the topic.

Work with your child to develop the skills necessary for success in this unit. Describe to your child an event from the past about which you have an opinion. Give background information so that he or she can understand the event, and elaborate on your opinion. Point out to your child how you use evidence and logical reasoning to support your claim about the event. Model how to acknowledge and refute opposing claims. Then put your opinion piece in writing for your child to study and explore.

Activity: Explore the unit topic, "tales from the past," with your child. Work together to make a timeline showing past events that people had strong opinions about, such as the Civil War. Discuss whether opinions are still divided on these events, and why. Pick two or three events your child is interested in and brainstorm ideas that could support his or her claim in an opinion piece on this event.

IN THIS UNIT, YOUR CHILD WILL...

- Learn how to write an opinion piece about an event from the past.

- Introduce a claim and acknowledge opposing claims.

- Support an argument with evidence and logical reasoning.

- Use trustworthy sources to gather information about a topic.

- Incorporate information from texts as evidence for an argument.

- Conclude an essay with a section that follows from and supports the argument.

- Write in a formal style that includes the correct punctuation of coordinate and cumulative adjectives, and that expresses ideas precisely and concisely.

NOTE: All of these learning goals for your child are based on the Grade 7 Common Core State Standards for English Language Arts.

WAYS TO HELP YOUR CHILD

Hold a debate with your child on an event from the past (either from history or from your family's past). You and your child should argue different sides. Take time to prepare by listing evidence and logical reasoning that supports each side. You may choose to have another family member moderate the debate and declare who better supported his or her claim.

> **ONLINE**
>
> **For more Home Connect activities, continue online at** sadlierconnect.com

Text Types and Purposes: Write Opinion Pieces

Essential Question:
How can writers support an analysis of a text?

W.7.1, W.7.1.a–b, W.7.1.d, WHST.7.1, WHST.7.1.a–b, WHST.7.1.d

CREATING AN ORGANIZATIONAL STRUCTURE

Marley used an outline like the one below to organize her essay and support her argument.

Title _____
  I. **Introduction**
     a. Claim: _____
     b. Give necessary background information on the topic: _____
  II. **Support Claim**
     a. Logical reasoning about _____
        1. Facts and evidence _____
        2. Facts and evidence _____
     b. Logical reasoning about _____
        1. Facts and evidence _____
        2. Facts and evidence _____
     c. Logical reasoning about _____
        1. Facts and evidence _____
        2. Facts and evidence _____
     d. Opposing claim(s) to address: _____
        1. Facts to address opposing claim _____
        2. Facts to address opposing claim _____
  III. **Conclusion**

INTRODUCTION

- Introduces the topic and presents the writer's claim

BACKGROUND

- Includes background information for the reader. This is especially important when discussing an historical issue with which the reader may not be familiar.

FORMAL STYLE

- Includes academic language
- Avoids slang, contractions, and personal statements
- Uses complete sentences and clear explanations

Read a Student Model

Marley is a student in Ms. White's seventh-grade Language Arts class. Ms. White gave Marley's class an assignment to write an opinion piece based on an event from the past. For this opinion piece, Marley must make a strong claim and then support it with clear reasons and relevant evidence. As you read Marley's essay, think about an historical event that you might choose to write about in your own opinion piece.

Preserving our Natural Heritage

Today, some people think that the natural world is there to be exploited and developed. Of course, there are places where development is reasonable. However, America's National Parks are far more valuable when preserved. The development that threatened what is now Grand Canyon National Park shows that designating these unique areas as national parks is essential to preserving America's heritage.

Background

For almost a century, America had no national parks. However, the discovery of California's Yosemite Valley in 1851 led many to advocate that the area be preserved so that it could be enjoyed by generations to come. In 1890, after Yellowstone became America's first national park, Yosemite was finally designated one, too. America's national parks now number in the hundreds.

W.7.1.a–b, WHST.7.1.a–b

The Grand Canyon

One of America's most amazing parks is Grand Canyon National Park, an incredible one-mile-deep canyon visited by nearly five million people a year. Even those who have not visited it are familiar with images of the deep canyon and the layers of rocks that reveal geological history from the ancient past. According to the National Park Service website, the park also contains human artifacts from nearly 12,000 years ago and is home to many species of plants and animals, including the rare California Condor.

SOURCES

Make sure the sources you use are credible. Trustworthy sites include .gov sites and reliable information providers such as news organizations and universities.

Circle the source the author cites in this paragraph.

The Need for Parks

Some might believe that these natural areas would be preserved even if they were not designated parks—that people's respect for them would prevent destruction and development. This is not true. In the 1860s, tourists who wanted to see Niagara Falls had to pay private landowners who claimed every good spot for viewing the natural wonder. In Arizona, the Mesa Verde cliff dwellings suffered looting and vandalism until the area became a national park.

ADDRESS OPPOSING CLAIMS

Acknowledge opposing claims—what people who disagree with you might say—and present evidence against them.

Put an asterisk next to the opposing claim in this paragraph.

The Grand Canyon

When President Theodore Roosevelt hoped to make the Grand Canyon a national park, he was opposed by local miners, settlers, and ranchers. Although he named the canyon a national monument in 1908, mining was still allowed, and hotel owner Ralph Cameron claimed the most scenic spots. Cameron built hotels, charged travelers tolls and high fees, and tried to build two dams and a platinum mine in the park.

LOGICAL REASONING

Use logical reasoning supported by evidence to strengthen your argument.

Underline the evidence that supports Marley's argument that President Roosevelt faced opposition.

W.7.1.a, W.7.1.c, W.7.1.e, W.7.9, W.7.9.b, WHST.7.1.a, WHST.7.1.c, WHST.7.1.e

CONNECT EVIDENCE

Use clear transition words, phrases, and clauses to connect your claims, reasons, and evidence.

Underline the word Marley uses to connect past images of the canyon to the reason for preserving it as a national park.

LOGICAL ORGANIZATION

Organize the information logically, and use subheads throughout the essay to make the organization clear and to create unity among sections and arguments.

Box the subhead that makes it clear that Marley has moved from an historical discussion of national parks to a modern one.

CONCLUSION

The conclusion of an opinion piece must follow from and support the essay's argument. Many opinion pieces end with a call to action to tell readers what they should do in response to this issue.

Circle the call to action in this conclusion.

Now that the Grand Canyon has become a national park, its trails are open to everyone. It is no longer cluttered with hotels, dams, or mines. Instead, the canyon is an incredible monument to history. The layers of its walls preserve a record of the past, and the canyon itself provides a safe home for native plants and animals. And it protects evidence of the ancient cultures that once lived there. If the canyon were developed, it would lose its majesty and primitive beauty; it would simply become like everywhere else.

Threats Today

Being declared a national park is no guarantee that a piece of wilderness will be safe forever. Today, national parks face threats from many sources, including invasive foreign plants and animal species, development on park borders, decreasing supplies of fresh water, and air pollution. Ironically, the park's popularity itself poses a threat: park visitors damage vegetation and leave trash behind, and sightseeing flights and boat rides cause disturbance and noise pollution.

Our Parks, Our Responsibility

America has a responsibility to protect the Grand Canyon and other national parks for future generations. We must not let these national treasures be developed or exploited. Tell those who want more development in our parks, or who want to reduce park funding, that our national resources must be protected. We would lose invaluable aspects of America if we no longer possessed these incredible parks.

W.7.1, W.7.1.a–e, W.7.4, W.7.5, W.7.6, W.7.7, W.7.8, W.7.9, W.7.9.b, W.7.10, WHST.7.1.a–e

Use this outline to organize your opinion piece about an event in the past for the Common Core Review on page 259. Be sure to draw evidence from literary and informational sources and to make connections between them to support your claim. Then write your first draft on another sheet of paper.

Title _____

I. **Introduction**

    a. Claim: _____

    b. Give necessary background information on the topic: _____

    _____

II. **Support Claim**

    a. Logical reasoning about _____

        1. Facts and evidence _____

        2. Facts and evidence _____

    b. Logical reasoning about _____

        1. Facts and evidence _____

        2. Facts and evidence _____

    c. Logical reasoning about _____

        1. Facts and evidence _____

        2. Facts and evidence _____

    d. Opposing claim(s) to address: _____

    _____

        1. Facts to address opposing claim _____

        2. Facts to address opposing claim _____

III. **Conclusion**

    _____

    _____

L.7.2.a

Coordinate and Cumulative Adjectives

Guided Instruction A string of adjectives is punctuated differently in a sentence depending on whether it uses **coordinate** or **cumulative** adjectives.

- **Coordinate adjectives** are adjectives that each separately modify the noun they come before. When a sentence contains a string of coordinate adjectives, the adjectives are separated by commas.

  The lazy, green, winding river was full of silver fish.

  The fierce, hungry, strong lion took down a zebra.

  Each adjective separately describes the noun. The river is lazy *and* green *and* winding; the lion is fierce *and* hungry *and* strong. The adjectives could be rearranged in the sentence and the meaning would remain the same.

- However, **cumulative adjectives** are formed when an adjective joins with the noun it comes before to make a unit.

  ruby slippers

  deserted island

  young child

  Since the adjective and noun have formed a unit, there should not be a comma between the preceding adjective and the unit.

  She was excited to wear the sparkling ruby slippers.

  They landed on a mysterious deserted island.

  The happy, excited young child opened the present.

- It can be difficult to determine the difference between coordinate and cumulative adjectives. Test by considering:

  If the adjectives in the sentence can be rearranged and still make sense in the sentence, they are coordinate.

  If the adjectives can be joined by the word "and" and still make sense, the adjectives are more likely to be coordinate.

Guided Practice Rewrite the sentences below, adding commas where necessary.

1. The wild untrained dog splashed mud all over me.

   _____

2. My friend lives in that big old rundown house.

   _____

3. The exhausted airline passengers trudged off the plane.

   _____

4. I spilled hot chunky spicy soup all over the white tile floor.

   _____

5. The long dirty hot hike finally came to an end at a sparkling blue lake.

   _____

Independent Practice Write one sentence using coordinate adjectives and one sentence using cumulative adjectives for each prompt.

Describe something you saw at the aquarium.

_____

_____

Describe a story or article you recently read.

_____

_____

Describe a meal you enjoyed.

_____

_____

L.7.3.a

Expressing Ideas Precisely and Concisely

Guided Instruction Writers should use language that expresses their ideas **precisely**, choosing the exact words to communicate their meanings. Writers should also share their ideas **concisely**. This means avoiding wordiness and redundancy. Wordiness is using too many words to describe something, and redundancy is saying the same thing more than once.

■ **Precise Language**

Choose the right word to share your meaning. Think carefully about the nouns and verbs that you choose.

Vague: *I saw many large vehicles on the road.*

Precise: *I saw many trucks and buses on the highway.*

Vague: *She jumped over the rock and walked quickly up the path.*

Precise: *She sprang over the rock and dashed up the path.*

To use precise language in your own writing, make sure you understand the meanings and connotations of the words you use. Choose the word that means exactly what you want to say, and try to stick to words that you're familiar with and understand.

■ **Concise Language**

To write concisely, keep your sentences sharp and to the point. Decide what you want a sentence to say and say it directly.

Wordy: *There is the belief among some people that all teenage boys and girls should experience paid employment.*

Concise: *Some people believe all teenagers should have a job.*

Redundant: *The giant trees were very tall and towered far above us.*

Concise: *The trees towered far above us.*

The best way to check for wordiness and redundancy is in the revision phase of your writing. Reread your work and note anywhere that the writing slows down. Revise these sections to say more directly what you want to share with the reader. Avoid language that puts your ideas in an unnaturally or overly formal style, and state your ideas simply and straightforwardly.

Guided Practice Rewrite each sentence to correct the error identified in parentheses.

1. (wordiness) All people on all the seven continents should gravely consider this issue.

_____

2. (vague language) The big house was old.

_____

3. (redundancy) The hot, blazing sun shone down on the overheated runners, making them very hot.

_____

4. (vague language) The furniture was ugly.

_____

_____

5. (wordiness) This is just one problem of the many, many problems that people have caused for the lions, elephants, giraffes, and zebras who live on the savannah.

_____

_____

Independent Practice Revise this paragraph to convey its ideas precisely and concisely.

Long ago, in the previous century in the 1940s, there was a terrible event. This event was when many Japanese Americans who were living peacefully in the United States were forcibly interned in internment camps by the United States government. Because the United States was at war with Japan, the government believed that people in the U.S. who were of Japanese descent might be sympathetic to Japan's side of the global conflict in which these two countries were engaged. Innocent men, women, children, and old people were put into the camps and lived in bad conditions for no reason.

_____

_____

_____

_____

SL.7.1.a–d, SL.7.3, SL.7.4, SL.7.6

Discuss the Essential Question

How can writers support an analysis of a text?

Prepare for a class discussion about the Essential Question by responding to the questions below. Support your points of view with reasons and examples.

1. How did Marley support her claim with logical reasoning and evidence?

_____

_____

_____

_____

2. How did Marley address opposing claims in her essay?

_____

_____

_____

3. Did Marley's analysis of informational texts work to support her argument?

_____

_____

Use your notes above as you discuss the Essential Question with your class or in small groups. Use the organizer below to record your ideas and what you hear in the discussion. Follow the discussion rules on the "Did I?" checklist (page 58).

Ideas I Agree or Disagree With		Questions I Asked
agree		
disagree		
New Ideas I Had During Discussion		Questions I Answered

W.7.1, W.7.1.a–c, WHST.7.1.a–c

Read this draft of an introductory paragraph and body paragraph from a student essay and answer the questions below.

Altamont Pass: A Terrible Idea

(1) In the 1970s, Americans began to look at alternative energy sources, such as wind energy. (2) A wind farm was built in California's Altamont Pass, known for its strong winds. (3) However, it was built in the wrong place, which led to the deaths of thousands of raptors, or hunting birds. (4) Some people think that the jobs and clean energy that resulted were worth the death of these birds, but clean energy should be cleaner than this wind farm. (5) Altamont Pass should never have been built.

(6) Altamont Pass is indeed an important source of clean energy for California. (7) However, the pass is also where many different type of birds hunt, such as Golden Eagles, Red-tailed Hawks, and Burrowing Owls. (8) According to Sierra Club information, several of these hunting animals are on the Endangered Species list! (9) It is not right to excuse these rare birds' deaths just because they are being killed by clean energy.

---

1. In what sentence does the writer acknowledge opposing claims about this issue?

  a. 1   **c.** 5

  d. 4   **d.** 7

2. What is the writer's claim about Altamont Pass?

  a. It should never have been built.

  b. It is a wind farm in California.

  c. The birds' deaths are sad but necessary.

  d. It kills many different types of birds.

3. Why does the writer cite the Sierra Club?

  a. to use precise language

  b. to provide an expert source

  c. to address an opposing argument

  d. to provide logical reasoning

4. What precise word would best replace the phrase "hunting animals" in sentence 8?

  a. birds   **c.** raptors

  b. eagles   **d.** prey

Read the conclusion from the student essay and answer the questions below.

W.7.1, W.7.1.b, W.7.1.d–e, W.7.4, W.7.5, W.7.6, W.7.7, W.7.8, W.7.9, W.7.9.b, W.7.10, L.7.2.a, L.7.3.a

(1) In poems and stories and books, birds often symbolize freedom, and symbolize escape, and these symbols encourage us to fly beyond our limitations. (2) We should fly beyond the need for energy that will harm Earth and its creatures. (3) Recently, there have been fewer raptor deaths at Altamont Pass. (4) We can't improve our planet's health if we harm these beautiful vital predatory birds.

5. How could the writer improve this conclusion?

   a. include a reference to literature

   b. restate the argument

   c. include a picture of a raptor

   d. include a call to action

6. What facts could the writer provide to serve as evidence for the claim?

   a. numbers of wind turbines at Altamont Pass

   b. types of birds in California

   c. numbers of birds killed by the turbines

   d. other causes of death for endangered birds

7. Underline the sentence that is redundant in this conclusion.

8. Restate sentence 2 in a formal style.

   _____

   _____

9. What explanation would support the statement in sentence 3?

   _____

10. Punctuate the adjectives in sentence 4 correctly.

   _____

Assignment: On separate paper, provide a final draft of the essay you began on page 253. Use what you learned about punctuating adjectives and writing concisely and precisely. Think about how you and your classmates answered the Essential Question. Check your outline to be sure you organized your ideas well. End with a conclusion that follows from and supports your claim.

Introducing UNIT 11

The word *transformation* refers to some sort of major change. Transformations can be scientific, such as when a caterpillar turns into a butterfly, or they can be social, such as when a nation undergoes a revolution. In this unit, you're going to read about different kinds of world transformations.

Integrating what you know with your reading skills makes reading nonfiction texts much more pleasurable. One way to approach a nonfiction text is to see if there is an audio, video, or multimedia version of it so you can compare the two versions. Even when the text is the same, its meaning is affected by the medium, or method of communication, it is presented in. Some nonfiction texts offer arguments about a certain topic. In such cases, it is a good idea to read a text that offers the opposite point of view and then compare the arguments. Whichever side of the argument you are reading, always look to see if the writer has supported his or her claim with strong reasoning and evidence.

Progress Check *Can I?*

Before Unit 11 | **After Unit 11**

- [ ] Compare a text to an audio, video, or multimedia version of it. [ ]
- [ ] Evaluate an argument in terms of the soundness of the evidence that supports it. [ ]
- [ ] Analyze how two authors writing about the same topic emphasize different evidence. [ ]
- [ ] Identify an author's point of view, based on loaded language and the inclusion of particular facts. [ ]
- [ ] Integrate visual information with other information in a text. [ ]
- [ ] Distinguish among facts, opinions, and reasoned judgments. [ ]
- [ ] Determine the central ideas of a text. [ ]
- [ ] Use the relationship between words to help understand their meaning. [ ]

HOME ◆ CONNECT...

IN THIS UNIT, YOUR CHILD WILL...

- Compare a text to an audio or video version of it.

- Evaluate an argument or claim in terms of its evidence and reasoning.

- Analyze how two authors writing about the same topic emphasize different evidence in support of their claims.

- Identify loaded language and understand how it reveals an author's point of view.

- Integrate visual information with information in a text.

- Distinguish among facts, opinions, reasoned judgments, and speculation.

- Use word relationships to figure out the meaning of words.

NOTE: All of these learning goals for your child are based on the Grade 7 Common Core State Standards for English Language Arts.

Your child will likely understand that when someone gives a speech on television, the speech had to be written down first. A concept that may be new, however, is that a text's medium impacts its meaning. Ask your child how a **written text changes when it is delivered by a speaker**. To get started with the concept, ask how the words of a play change when actors act them out. Then talk about other kinds of texts that are performed or delivered, such as speeches.

Your child may have engaged in arguments with siblings or friends. Encourage him or her to talk about winning or losing arguments and what the outcome had to do with how well he or she **reasoned in support of his or her position**. When two people are arguing about something, each must present strong reasoning and evidence in order to convince the other.

When your child encounters an unfamiliar word, looking at other, **related words like synonyms or antonyms** can be helpful. Brainstorm pairs of synonyms and antonyms with your child. Talk about how related words help with understanding meaning.

WAYS TO HELP YOUR CHILD

Discuss with your child the difference among facts, opinions, and reasoned judgments. Explain that facts can be verified and that opinions are personal beliefs. Reasoned judgments are opinions supported by evidence. Offer examples of each from your personal life and then have your child do the same.

ONLINE

For more Home Connect activities, continue online at sadlierconnect.com

Activity: Play a game with your child in which you try to think of as many different kinds of transformations as possible. Encourage your child to think about changes that happen in science, history, and current events. Your child may also think about big changes in his or her own life—such as starting a new school or moving from one city to another.

Reading Informational Text: Integration of Knowledge and Ideas

Essential Question:
How can readers analyze texts presented in multiple formats?

Guided Instruction

RI.7.7, RH.7.8

WORDS TO KNOW

desolate

oratorical

sheer

tyranny

The **medium**, or form of communication, by which information is delivered can affect the meaning of the information itself.

CITE EVIDENCE

A **Media** are the means by which information is delivered. Public officials like presidents deliver information in a variety of media, such as audio, video, newspapers, and Internet sites. Place an asterisk by the word that tells you what medium this text is in.

B Texts will contain **facts**, which are true pieces of information that can be verified; **opinions**, which express personal beliefs; and **reasoned judgments**, which are opinions that are supported by evidence. Underline a fact that tells when D-Day occurred.

The 40th Anniversary of D-Day

Excerpt of remarks by President Ronald Reagan, June 6, 1984

(Genre: Speech)

1   We are here to mark that day in history when the Allied armies joined in battle to reclaim this continent to liberty. For four long years, much of Europe had been under a terrible shadow. Free nations had fallen, Jews cried out in the camps— millions cried out for liberation. Europe was enslaved, and the world prayed for its rescue. Here in Normandy the rescue began. Here the Allies stood and fought against **tyranny** in a giant undertaking unparalleled in human history.

2   We stand on a lonely, windswept point on the northern shore of France. The air is soft, but forty years ago at this moment, the air was dense with smoke and the cries of men, and the air was filled with the crack of rifle fire and the roar of cannon. At dawn, on the morning of the 6th of June, 1944, 225 Rangers jumped off the British landing craft and ran to the bottom of these cliffs. Their mission was one of the most difficult and daring of the invasion: to climb these **sheer** and **desolate** cliffs and take out the enemy guns. . . .

3   The Rangers looked up and saw the enemy soldiers at the edge of the cliffs shooting down at them with machine guns and throwing grenades. And the American Rangers began to climb . . . Soon, one by one, the Rangers pulled themselves over the top, and in seizing the firm land at the top of these cliffs, they began to seize back the continent of Europe. Two hundred and twenty-five came here. After 2 days of fighting, only 90 could still bear arms.

Reconsidering Reagan

Transcript of a television interview

(Genre: Reaction to a Speech)

1 **RON BLAKE, journalist:** Tonight my guest is presidential historian Nancy Busch Jameson, and she specializes in the presidency of Ronald Reagan. I want to begin with what may be Reagan's finest **oratorical** achievement: the speech he gave on the fortieth anniversary of D-Day. Let's watch a video clip.

(video clip of Reagan speaking)

2 **NANCY BUSCH JAMESON, historian:** Ron, I was actually at this speech in person and I remember feeling at the time that it was going to be a speech—and a delivery of a speech—for which Reagan would be long remembered.

3 But first, let's be clear: the speech works extremely well even if you just read it on paper. Reagan's gift for word choice is apparent; for example, he uses the word *prayed*, and that is such a Reagan-esque word, if you will. Reagan liked to evoke his religious faith during tough times.

4 Listening to the video, however, shows how he emphasized words effectively. A good example is the way he stressed *unparalleled*; his delivery of that word really communicates that what happened on D-Day was special and unique in history.

5 His phrasing is wonderful, too: he pauses slightly before he says "and the cries of men," which highlights the emotional meaning of that phrase.

Comprehension Check

How does Reagan's delivery of the speech affect the impact of the words? Cite some specifics from the interview.

CITE EVIDENCE

C Double underline a word in Reagan's speech that is effective both as written and as spoken, according to Nancy Busch Jameson.

D Circle a word and a phrase in the speech that Jameson mentions as examples of effects that one can get only from listening to Reagan's delivery.

E Box the aspects of Reagan's delivery mentioned in the interview that Jameson says are particularly effective. What other information could you get from watching a video of Reagan's speech?

The 40th Anniversary of D-Day *continued*

RH.7.6

WORDS TO KNOW

anecdote

bagpipes

buoyancy

valor

CITE EVIDENCE

A A speaker's point of view is revealed in a number of ways, one of which is the use of **loaded language**. Loaded language consists of words and phrases that have highly emotional connotations beyond their literal meanings. For example, the word *champions* in paragraph 5 has a connotation that these men were heroes. Circle a loaded word in paragraph 9 that has a connotation of "noble courage."

B Loaded language is often used to persuade an audience to feel a certain way about something. Put a box around a section of loaded language that is humorous but is meant to make the audience appreciate one soldier's remarkable modesty in the face of war.

4   Behind me is a memorial that symbolizes the Ranger daggers that were thrust into the top of these cliffs. And before me are the men who put them there.

5   These are the boys of Pointe du Hoc. These are the men who took the cliffs. These are the champions who helped free a continent. These are the heroes who helped end a war.

6   Gentlemen, I look at you and I think of the words of Stephen Spender's poem. You are men who in your "lives fought for life . . . and left the vivid air signed with your honor."

7   I think I know what you may be thinking right now—thinking "we were just part of a bigger effort; everyone was brave that day." Well, everyone was. Do you remember the story of Bill Millin of the 51st Highlanders? Forty years ago today, British troops were pinned down near a bridge, waiting desperately for help. Suddenly, they heard the sound of **bagpipes**, and some thought they were dreaming. Well, they weren't. They looked up and saw Bill Millin with his bagpipes, leading the reinforcements and ignoring the smack of the bullets into the ground around him.

8   Lord Lovat was with him—Lord Lovat of Scotland, who calmly announced when he got to the bridge, "Sorry I'm a few minutes late," as if he'd been delayed by a traffic jam, when in truth he'd just come from the bloody fighting on Sword Beach, which he and his men had just taken.

9   There was the impossible **valor** of the Poles who threw themselves between the enemy and the rest of Europe as the invasion took hold, and the unsurpassed courage of the Canadians who had already seen the horrors of war on this coast. They knew what awaited them there, but they would not be deterred. And once they hit Juno Beach, they never looked back. . . .

Reconsidering Reagan *continued*

RI.7.7, RH.7.6

6 **NANCY BUSCH JAMESON:** In the video clip of this section, we experience more of Reagan's oratorical skills.

7 The **anecdote** about Lord Lovat is classic Reagan; he had such a marvelous sense of humor and often peppered his speeches with it. And yet the humor is a device; it serves to make us chuckle but it also highlights a serious point about how these men maintained incredible humility in the face of extraordinary events. It's a section that reads just as well as it sounds, I might add.

8 I'm struck by Reagan's pace in the clip you just showed. He moves on steadily and never rushes. He had such a good touch; you feel the weight of what he's saying, yet there's a lightness and **buoyancy** as well. He's very listenable.

9 The physical setting of the speech is so effective, too. When Reagan speaks repeatedly of "these cliffs" and then you see the wind whipping around him with the English Channel in the background, the stories in the speech really come alive.

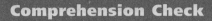

Comprehension Check

How does learning about the various aspects of Reagan's speech help you understand its meaning? Cite specifics from the interview as part of your answer.

CITE EVIDENCE

C Another way a speaker expresses a point of view is by **including—or omitting—particular facts about a topic**. For example, Reagan mentions the contributions of countries other than the United States. Find those nationalities in the speech and place an asterisk next to them. What does their inclusion tell you about Reagan's point of view of D-Day?

D Underline in Jameson's remarks the effects that one can get only from watching the video (or listening to the audio) of Reagan's delivery of the speech.

Guided Practice

RI.7.7, RH.7.6

WORDS TO KNOW

affinity

beachhead

devised

evoke

liberation

CITE EVIDENCE

A Reagan's use of the word *boys* in paragraph 10 is an example of loaded language. What is his purpose in using this word? Circle a phrase with a strong emotional connotation.

B Put a box around the loaded language in paragraph 13 that evokes a feeling of people living in small town America.

C Review what Jameson says on page 269 about patriotic symbols, and then underline a phrase in paragraph 13 that would have an impact in both written and spoken media. Then work with a partner and practice speaking this phrase out loud with different pace, phrasing, and emphasis.

The 40th Anniversary of D-Day *continued*

10   Forty summers have passed since the battle that you fought here. You were young the day you took these cliffs; some of you were hardly more than boys, with the deepest joys of life before you. Yet, you risked everything here. Why? Why did you do it? What impelled you to put aside the instinct for self-preservation and risk your lives to take these cliffs? What inspired all the men of the armies that met here? We look at you, and somehow we know the answer. It was faith and belief; it was loyalty and love.

11   The men of Normandy had faith that what they were doing was right, faith that they fought for all humanity, faith that a just God would grant them mercy on this **beachhead** or on the next. It was the deep knowledge—and pray God we have not lost it—that there is a profound, moral difference between the use of force for **liberation** and the use of force for conquest. You were here to liberate, not to conquer, and so you and those others did not doubt your cause. And you were right not to doubt.

12   You all knew that some things are worth dying for. One's country is worth dying for, and democracy is worth dying for, because it's the most deeply honorable form of government ever **devised** by man. All of you loved liberty. All of you were willing to fight tyranny, and you knew the people of your countries were behind you.

13   The Americans who fought here that morning knew word of the invasion was spreading through the darkness back home. They fought—or felt in their hearts, though they couldn't know in fact, that in Georgia they were filling the churches at 4 a.m., in Kansas they were kneeling on their porches and praying, and in Philadelphia they were ringing the Liberty Bell. . . .

10 **NANCY BUSCH JAMESON:** In this section, as before, Reagan **evokes** religion; however it's interesting to hear how he also weaves in the Liberty Bell. Reagan had a strong **affinity** for America's patriotic symbols, and here he connects one to religious images in a subtle but effective way.

11   Seeing the video of the speech after all these years also reminds me that Reagan's voice had a very natural gentleness to it, and that he rarely shouted or bellowed as some politicians do—he didn't need to!

Comprehension Check

1. Jameson mentions Reagan's gentle voice. In what medium would you NOT experience this aspect of his delivery?

   a. a video of his second inaugural address

   b. a sound clip from his first State of the Union address

   c. a poster from his 1984 reelection campaign

   d. a television interview with a journalist

2. What aspect of Reagan's delivery does Jameson mention in this section of her interview?

   a. volume

   b. pace

   c. body language

   d. humor

3. Which of the following is an opinion, and not a reasoned judgment, of Jameson's?

   a. Reagan did not need to shout.

   b. Reagan rarely shouted.

   c. Reagan's voice was gentle.

   d. Reagan had an affinity for patriotic symbols.

4. Which fact reinforces the religious theme in Reagan's speech?

   a. D-Day involved 156,000 Allied troops.

   b. A radio journalist broadcasted a D-Day report from the deck of a naval ship.

   c. More than 9,000 Allied soldiers died on the first day of the D-Day invasion.

   d. People in the United States attended church services on D-Day.

5. Why is it important to distinguish among facts, opinions, and reasoned judgments when you read about history? Consider the question with a partner and then tell why.

_____

_____

_____

_____

The 40th Anniversary of D-Day *continued*

RH.7.6

WORDS TO KNOW

daunting

forsake

reconciliation

vow

CITE EVIDENCE

A Circle in paragraph 15 a phrase made up of a list of loaded words. What is the connotation of the phrase? What is Reagan's purpose for including these particular words?

B Direct address is a powerful method of relating one's point of view to one's audience. Underline the sentences in paragraph 16 in which Reagan directly addresses his audience.

14 When the war was over, there were lives to be rebuilt and governments to be returned to the people. There were nations to be reborn. Above all, there was a new peace to be assured. These were huge and **daunting** tasks. But the Allies summoned strength from the faith, belief, loyalty, and love of those who fell here. They rebuilt a new Europe together.

15 There was first a great **reconciliation** among those who had been enemies, all of whom had suffered so greatly. The United States did its part, creating the Marshall Plan to help rebuild our allies and our former enemies. The Marshall Plan led to the Atlantic alliance—a great alliance that serves to this day as our shield for freedom, for prosperity, and for peace. . . .

16 We are bound today by what bound us 40 years ago, the same loyalties, traditions, and beliefs. We're bound by reality. The strength of America's allies is vital to the United States, and the American security guarantee is essential to the continued freedom of Europe's democracies. We were with you then; we are with you now. Your hopes are our hopes, and your destiny is our destiny.

17 Here, in this place where the West held together, let us make a **vow** to our dead. Let us show them by our actions that we understand what they died for. Let our actions say to them the words for which [U.S. Army general] Matthew Ridgway listened: "I will not fail thee nor **forsake** thee."

18 Strengthened by their courage, heartened by their [valor], and borne by their memory, let us continue to stand for the ideals for which they lived and died.

19 Thank you very much, and God bless you all.

12 **NANCY BUSCH JAMESON:** Here we get a few good examples of how Reagan used lists of loaded words to great effect. As I was listening to him pause slightly between each of the words "faith, belief, loyalty, and love" when describing what the Allies leaned on for support, I thought, I love how Reagan does that! He also uses repetition very effectively in this section; he repeats words and phrases for emphasis. This entire speech demonstrates that Reagan was a great communicator.

Comprehension Check   (MORE ONLINE) **sadlierconnect.com**

1. Which phrase from the speech is NOT an example of Reagan's use of repetition?

   a. "We were with you then; we are with you now."

   b. "Your hopes are our hopes, and your destiny is our destiny."

   c. "The United States did its part, creating the Marshall Plan."

   d. "We are bound today by what bound us 40 years ago . . . We're bound by reality."

2. Which statement expresses a reasoned judgment by Jameson?

   a. Ronald Reagan was a great communicator.

   b. In the speech, Reagan often repeats words.

   c. She loves how Reagan pauses slightly.

   d. Reagan uses lists of loaded words.

3. Which of the following can be experienced only by watching or listening to the speech?

   a. Reagan's use of repetition

   b. Reagan's pausing between lists of words

   c. Reagan's making references to religion

   d. Reagan's use of loaded language

4. Which fact is excluded from this part of Reagan's speech?

   a. The United States created the Marshall Plan.

   b. The Marshall Plan led to the Atlantic alliance.

   c. The Atlantic alliance was in effect 40 years after D-Day.

   d. The former Soviet Union was strongly opposed to the Marshall Plan.

5. Analyze the effectiveness of Reagan's words in both written and spoken media. In what way do the words work solely on the page? What does Reagan's oral delivery add to them? Is one more effective than the other? Cite specifics from the text.

   _____

   _____

   _____

   _____

Guided Instruction

RI.7.8, RST.7.8

WORDS TO KNOW

deforestation

forestry

hectare

renewable resource

timber

When a writer is making an argument, you should look for **sound reasoning**, as well as **specific evidence that offers support** for the writer's claim.

CITE EVIDENCE

A   A piece of writing that offers an argument should **state a specific claim** plainly and clearly. Put an asterisk next to the sentence that contains Alvarado's specific argument.

B   Writers who are making arguments will provide **facts** to support their claims. A fact is a true piece of information that can be verified. Underline in paragraph 2 an economic fact that supports the claim that forest industries are vital to many.

What Forests Offer Us

By Ricardo Z. Alvarado, MS in Forestry

http://www.futureofforestry.net/What_Forests_Offer_Us/index.html

(Genre: Web article/opinion piece)

1   Amidst all the talk of how damaging **deforestation** is to the environment, there are few voices speaking out in favor of the practice. I am posting this article because I believe that the clearing of forested land, despite its drawbacks, is actually a "necessary evil." Earth's forests provide land, resources, and jobs upon which millions of people all over the world depend every day.

2   To begin with, forest-related industries employ 60 million people, according to United Nations estimates. These include **forestry**, which is the management of forests, as well as the logging, timber, and paper industries. Every year, nearly $300 billion in forest products are traded around the world. The economic livelihood of many poor communities depends heavily on forest resources. Combating deforestation endangers these communities.

Logging

3   The logging industry involves cutting down trees and turning them into usable **timber**. Timber is an important raw material used to build homes and buildings. Wood is also a significant energy source; in rural societies, it is burned for heat and to cook food. Wood is of course also used to make paper. Trees must be cut down in order for them to be used.

4   The logging industry has shown a commitment to what is termed "selective logging," which is the cutting down of only selected trees. In this way, entire forests are not decimated—only the most desirable trees are harvested. It is also important to note that

trees are a **renewable resource**, which means they can be replanted and grown back. In recent years, many countries have engaged in the practice of large-scale tree replanting. This practice has resulted in a drop in the number of **hectares** of forest being lost every year, according to a United Nations study.

Cattle Ranching

5   When forested land is deliberately cleared, it is usually for an important reason. One such reason is for cattle ranching. In the rural areas of many countries, the raising of cattle for meat is a vitally important economic practice. Raising cattle requires many acres of land on which the cattle may roam, and so the felling of trees is sometimes necessary.

6   In Brazil—a country with a population of 200 million—cattle ranching is essential to the economy. Brazil is the world's largest producer and exporter of beef, which accounts for an important portion of its annual exports of $242 billion. Brazil's impressive cattle ranches, located in sections of cleared Amazon rainforest, are spread out over 283,000 square miles. Cutting down areas of the Brazilian rainforest in order to support Brazil's cattle-ranching industry is entirely justified. In fact, since 2003, Brazil's economy has boomed, thanks in large part to the growth of its beef cattle industry.

Agriculture

7   For many countries, agriculture also depends on clearing forested land. For example, in El Salvador, coffee is an important crop grown on land that was previously forested. Thousands of hectares of "coffee forests" are used to produce this important crop and employ many people. A full ten percent of El Salvador's economy is agriculture. Coffee is important to the economies of many Central American countries; some 2.5 million acres of Central American forest has been cleared for coffee farming. It is an important use of deforested land.

Comprehension Check

Evaluate Alvarado's claim that deforestation is a "necessary evil." Explain your position by citing specific evidence from the opinion piece.

CITE EVIDENCE

C   Writers also include their own **opinions** about the subject. An opinion is a personal belief about a topic that is not supported by sound reasoning or substantial evidence. Circle in paragraph 6 a word that expresses Alvarado's opinion about Brazil's cattle ranches.

D   An opinion that is supported by substantial evidence is called a **reasoned judgment**. Find a sentence in paragraph 6 that offers reasoning for the assertion that cattle ranching is an important part of Brazil's economy and double underline it.

E   As you read an argument, assess whether the writer is using **sound reasoning** and **relevant evidence**. In paragraph 7, there is one sentence that is not relevant to the claim that growing coffee is important and depends on clearing forested land. Draw a box around it. What would be a more relevant fact in this case?

RI.7.8, RST.7.8

WORDS TO KNOW

biofuel

plantation

processed food

sustainable

CITE EVIDENCE

A Draw an asterisk next to the sentence that offers sound evidence for the assertion that slash-and-burn practices provide environmental benefits.

B Circle the word in paragraph 13 that reveals the writer's claim about processed foods that use palm oil. Then explain why that entire sentence is actually offering a fact.

What Forests Offer Us *continued*

Benefits of Slash-and-Burn

8   A discussion of the use of deforested land to raise crops is a good opportunity to raise the controversial issue of clearing forests by a method called slash-and-burn.

9   In slash-and-burn, trees are cut down and then burned where they lie on the forest floor. While this may sound like a harsh practice, it is actually full of environmental benefits. Studies have shown that the ash left behind by the burned trees is an excellent fertilizer. The soil actually benefits from slashing-and-burning.

Palm Oil

10   Previously, I mentioned that many countries participate in large-scale reforestation. Some places actually replace the old trees with different kinds—specific types of trees that provide important economic benefits.

11   In countries like Malaysia and Indonesia, rainforests are being cleared to plant palm trees from which palm oil is then harvested. Palm oil has emerged as one of the world's most important **biofuels**. A biofuel is any fuel that is created from a renewable biological resource. Palm oil is an exciting alternative to fossil fuels. For example, it is being used to run electric plants in Europe.

12   The economies of Malaysia and Indonesia have boomed ever since they concentrated on growing palm trees for the purpose of producing and exporting palm oil. In a sense, it's an environmental trade-off: the clearing of rainforests is compensated by the creation of a clean energy source (palm oil) that reduces dependence on fossil fuels like oil and coal.

RI.7.8, RST.7.8

13   Furthermore, palm oil is an important part of our daily life, though you may not realize it. It is found in many delicious **processed foods** like potato chips, bread, mayonnaise, and ice cream. It is also used in soap, detergent, and paint. Cutting down trees and replacing them with palm trees is a logical practice.

Rubber Trees

14   It's worth mentioning that rubber trees are also big business in many countries. Their development requires the clearing of forested land. The economies of Indonesia, Malaysia, and Thailand all depend on the production of rubber, which is tapped from rubber trees on huge **plantations**. One rubber tree can produce as much as 30 pounds of rubber in one year. As the world's demand for rubber products such as automobile tires increases, these countries feel the benefit.

15   Leading manufacturers all over the world are doing their best to make the production of oil and rubber more **sustainable**. In many countries, these efforts are paying off tremendously. Indonesia, for example, has seen a steep drop in its rate of deforestation in the last 20 years.

Building Boom

16   An obvious reason to deforest land is to build homes and communities for people to live in. While critics have applied the term *urban sprawl* to describe the rapid growth of cities, there are benefits to living in cities and many reasons to encourage their continued expansion.

17   When people's standard of living goes up, they can afford to own their own homes. Further, they often want to move out of the city center and build larger domiciles. This desire for increased living space is legitimate. The clearing of forested areas for the purpose of developing larger homes and residential areas should be encouraged.

Comprehension Check

Does Alvarado cite relevant evidence on pages 274 and 275 to support his overall argument that deforestation is necessary? Offer specifics in your answer.

CITE EVIDENCE

C Box the sentence in paragraph 15 that expresses an opinion that is not supported by any evidence.

D Double underline the sentence in paragraph 15 that expresses a reasoned judgment that is supported by the sentence that immediately follows it.

E Read the last sentence of paragraph 17 and circle the sentence if it is an unsupported opinion. If it demonstrates reasoned judgment, double underline it. Explain your answer.

A woman taps a rubber tree.

EVALUATING ARGUMENTS

Guided Practice

RI.7.8, RST.7.8

WORDS TO KNOW

generate

hydroelectric dam

water cycle

watt

CITE EVIDENCE

A Draw an asterisk next to the sentence on this page that clearly states the writer's claim for this section of the text.

B Underline in paragraph 19 the sentence that expresses a reasoned judgment about building hydroelectric dams. Then discuss with a partner how paragraph 19 would have to be different in order for this sentence to be an opinion.

Hydroelectric Dams

18   I've already cited a number of ways in which the clearing of forested lands is often necessary to improve the lives of the people that exist there. Another example of this is the building of **hydroelectric dams**, which often requires deforestation.

19   A hydroelectric dam harnesses the incredible power of a raging river and turns it into electricity that can be used by local communities to improve their daily lives. A hydroelectric dam takes advantage of another renewable process—the **water cycle**. When water evaporates, rises, condenses, and then falls as rain, the power supply of a hydroelectric dam is replenished. In this way, hydroelectric dams are environmentally friendly.

20   The building of a hydroelectric dam often requires the clearing—and then flooding—of large areas of forest. The benefits far outweigh the negatives of this practice, however. One example of this is the Three Gorges Dam in China, the world's largest hydroelectric power plant. It is still being completed, but at its peak it will **generate** more than a billion **watts** of power. Not only will millions of people in China have access to affordable energy because of the dam, those same people will be provided with a supply of clean water. Furthermore, the construction of the dam is employing some 250,000 people.

Mining

21   Another practice that concerns opponents of deforestation is mining, because building a mine typically necessitates the removal of many acres of forest. However, the benefits of mining cannot be overlooked. Some might object to the difficult working conditions, but the mining industry employs millions of people all over the world, including 80,000 people in the United States.

22   Mining is also very important to the economies of many South American nations, almost all of which are rich in mineral deposits. Selling mined metals such as gold, silver, copper, tin, and zinc generates significant revenue that can be spent on public works projects like road building.

23   In the United States, the mining of coal is absolutely vital to coal-rich states like West Virginia and Kentucky. With half of the country's electricity generated from the burning of coal, coal mining must continue despite its effect on forests.

Comprehension Check

1. Which of the following ideas from the text expresses an opinion?

    a. Coal mining must continue, despite what it does to forests.

    b. Many South American countries are rich in mineral deposits.

    c. Half the electricity used in the United States is generated from burning coal.

    d. Mining employs millions of people.

2. Which idea from the text does NOT support the claim that the benefits of clearing forests to build the Three Gorges Dam outweigh the negatives?

    a. The dam will generate billions of watts of power.

    b. The dam will supply clean water.

    c. The dam has created thousands of jobs.

    d. The forest was dying out anyway.

3. Which of the following expresses a fact related to hydroelectric dams?

    a. The power of a raging river is incredible.

    b. Hydroelectric dams are environmentally friendly.

    c. Building a hydroelectric dam often requires clearing forested land.

    d. Building hydroelectric dams improves people's daily lives.

4. Based on the text, which of the following is a reasoned judgment about mining?

    a. Selling mined metals generates revenue.

    b. Coal mining must continue, despite what it does to forests.

    c. Mining revenue can be spent on public works projects.

    d. Coal mining is vital to states like Kentucky.

5. Work with a partner to find examples of facts, opinions, and reasoned judgments on pages 276 and 277. Then explain how identifying facts, opinions, and judgments helps you understand the central claim of the entire article.

_____

_____

_____

_____

_____

_____

Independent Practice

RI.7.8, RST.7.8

WORDS TO KNOW

decimation

erosion

primary forest

secondary forest

CITE EVIDENCE

A What specific claim do the details in paragraphs 25 and 26 support? Draw an asterisk next to the sentence that contains the claim.

B Underline a reasoned judgment the writer makes regarding governmental efforts to fight deforestation. What relevant evidence does the writer offer in support?

Reforestation

24   Despite the efforts of anti-deforestation groups to vilify any company that clears forests as part of its development, the truth is that reforestation is alive and well among many companies.

25   One company that has emerged as a leader in reforestation is Nestlé, which is famous for its chocolate but also manufactures baby food, bottled water, and coffee, among other products. As part of its Creating Shared Value initiative, Nestlé is reforesting areas that have been affected by the production of their food products (coffee and chocolate, especially).

26   In 2011, Nestlé announced a plan to plant 750,000 trees in Malaysia, 100,000 of which would be planted in the first year alone. When all the trees are planted, they will cover an astonishing 2,400 hectares of land.

Government Efforts

27   The governments of many countries whose economies rely on deforested land are making a positive difference as well. For example, in Indonesia, the government planted an incredible 79 million trees in 2007. In Brazil, the government is working with international environmental organizations to slow the rate of deforestation. The work is producing results, too; the rate of deforestation in that country has fallen since 1990. A national law was passed in 2012 that will protect Brazilian forests from **decimation**.

Exotic Trees

28   One reforestation practice that has shown positive results is the planting of exotic trees like eucalyptus trees. Eucalyptus grows quickly and can efficiently replenish the soil with needed nutrients. Also, the quicker replacement trees grow, the better the fight against soil **erosion**.

Secondary Forests

29   In addition to human-driven reforestation efforts, Mother Nature rejuvenates herself by growing **secondary forests**. Secondary forests grow back after a catastrophic event, like a forest fire or flood. A **primary forest**, then, is an original forest that has remained largely untouched by humans.

278

RI.7.8

Conclusion

30   No one, including me, denies that deforestation is an environmental problem. It may even be a crisis. Yet let's not completely lose perspective as we tackle this issue. Most of the time, forested land is cleared for important economic reasons. I can only restate my claim even more strongly: deforestation may be an evil, but it is necessary.

Comprehension Check   MORE ONLINE sadlierconnect.com

1. Based on the text, which is NOT true about eucalyptus trees?

   a. Eucalyptus grows quickly.

   b. Planting eucalyptus does not impact the effects of deforestation.

   c. Eucalyptus replenishes the soil with essential nutrients.

   d. Planting eucalyptus helps combat soil erosion.

2. What claim does the section on secondary forests support?

   a. There are a number of ways that deforestation is being slowed.

   b. Deforestation is a serious crisis.

   c. Many companies are concerned about deforestation.

   d. World governments are ignoring the issue of deforestation.

3. Which idea from the text expresses an opinion, as opposed to a reasoned judgment or a fact?

   a. Deforestation may be evil, but it is necessary.

   b. Reforestation is alive and well among many companies.

   c. Deforestation may even be a crisis.

   d. Secondary forests grow back after a catastrophic event.

4. Which detail described in the text is irrelevant to the writer's central claim about deforestation?

   a. Most of the time, forested land is cleared for important economic reasons.

   b. A primary forest is an original, untouched forest.

   c. Deforestation may be a crisis.

   d. Many companies are engaged in reforestation.

5. Is Alvarado's claim that the benefits of deforestation outweigh its drawbacks a reasoned judgment? Explain your answer with specifics from the text.

   _____

   _____

   _____

   _____

Guided Instruction

RI.7.9, RST.7.2

WORDS TO KNOW

forest canopy

refute

restraint

unassailable

A writer expressing an opinion different from another writer's on the same topic will offer **different evidence** and **interpret the same facts differently**.

CITE EVIDENCE

A A writer's central idea is often found in the first few paragraphs. Draw an asterisk next to the sentence in paragraph 3 that expresses Nguyen's central idea.

B In offering a different opinion on deforestation, Nguyen **interprets facts differently.** Underline in paragraph 8 a point that Alvarado stated that Nguyen challenges.

Save the World's Forests
By Karen X. Nguyen, Ph.D.
(**Genre**: Scientific Text/Opinion Piece)

1   I have read Ricardo Alvarado's opinion piece on deforestation and I am stunned, outraged, and deeply concerned. Mr. Alvarado points out that the world depends on forests in a variety of ways, but that does not mean that deforestation should be allowed to go on without **restraint**.

2   Mr. Alvarado has a habit of peppering his piece with tidy, **unassailable** truths that sound nice but ignore deeper environmental issues. For example, he says that "trees must be cut down in order for them to be used." This is hardly a disputable fact, but what about deforestation's impact?

3   I will take Mr. Alvarado's claims point by point and **refute** his argument that deforestation is a "necessary evil." Deforestation is wreaking havoc on our environment, and it must be controlled.

Logging

4   Mr. Alvarado's defense of the logging industry involves a discussion of "selective logging." He infers that this practice saves trees. In fact, the opposite is true. "Selective logging" does refer to felling only the most valuable trees, but when these trees are cut down, they usually fall on other trees and bring those down with them.

5   Logging also destroys the **forest canopy**, the protective layer formed by very tall trees that prevents sunlight from hitting the forest floor. The forest canopy keeps the soil moist and the

temperature of the forest cool. Entire species of plants and insects that thrive in cool, moist conditions have been wiped out because forest canopies have been eliminated. The forest canopy also prevents soil erosion by protecting the forest floor from torrential rains.

6   Not only is the cutting down of trees harmful to forests, but logging requires heavy machinery and trucks that crush plants and animals when they drive over the forest floor.

7   Alvarado's solution to the impact of logging is weak. He suggests replanting trees as a way of replenishing lost forests. He neglects to mention that it takes a very, very long time for a forest to grow back to its previous fullness. Reforestation is not a complete solution.

8   Alvarado reports that deforestation is down in some places because "many countries have engaged in the practice of large-scale replanting of trees." Yet the United Nations study he cites shows that overall we are still losing the battle, particularly in South America and Africa. Reforestation will never make a serious dent in the problem of deforestation.

Cattle and Crops

9   Mr. Alvarado's discussion of farmers' and cattle ranchers' need for cleared land makes logical sense, but again, he avoids any of the real impact on forests.

10   To begin with, the practice of slash-and-burn is harmful, not helpful, to forests. Despite his claims about tree ash, clearing forested land in this way leaves thousands of acres of un-farmable, barren land. The soil left behind after burning a forest soon becomes devoid of nutrients.

11   The cleared land is also susceptible to flooding. The trees that had acted as a barrier to storm surges and heavy rains are removed. Small coastal villages in particular have felt the impact of deforestation in this way.

Comprehension Check

How does Nguyen use evidence that differs from Alvarado's to shape her argument thus far? Cite specifics in your answer.

CITE EVIDENCE

C Nguyen is putting forth a different viewpoint and offers opinions that are different from those of Alvarado. In paragraph 7, box in Nguyen's opinion about reforestation. Then give a summary of her point of view of what logging does to forests.

D You have learned about facts, opinions, and reasoned judgments. **Speculation** is an unsupported conclusion reached by merely guessing. Find the speculation in paragraph 8 and circle it.

E Writers with different viewpoints will also offer and **emphasize different evidence** on a topic to support their opinions. Find in paragraph 10 the evidence about slash-and-burn that Alvarado did not offer and double underline it.

Guided Instruction

Save the World's Forests *continued*

RI.7.9, RH.7.7

WORDS TO KNOW

archipelago

fertilizer

indigenous

peat

subsidizing

CITE EVIDENCE

A Writers may introduce **visual information** that can be integrated into information presented in the text. On the map, find the islands of Borneo and Sumatra and circle them. Then underline in paragraph 13 a fact about these two islands. Then tell how the map supports what the text states about Borneo and Sumatra.

B In paragraph 14, place an asterisk beside the evidence Nguyen offers about the usefulness of palm oil that differs from Alvarado's statement.

Case Study: Indonesia

12 One of the countries Mr. Alvarado cites as a beneficiary of clearing forested land is Indonesia. Indonesia is an **archipelago** in Southeast Asia. It is home to more than 251 million people. While much of what Mr. Alvarado says about Indonesia is true—that its economy has benefitted from increased production of palm oil and rubber—he conveniently leaves out the negative impact the palm oil and rubber industries have had on the environment.

13 The rainforests of Indonesia have been cleared for the planting of palm and rubber trees; this is a fact Mr. Alvarado himself offers in his article. What he neglects to mention is that in 2007, the United Nations Environment Program warned that two of Indonesia's islands, Borneo and Sumatra, could see 98% of their rainforests destroyed by 2022.

14 Mr. Alvarado's emphasis on the utility of palm oil (it "is an important part of our daily life," he writes) is also misleading. It is precisely because so many manufacturers use palm oil to make their products (ice cream, detergent, and so forth) that the clearing of forested land continues.

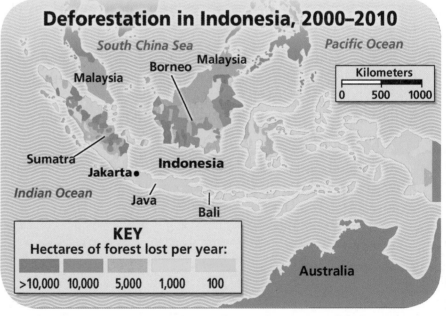

Deforestation in Indonesia, 2000–2010

KEY
Hectares of forest lost per year:
>10,000   10,000   5,000   1,000   100

A Dangerous Alternative

15   Mr. Alvarado's praise of palm oil as a biofuel is misguided. It's true that palm oil is used as an alternative to fossil fuels, but it presents its own environmental dangers.

16   In Indonesia and Malaysia, much of the land that is cleared to grow palm plantations is peatland. **Peat** is a dark, rich material made up of decayed organisms and is usually added to soil to make it more nutritious. Peatland is 90% water, and when it is drained (or burned), carbon is released into the air. Carbon emissions are the cause of global warming. By 2007, Indonesia was the third-leading producer of carbon emissions in the world.

17   Because of these emissions, many countries have decided to stop **subsidizing**, or helping to pay for, the development of palm oil as an energy alternative. Still others are considering an outright ban on the use of palm oil as a biofuel.

18   Another detail of palm oil deforestation Mr. Alvarado leaves out has to do with the harsh chemical **fertilizers** used to grow the palm trees. These fertilizers damage the surrounding environment. Palm oil has been called an "ecological disaster," and I agree.

Displacing Native People

19   An underreported side effect of deforestation is the displacement of **indigenous** people who live in forests. Very often, indigenous people have no legal ownership of the land they live on. Governments and big corporations can—and do—simply push people off their land and raze it. Displacing indigenous people from their native environment does unimaginable damage to their culture.

Comprehension Check

How does the map that shows deforestation in Indonesia support your overall comprehension of the topic? Explain your answer.

CITE EVIDENCE

C Underline the sentences in paragraph 16 that demonstrate Nguyen's different interpretation of the fact that palm oil is an alternative to fossil fuels.

D Double underline in paragraph 18 the sentence that expresses Nguyen's reasoned judgment about palm oil.

E You should use your own **personal experience**, as well as what you know about **language and culture**, to think analytically. Draw a box around the paragraph on page 283 that deals with a cultural aspect of the problem of deforestation. Then offer in your own words an argument against deforestation from a cultural perspective.

Guided Practice

Save the World's Forests *continued*

Dams and Mines

RI.7.9

WORDS TO KNOW

gaudy

gloss over

marvel

permit

CITE EVIDENCE

A Underline in paragraph 21 a sentence or phrase that shows that Nguyen is interpreting differently the fact that building a dam requires deforestation.

B What new piece of evidence regarding mining does Nguyen introduce in paragraph 23? Box it and tell how it strengthens or weakens her overall argument about deforestation.

20   Mr. Alvarado's section on hydroelectric dams is interesting, for while he sings their praises as mechanical **marvels** that transform communities—and they are—he conveniently **glosses over** their negative impact.

21   First, he does admit that a hydroelectric dam requires deforestation. When this happens, however, it is common for local populations to be displaced, for their land is needed for the construction of the dam. Second, the construction of a dam requires heavy machinery that damages what land remains. A dam also brings additional roads, which means more cars, which equals pollution. Deforesting land for dams also means loggers using bulldozers and tree cutters.

22   I was impressed that Mr. Alvarado mentioned that sometimes forested land is flooded, rather than cleared, before a dam is built. However, he left out the fact that the flood water can interact with the soil and release harmful gases into the air. He cites a dam's employment of the water cycle as evidence that dams are environmentally friendly. The truth is that they are not.

23   Mining is another industry that Mr. Alvarado is quick to praise. Mining, however, demands extensive deforestation. Indeed, it is not unusual for entire forests to be removed. In 2008, the government of Venezuela courageously denied a **permit** to a huge mining company, Crystallex International Corp., because of "sensitivities surrounding indigenous peoples . . . and the environment." Had it been allowed to go forward, the company would have built the largest gold and copper mines in Venezuela.

An iron mine in Venezuela

Urban Sprawl

24   What Mr. Alvarado wrote about the relationship between deforestation and urban sprawl is a good example of his shortsightedness. Mr. Alvarado appears to believe that the desire to live in big, **gaudy** homes is more important than preserving the forest habitats of plants, animals, and insects. Depressingly, deforestation has no hope of decreasing in the coming years.

Comprehension Check

1. Nguyen's central idea about dams is

   a. they impact communities in negative ways as well as positive ways.

   b. they are worthy of Alvarado's praise because of their environmental impact.

   c. they are not worth building.

   d. they provide people with jobs.

2. Which of the following pieces of visual information would be most relevant to this section?

   a. a deforestation map of Venezuela

   b. a technical diagram showing how a hydroelectric dam is constructed

   c. a chart comparing a city's population with the rate of deforestation

   d. a photograph of the president of Crystallex International Corporation

3. Which key fact is NOT emphasized by either writer?

   a. Building hydroelectric dams requires deforestation.

   b. Before a dam is built, sometimes the forested land is flooded.

   c. During the building of a dam, local people are displaced.

   d. Hydroelectric dams are mechanical marvels.

4. Which is an example of speculation?

   a. Deforestation has no hope of decreasing in the coming years.

   b. Crystallex would have built the largest gold and copper mines in Venezuela.

   c. The construction of a dam requires heavy machinery.

   d. Dams are environmentally friendly.

5. Work with a partner and tell how comparing and contrasting the two writers' claims helps you better understand the topic of deforestation.

_____

_____

_____

_____

Independent Practice

Save the World's Forests *continued*

RI.7.9, RST.7.8

Global Warming

25 My argument is rooted in one central fact: deforestation contributes to global warming. Global warming is the gradual warming of the Earth's temperature due to the release of **greenhouse gases** into the atmosphere. Greenhouse gases are generated by the burning of carbon-based fossil fuels like coal and oil. When they are present in the atmosphere, the surface temperature of the Earth warms. Warmer temperatures cause rising sea levels, changing weather patterns, and many other effects.

26 Earth's forests are a **combatant** to global warming. Trees absorb carbon dioxide, which is a greenhouse gas. If trees are cut down and carbon dioxide is not absorbed, it stays in the air and contributes to global warming.

27 Scientists track the amount of carbon dioxide in the atmosphere by looking at **carbon footprints**. A carbon footprint is the amount of carbon dioxide released into the atmosphere by a population, a place, or an event. Just as we make footprints in wet sand, we make a carbon footprint on the environment when we use carbon-based energy sources. It is estimated that the carbon footprint of four years of deforestation is about the same as the combined carbon footprint of every airplane since those machines were invented—running up until the year 2025! That is an enormous amount of carbon, and it accelerates global warming.

Biodiversity

28 The environmental impact of deforestation does not stop with global warming. Cutting down a rainforest, for example, severely impacts **biodiversity**. It is estimated that nearly half of all plant and animal species exist in rainforests. In addition to fighting the threat of extinction, rainforest life forms are worth protecting because they hold medicinal properties and may help cure disease.

WORDS TO KNOW

biodiversity

carbon footprint

combatant

greenhouse gases

CITE EVIDENCE

A Find the central fact that Nguyen is offering in this section and underline it. Is it truly a fact, or is it a reasoned judgment? Explain your answer.

B Circle a word in Nguyen's conclusion that shows that she and Alvarado agree on one aspect of deforestation. Then tell how her interpretation of this fact departs from Alvarado's.

Conclusion

29   Mr. Alvarado argues that deforestation is a "necessary evil" because there are so many human activities that need it in order to succeed. I don't dispute the latter point; however, he omits the downside of deforestation. I've attempted to address it in this article, and I hope the reader will come to agree that deforestation is in fact an evil that is unnecessary.

Comprehension Check   (MORE ONLINE) **sadlierconnect.com**

1. Which evidence emphasized by Nguyen in this section is mentioned by Alvarado in his opinion piece?

    a. Deforestation impacts Earth's biodiversity.

    b. Many human activities require the clearing of forested land.

    c. Deforestation is one of the major culprits of global warming.

    d. Earth's forests combat global warming.

2. Choose the answer that best describes this sentence: *The environmental impact of deforestation does not stop with global warming.*

    a. fact

    b. opinion

    c. reasoned judgment

    d. speculation

3. Which does NOT support Nguyen's reasoned judgment that rainforests are worth saving?

    a. Rainforests are a source of biodiversity.

    b. Animal and plant species living in rainforests face extinction.

    c. Rainforest land has rich, farmable soil.

    d. Rainforest life forms may hold the cure to diseases.

4. Which visual element would be most helpful in explaining carbon footprints?

    a. a photograph of a human footprint

    b. a film showing real-time carbon emissions

    c. a map of Brazil

    d. a product label that estimates that product's carbon footprint

5. Review Alvarado's concluding paragraph on page 279, and summarize how it differs from Nguyen's conclusion on this page.

    _____

    _____

    _____

    _____

    _____

Deeply Flawed Book

(Genre: Letter to the Editor)

Dear Editor:

1   I was surprised to read in your last issue Marc Sargent's positive review of *Dark Wyoming*, Melissa Christensen's new book about the Johnson County War. I was surprised because the book is not only full of historical errors, but it conjures up a feeling of sympathy for the rich cattle barons of the era that is very misplaced.

2   There has been some very fine recent scholarship about the Johnson County War that Ms. Christensen seems to have missed. Court records, government documents, and contemporary newspaper accounts reveal that the powerful Wyoming cattle barons were not justified in their attack on the local cattlemen of Johnson County. Ms. Christensen's book, however, suggests that they were.

3   I teach a course on the range wars of the American West as part of my curriculum at Beaver Creek Community College, and I feel compelled to correct Ms. Christensen's mistakes.

4   Ms. Christensen devotes the first part of her book to setting the stage for the events of the war. From her point of view, the all-powerful cattle ranchers who raised herds of cattle on huge tracts of land were victims of widespread cattle theft, especially in Johnson County. The cattlemen complained that local authorities were not doing their job sufficiently and that they had no choice but to take matters into their own hands and pursue the thieves.

5   In fact, Johnson County was largely made up of small ranch owners who were doing their utmost to survive. The big cattlemen had overstocked their ranches, creating a supply of steer that market demand could simply not keep up with. The price of beef dropped, and no one was more hurt by this than the small cattle ranchers. Ms. Christensen does not draw this conclusion in her book. She fails to incorporate the experience of the small ranchers into her narrative.

6   When the large cattle barons decided to take matters into their own hands in 1891, they went after a number of suspected thieves, including a man named Nate Champion. Champion allowed his cattle to roam and graze on public land alongside the cattle of the big barons. He was within his legal right to do so, but the barons did not like it. Christensen reports that a local

newspaper began running negative stories about Champion, but she does not include the fact that the newspaper was controlled by the cattle barons. In the book, Champion comes off as a guilty party, when in fact, technically he was not.

7   By this point, the cattle barons, organized under a group called the Wyoming Stock Growers Association, had decided to make Champion their number-one target. They organized a group of men to assassinate Champion. The assassination squad engaged Champion at the small cabin in which he lived. Champion fought back and one of the assassins was killed.

8   Christensen's description of the scene in the cabin is a thrilling read, but I doubt the accuracy of her facts. Some details she simply gets wrong. For example, Champion did not have a beard. Other details cannot be verified—like the color of Champion's boots.

9   Furthermore, Christensen's book, which is being advertised as nonfiction, transforms into a work of historical fiction at this point. I appreciate her effort to make the confrontation in Champion's cabin dramatic, but I could do with less excitation and more finely researched storytelling.

10   Another member of the squad was soon captured after the Champion incident. This man told two local ranchers the names of the other members of the group. The big cattle barons were frightened. These two witnesses had enough information to link the barons to the assassination squad. They could be arrested, thrown in jail, or worse.

11   The two witnesses ended up being killed at the hands of the assassination squad, and the people of Johnson County were outraged. The strongest evidence of their indignation were stories that ran in newspapers friendly to the small ranchers. Again, Christensen has no mention of these reports.

12   Christensen transforms her book yet again at this moment in the story; the trial against Champion's would-be killer feels like a scene out of the movies. Christensen's language is full of detail; we know everything from the size of the courtroom to the type of wood used to construct the judge's bench (mahogany).

13   But despite the addition of all these flourishes, she misses some major points. First, the accused man was named Joe Elliott, not John Elliott. Second, Elliott worked as a detective for the Wyoming Stock Growers Association. That directly linked him to the big cattle barons. She somehow missed this key point in her research, for she strongly implies that the barons and Elliott were disjoined.

14   Her story gets back on track as an invading gang of cattle barons and their men headed straight from the capital city of Cheyenne into Johnson County. Upon receiving intelligence that a group of local ranchers—including Champion—were located nearby, the invaders decided to attack.

Deeply Flawed Book *continued*

15 Champion was with a friend when the invaders reached his cabin. After his friend was killed, Champion held off the invaders until he was forced from his cabin and struck down. Local citizens arrived in a fury and surrounded the cabin to which the cattle barons' gang had fled. So began a three-day siege. This was the height of the Johnson County War.

16 The war was not active. The citizen's posse spent most of the three days in a tense state of surveillance. Before they could make their move, however, federal soldiers arrived. The governor had appealed to President Benjamin Harrison himself for help.

17 Christensen is not up to speed with current scholarship yet again. She writes that the governor was ignorant of the situation, but in fact he knew exactly what was happening and was sympathetic to the encircled cattle barons.

18 Christensen gets the main fact related to the resolution of the war correct, but she fumbles the political intrigue that followed. The federal troops arrested the invaders. The governor was not about to let accusations against big cattle barons go forward, so the investigation was stymied.

19 Neither did a trial ever get off the ground. It was too difficult to find a jury, and the financial strain the trial put on Johnson County was too great. Christensen's explanation of the financial challenges is excellent; it's a thorny subject that she gets right.

20 I appreciate that Melissa Christensen has made the story of the Johnson County War exciting to read, but I wish she had paid more attention to historical accuracy. *Dark Wyoming* is a deeply flawed book that does not do its subject justice.

Dark Wyoming

(Genre: Movie Review)

1 Most American history textbooks careen through the range wars of the Old West as quickly as a hurricane's wind. This compelling period of history is largely unknown to most Americans, so Damon Armijo's new film, *Dark Wyoming*, based on Melissa Christensen's book of the same name, is welcome. It is not only a fine film, but it places the Johnson County War in its rightful place as a key event in American history.

An Epic of the American West

Dark Wyoming

2 Armijo has successfully re-created the two worlds of the range war era: the bleak, dusty life of small-scale ranchers, and the realm of wealthy, decadent cattle barons. The scenes featuring the ranchers take place outside in bright, oppressive sunlight. The audience squints its eyes along with them. In contrast, the immoral barons are seen in their offices colored with dark brown woods and burgundy rugs.

3 There is no mistaking Armijo's point of view. The film is firmly on the side of the local ranchers, who are persecuted by the forceful, greedy barons. It's interesting to

note that the film diverges from the book in this respect. Christensen's portrait of the barons is more sympathetic.

4   The film has two major sequences: the trial of the attempted murderer of Nate Champion, a local rancher, and the final attack on Champion's tiny cabin in which federal soldiers come to the rescue. I wish I could report that both are excellently done, but only one of them is.

5   The trial scene is interminable; it's like listening to your least favorite relative go on for too long at Thanksgiving dinner.

6   The film's shoot-'em-up climax is thrilling, however. The widescreen shot of the soldiers riding in on horseback is a triumph and it tells the viewer that Champion will be saved.

Dark Wyoming *coming soon!*

7   The uplifting ending is another departure from the book, but it's not uncommon for Hollywood to change a book's ending for a film version. However I couldn't help feeling that the final scene of Champion curling up in front of the fire with his dog rang false, especially in light of the violence that came before. But it's a detail easily forgiven in the larger context of this fine film about a fascinating subject.

Comprehension Check

1A. According to the review, how does the movie portray the cattle barons?

    a. as greedy and evil

    b. as sympathetic

    c. as barely getting by each day

    d. as a powerful force for good

1B. What phrase from the movie review supports the answer to Part A?

    a. "the bleak, dusty life"

    b. "a tense state of surveillance"

    c. "the realm of wealthy, decadent"

    d. "in bright, oppressive sunlight"

2A. The idea about the barons expressed in the Letter to the Editor is that they were

    a. justified in pursuing Nate Champion.

    b. powerless in the local community.

    c. poor victims of local crime.

    d. ruthless manipulators.

2B. What fact from the Letter to the Editor supports the answer to Part A?

    a. Nate Champion was found guilty.

    b. Joe Elliott was linked to the barons.

    c. Nate Champion allowed his cattle to graze on public land.

    d. Johnson County was largely made up of small-ranch owners.

3A. Which of the following characterizes the Letter to the Editor on page 288?

   a. a list of facts and reasoned judgments that stem from those facts

   b. a strong personal opinion based on an audience member's reaction

   c. speculation about how a specific work could have been improved

   d. fine scholarship that avoids personal commentary

3B. What phrase from the text supports the answer to Part A?

   a. "The big cattle barons were frightened."

   b. "This was the height of the Johnson County War."

   c. "The federal troops arrested the citizen posse."

   d. "I wish she had paid more attention to historical accuracy."

4A. Which statement best summarizes the letter writer's central claim?

   a. *Dark Wyoming* is a brilliant work of historical fiction.

   b. *Dark Wyoming* does not tell a complete or accurate story of the Johnson County War.

   c. *Dark Wyoming* should be regarded as the finest book on its subject.

   d. *Dark Wyoming* is a complete failure, for it gets all its details wrong.

4B. Which phrase from the text supports the answer to Part A?

   a. "I feel compelled to correct Ms. Christensen's mistakes."

   b. "Christensen transforms her book yet again at this moment in the story."

   c. "Christensen's explanation of the financial challenges is excellent."

   d. "Christensen gets the main fact related to the resolution of the war correct."

5A. How can the medium of film portray an event that a nonfiction text cannot?

   a. by having interesting characters

   b. by having realistic dialogue

   c. by using angles and effects to bring out emotion

   d. by describing the landscape's colorful scenery

5B. Which phrase from the movie review supports the answer to Part A?

   a. "The uplifting ending is another departure from the book."

   b. "The widescreen shot of the soldiers riding in on horseback is a triumph."

   c. "The trial scene is interminable."

   d. "The film has two major sequences."

6. What evidence does the Letter to the Editor writer offer to support his claim that Christensen has included errors or avoided certain facts? Offer specifics.

_____

_____

_____

7. From your interpretation of the movie review, how is the film version of *Dark Wyoming* different from the nonfiction text? In what way are these differences due to the differences between media? Cite specifics.

_____

_____

_____

8. Does the Letter to the Editor writer offer sound reasoning to support his claim that Christensen portrays the cattle barons too sympathetically? Why or why not? Cite specifics.

_____

_____

_____

_____

9. Analyze what the nonfiction text version of *Dark Wyoming* can offer that other versions cannot. Then think about what it would be like to listen to an audiobook of *Dark Wyoming*. What would that version offer? How might it change the meaning of the book?

_____

_____

_____

_____

10. How do both the Letter to the Editor writer and the movie reviewer shape their arguments about *Dark Wyoming*? What evidence do they each emphasize to support their claims?

_____

_____

_____

_____

_____

Compare and Contrast Texts

RI.7.9, SL.7.1.a, SL.7.1.c–d

In this unit you've read texts that offer arguments about a topic. You've learned that it is important to offer specific evidence and sound reasoning to support a claim. Fill in the center column of the chart below with the specific claim from each of the four texts listed. Then fill in the last column with at least one piece of sound reasoning that supports the claim. Make sure this reasoning follows from the texts' main ideas and supporting details. Finally, discuss your completed table in a small group.

Text	Claim	Reasoning
"What Forests Offer Us"		
"Save the World's Forests"		
"Deeply Flawed Book": Letter to the Editor		
Dark Wyoming: Movie Review		

Return to the Essential Question

How can readers analyze texts presented in multiple formats?

In small groups or as a class, discuss the Essential Question. Pose questions to your classmates about what they have learned about how written stories compare to versions in other media, how arguments and claims in a text are supported by evidence, and how two or more authors writing about the same topic will emphasize and interpret different evidence. Acknowledge the information your classmates express and, if necessary, ask them to elaborate. Then respond with relevant observations of your own while remaining open to their ideas. Use evidence from the texts in this unit to answer the question.

Word Relationships

Guided Instruction When you have difficulty with the meaning of a word, look for nearby words or phrases that have a relationship to the word. You may find a **synonym**, which is a word that means the same as another word. An **antonym** means the opposite of a word. An **analogy** is a comparison that is made between two words that are alike in some way. Look at the chart below for some examples from this unit's selections.

Word	Related Word(s)	Type	Meaning
decadent	immoral	synonym	corrupt
accuracy	gets wrong	antonym	correctness
careen	as quickly as a hurricane's wind	analogy	to go forward quickly

Guided Practice Read the following sentences from the texts. Circle the word or phrase that is a synonym, antonym, or analogy of the underlined word. Then write the meaning of the underlined word on the line.

1. I appreciate her effort to make the confrontation in Champion's cabin dramatic, but I could do with less <u>excitation</u> and more finely researched storytelling.

   _____

2. The trial scene is <u>interminable</u>; it's like listening to your least favorite relative go on for too long at Thanksgiving dinner. _____

3. The governor was not about to let accusations against big cattle barons go forward, so the investigation was <u>stymied</u>. _____

Independent Practice Read the following sentences from the texts. A word or phrase is underlined. Find the word or term it is related to and tell whether it is a synonym, antonym, or analogy. Write the word and the meaning on the lines.

1. "The people of Johnson County were <u>outraged</u>. The strongest evidence of their indignation was stories that ran in newspapers friendly to the small ranchers."

   _____

2. "Just as we make <u>footprints in wet sand</u>, we make a carbon footprint on the environment when we use carbon-based energy sources." _____

   _____

RI.7.7, RI.7.8, RI.7.9, L.7.5.b

Read the following texts that compare a text to its audio version. Evaluate the reasoning behind specific claims and analyze how two different authors approach the same topic. Then answer the questions on pages 297 and 298.

Cloud Computing: An Interview

1 RADIO HOST: Tonight we welcome Paula Koh, a technology expert. She's going to tell us about a technology that is changing the way we work. Ms. Koh, can you explain cloud computing?

2 PAULA KOH: Well, the cloud is a network of computers that offers a gargantuan amount of space in which enormous amounts of data can be stored. The word *cloud* is used because the data is not stored on physical computers in the user's home or office; it's floating out there like a cloud in the sky. Cloud computing, then, means that businesses can access their data from the cloud, rather than the local computers they keep in the office.

3 RADIO HOST: How is it transforming how businesses are working?

4 PAULA KOH: It can save a lot of space. For example, employees often need software applications installed on their computers; that software can now be stored on the cloud. Their computers will run faster because the software will run from the cloud.

5 Large computers called servers administer the whole system, and there are also computers just for data storage.

Cloud Computing: An Opinion

1 For today's computer trends blog, I downloaded audio of an interview with Paula Koh, cloud systems expert.

2 Ms. Koh did a good job of explaining cloud computing (although I could barely hear her, the recording was so poor), but she didn't sound excited about it. And of course I couldn't see the diagram she kept referring to.

3 The interviewer also failed to ask her about the drawbacks of the cloud, such as questionable data security.

4 For example, more than 40% of U.S. businesses operating in China are concerned with data theft in China's cloud. I'm sure it's only a matter of time before a business has all its data stolen and experiences a major meltdown.

Circle the letter next to the best answer.

RI.7.7, RI.7.8, RI.7.9, L.7.5.b

1A. What is Koh's central claim about cloud computing?

   a. It is unsafe.

   b. It is changing the way we work.

   c. It is available only in China.

   d. It is years away from being widely available.

1B. What phrase from the text is evidence that supports the answer to Part A?

   a. "the recording was so poor"

   b. "U.S. businesses operating in China are concerned with data theft"

   c. "employees often need software"

   d. "software will run from the cloud"

2A. What is the blogger's central claim?

   a. China is stealing data from U.S. businesses operating there.

   b. Data stored in the cloud is easily accessible.

   c. Data stored in the cloud may not be totally secure.

   d. The cloud is made up of a network of computers.

2B. What phrase from the text is evidence that supports the answer to Part A?

   a. "Ms. Koh did a good job of explaining cloud computing"

   b. "I couldn't see the diagram she kept referring to"

   c. "the data is not stored on physical computers in an office"

   d. "U.S. businesses operating in China are concerned with data theft"

3A. What is the cloud?

   a. one very large computer

   b. the Internet

   c. a portable storage device

   d. a network of computers

3B. Which kind of word relationship did Koh use to explain the cloud?

   a. synonym

   b. antonym

   c. analogy

   d. metaphor

4A. What does *gargantuan* mean?

   a. extremely small

   b. extremely large

   c. extremely powerful

   d. extremely fast

4B. Rereading paragraph 2, which word relationship can you use to help you with the meaning of *gargantuan*?

   a. synonym

   b. antonym

   c. analogy

   d. simile

5A. Look at the diagram. Which of the following is NOT part of the cloud?

   a. servers

   b. storage computers

   c. client computers

   d. control nodes

5B. What phrase from the text is evidence that supports the answer to Part A?

   a. "rather than the local computers they keep in the office"

   b. "computers called servers administer the whole system"

   c. "employees often need software applications installed on their computers"

   d. "there are also computers just for data storage"

6A. Which of the following does the blogger use to show that he is not alone in his fears about data security?

    a. an opinion

    b. a fact

    c. speculation

    d. a reasoned judgment

6B. Which phrase from the text supports the answer to Part A?

    a. "Ms. Koh did a good job of explaining cloud computing"

    b. "she didn't sound excited about it"

    c. "it's only a matter of time before a business has all its data stolen"

    d. "more than 40% of U.S. businesses operating in China are concerned"

7. What is the blogger's point of view about cloud security? How does he reveal it? Does he use any loaded language? Does he offer any facts that Koh did not mention?

_____

_____

_____

_____

8. Based on both texts, does it seem reasonable that someday a business's cloud will be hacked? Use your own experience and reasoning to answer the question.

_____

_____

_____

_____

9. Think about both arguments, and tell which is supported by more sound reasoning. Explain your answer with specifics from the text.

_____

_____

_____

10. How does the fact that the blogger listens to a recording of Koh's interview (as opposed to seeing it in person) impact what he thinks of her claim? How would reading a technical article about cloud computing compare with Koh's interview? Explain.

_____

_____

_____

_____

Writing Handbook

This year, you will write narratives, informative/explanatory texts, an opinion piece, an evidence-based essay, and a research report. This handbook is your guide to writing all these types of texts. It takes you through the steps of the writing process, which help you go from ideas to a finished piece of writing. Once you know the steps, you can use them for any kind of writing.

W.7.2, W.7.4, W.7.5, W.7.6, W.7.7, W.7.8, W.7.9.b, W.7.10

STEP 1 Planning

Suppose you have to write a research report. Writers write research reports to share what they have learned about a topic that interests them. Let's say you want to know more about an activity that is good for the environment, such as composting. The process of good writing begins with planning. For any kind of writing you do, start by asking yourself some questions:

- **What** am I writing?

You are writing a research report. This type of writing involves identifying questions about a topic, researching the answers in multiple sources, and then sharing what you have learned. You must organize the information in a logical way, provide accurate details, and cite your sources of information. In your report, you should paraphrase, summarize, and quote information from your sources.

- **Why** am I writing? What is my **purpose**?

Your purpose is your reason for writing. The purpose of a research report is to inform readers. Do this by sharing the relevant information you find during your research. The information you provide should answer the questions that came up during your planning and research.

- **Who** is my audience? Who will read my writing?

Initially, your audience is your teacher and classmates, but if you decide to publish your paper, your audience will broaden to include anyone who is interested in environmental issues, or specifically interested in composting, such as gardeners.

Planning and Research

- **Choose a topic that interests you.**

Your first idea may be a broad topic, such as music or scientific discoveries, that has to be narrowed down. Start by thinking about what you already know about the topic. For many informational writing assignments, you cannot rely simply on your own knowledge of a subject, so you must do some research. As you read sources of information, you will likely think of questions to ask about your topic. These questions—and the answers you uncover— will help you focus the topic for your report. If you were writing a fictional narrative, at this stage of the process you might start by thinking about a character and a problem that requires a solution.

- **Find supporting evidence.**

When you write informational text, you must support your topic with evidence: facts, details, definitions, examples, and quotations from experts. This evidence must come from reliable sources. Reliable sources are writings or quotations from experts in a particular field, found in trustworthy books, periodicals, and Web sites.

If you were writing a fictional or nonfictional narrative, your details would consist of descriptions of people, places, and things, as well as dialogue.

One way to plan a piece of writing is to make an outline. Here's what an outline for a research report about composting might look like. The outline shows the introduction, the subtopics, and the conclusion. It also notes the sources you used.

Composting for the Environment

I. Introduction

Topic: Composting is an effective and natural way to get rid of food waste. It is easy to do and has many benefits.

II. Body: Compost and its importance

Subtopic 1: Composting is an ancient process of using plant waste to enrich the soil.

Supporting Facts: The discovery of compost helped ancient people grow more food and survive.

Subtopic 2: The composting process

Supporting Facts: Mix of "browns" and "greens," air, and water allows microbes to break down materials into compost.

Subtopic 3: Benefits of composting

Supporting Facts: It reduces pollution; slows overfilling landfills.

Subtopic 4: Builds personal awareness

Supporting Facts: Composting makes people more aware of food production and its impact on the world.

III. Conclusion: Compost, or "black gold," is valuable for everyone.

IV. Sources: Land Encyclopedia Online, How Your Garden Grows Online Magazine, Rotten Riches: Why Compost Is Black Gold.

If you were writing a fictional narrative, your outline would be a chronological sequence of events showing what happens first, next, and last in the story.

DIGITAL TIPS

You can write your outline by hand or by using a word processing program on a computer. A word processing program makes it easier to add and delete text, as well as to change and move text around—which happens a lot in the planning process!

PLANNING TOGETHER

You can work with a partner during the planning stage of any kind of writing. You can brainstorm ideas for topics, as well as ask each other questions to see how much you know (or need to find out) about a topic that interests you.

Researching Your Topic

The planning step involves finding good sources of information. If you are writing an informational essay, a research report, or an opinion piece, you should present relevant and up-to-date information. This information can come from print or online sources, but those sources must be reliable, accurate, and credible.

■ **Where to Look:** Go to the library or use the Internet to find sources. Find a number of sources and create a good balance of print and online materials. Since virtually anyone can post anything on the Internet, it's a good idea to steer clear of most .com sources unless they represent reputable institutions or publications (city newspapers, established magazines, and the like). The reference database section on your public library's Web site, as well as government (.gov), education (.edu), and many public organization (.org) websites, are usually reliable. Avoid commercial sites, as well as sites that present a one-sided, or biased, point of view.

■ **How to Search:** Use search terms to find appropriate print and online sources. Search terms should be neither too broad nor too narrow. For example, if you were interested in composting at home, *composting* would be too broad as a search term. The more focused search term *composting for beginners* would bring you much closer to the specific information you need. If you already knew something about composting and wanted to focus on a specific method, narrower search terms such as *trench composting* or *worm composting* would bring you more quickly to the information you need. Review the search entries you get by reading the summaries to see which entries best fit what you are looking for.

■ **How to Judge:** Credible sources include respected print and online encyclopedias, newspapers and magazines, professional journals and newsletters, and books and Web sites written by experts. Compare and contrast information in your sources to make sure the information is accurate. Also, notice when a source was published. In general, especially for science and current events topics, you will want to use recent sources to be sure your information is up-to-date.

■ **How to Take Notes:** Take notes on index cards, or create individual files on a computer. Carefully record the source of each note. Paraphrase and summarize the general information. If you find a good quotation, copy it exactly, placing it inside quotation marks. Finally, sort your notes into logical categories that follow your outline.

■ **How to Cite Sources:** As you take notes, be sure to identify the title, author, and publication information of each source. You will need to be able to tell your readers where you got your information. You can use an informal citation, such as: **Author. Title. Publisher. Date. Page number.** For online sources, you will have to identify the source as "Web" and may be asked to include the URL and the date you accessed the information.

> **RESEARCH TIP**
>
> Choose sources that are:
> - up-to-date
> - written by an expert on the subject
> - carefully documented, so that you can verify their credibility and accuracy
> - well-written
> - unbiased

W.7.2, W.7.4, W.7.5, W.7.6, W.7.7, W.7.8, W.7.9.b, W.7.10

STEP 2 Drafting

Follow your outline as you write your draft. Get your ideas on the page, and don't worry about spelling and grammar at this point. Writing on a computer will make revising easy later. If you are writing by hand, leave room for revisions by skipping every other line. Here is a draft of a research report about composting.

Composting

Composting is a great way to get rid of plant waste because it is easy to do and has many benefits for the planet.

Composting uses the process that plant materials undergo when they die. Experts think composting is a very old practice. Someone must have discovered that plants grew better in dirt covered by rotting leaves, grass, and manure. Growing more food meant more people could survive long winters or unexpected events.

Compost involves mixing equal amounts of "browns" (carbon-rich dead leaves, wood chips, and manure) and "greens" (nitrogen-rich grass clippings and fruit and vegetable peelings). Add in a little soil, water, and air. Then microbes from the soil begin the process of respiration. They break down the stuff into small parts, releasing carbon dioxide. Over time, a compost pile gets transformed into humus. You can use it to enrich the soil.

One benefit to composting is personal. When people compost, they think about where their food comes from and where it goes. As they add banana peels or moldy bread to a compost pile, they might wonder who grew the food they ate and how and where it was grown.

Composting helps with pollution. The Environmental Protection agency says that "In 2011 alone, more than 36 tons of food waste was generated, with only 4 percent [composted]." The food waste left rotting in landfills generates methane. Also, some cities incinerate their waste. The smoke settles over the land and water and gets into our drinking supplies.

Composting has many benefits and no downside. It reduces pollution. It can inspire people to think about where food comes from. Composting is good for the environment.

W.7.2, W.7.4, W.7.5, W.7.9.b, W.7.10, L.7.3.a, L.7.4.c, L.7.4.d

STEP 3 Revising

When you revise, you think about how to improve your writing. This step is about checking your ideas and how clearly you have expressed them, not about the finer points of spelling and grammar. Use the items in the checklist below to evaluate your draft. If you are using a computer, read the draft on your screen and enter changes as you go. If you are using a pencil and paper to write, mark up your draft by making notes between the lines and in the margins.

REVISING CHECKLIST

Ideas and Voice

- ☐ Have I developed my ideas by including enough supporting evidence?
- ☐ Have I included accurate and reliable information from my research?
- ☐ Does my writer's voice sound interesting and well informed?
- ☐ Have I conveyed the information in an unbiased and balanced way?

Organization and Coherence

- ☐ Does the beginning introduce the topic clearly?
- ☐ Is the information presented in a logical fashion?
- ☐ Have I used linking words to connect ideas between sentences and across paragraphs?
- ☐ Do I have a concluding section that relates to my topic?
- ☐ Have I combined sentences for better style or to clarify meaning?

Word Choice

- ☐ Have I used specialized terms correctly and checked their definitions?
- ☐ Have I provided definitions for terms readers may not know?
- ☐ Have I avoided using the same words over and over?
- ☐ Have I used formal English and avoided slang or informal language?

REVISING TOGETHER

It is helpful to work with a partner as you revise your writing. Have your partner read your draft and give you feedback. Together, go through the Revising Checklist to identify areas that need revision. Then, read your draft aloud to yourself or to your partner. Determine if you wish to make any more improvements based on the items you checked off in the checklist.

W.7.1, W.7.5, W.7.6, L.7.1.a, L.7.1.c, L.7.1.f, L.7.1.g, L.7.2.c, L.7.3.c

Here is a draft with notes and changes for revisions.
To see the revised draft, turn to page 307.

I want my title to grab the reader's attention.

Composting ∧ : Black Gold for the Planet

Composting is a great way to get rid of plant waste because it is easy to do and has many benefits for the planet.

My introduction should say something more specific about the benefits of composting.

Composting uses the process that plant materials undergo when they die. Experts think composting is ~~a very old~~ *an ancient* practice. Someone must have discovered that plants grew better in dirt covered by rotting leaves, grass, and manure. Growing more food meant more people could survive long winters or unexpected events. ∧ Today, compost can help people survive by reducing waste and pollution.

I need to improve the flow of this paragraph. smoothly.

Compost involves mixing equal amounts of "browns" (carbon-rich dead leaves, wood chips, and manure) and "greens" (nitrogen-rich grass clippings and fruit and vegetable peelings). Add in a little soil, water, and air. Then microbes from the soil begin the process of respiration. They break ∧ing down the stuff into small parts, *and* releasing carbon dioxide. Over time, a compost pile gets transformed into a dark crumbly material called humus. You can use it to enrich the soil. ∧ Because the material is so dark, rich and full of nutrients, gardeners refer to it as "black gold."

I want to combine some sentences to get rid of choppiness.

I need to better explain the phrase "black gold" that's in my title.

One benefit to composting is personal. When people compost, they think about where their food comes from and where it goes. As they add banana peels or moldy bread to a compost pile, they might wonder who grew the food they ate and how and where it was grown.

I need to switch the order of paragraphs 4 and 5 so the organization is more logical.

Composting helps with pollution. The Environmental Protection agency says that, "In 2011 alone, more than 36 tons of food waste was generated, with only 4 percent [composted]." The food waste left rotting in landfills generates methane. ~~Also, some cities incinerate their waste. The smoke settles over the land and water and gets into our drinking supplies.~~ ∧ Cities that incinerate their waste create smoke that gets into groundwater and then into our drinking water.

I need a stronger, more memorable conclusion.

Composting has many benefits and no downside. It reduces pollution. It can inspire people to think about where food comes from. ~~Composting is good for the environment.~~ Composting truly is as precious as gold because of the value that it provides to the entire planet.

WRITING HANDBOOK

W.7.2, W.7.4, W.7.5, W.7.6, L.7.1, L.7.2, L.7.3.a, L.7.4.c, L.7.4.d

STEP 4 Editing

The editing step is about making your writing correct. Read your revised draft carefully. Use the Editing Checklist below and the Proofreading Marks on page 307 to mark the errors in your draft. Always proofread and correct your own work. Seeing your own mistakes can be difficult, though, so asking a partner to also check your work can help.

EDITING CHECKLIST

Sentences

- ☐ Every sentence is a complete sentence.
- ☐ I have a good mix of simple, compound, and complex sentences.
- ☐ None of my sentences contain a misplaced or dangling modifier.
- ☐ I have not left out any words, and I have deleted any extra words.

Grammar and Usage

- ☐ The subject and verb of every sentence agree.
- ☐ Verb tenses are used correctly and consistently.
- ☐ Pronouns match the nouns they replace.
- ☐ Conjunctions, prepositions, and interjections are used correctly.
- ☐ Correlative conjunctions are used correctly.
- ☐ Linking words and phrases are used correctly to show relationships between ideas.

Mechanics

- ☐ Every sentence begins with a capital letter and ends with the correct punctuation mark.
- ☐ Quotation marks and other punctuation marks are used correctly, and no marks are missing.
- ☐ Commas are used correctly to separate coordinate adjectives, items in a series, and introductory words and phrases from the rest of a sentence.
- ☐ The title and all proper nouns are capitalized.
- ☐ Paragraphs are all indented.

Spelling

- ☐ I have used a print or online dictionary to check spellings I am unsure about.
- ☐ I have correctly used frequently confused words, such as homophones (*their/there/they're; two/to/too; sew/so*)

W.7.2, W.7.4, W.7.5, W.7.6, L.7.1, L.7.2.a–b, L.7.3.a, L.7.4.c, L.7.4.d

PROOFREADING MARKS

∧ Add

⊙ Period

∼ Change order

ℐ Take out

≡ Capital letter

¶ Indent paragraph

/ Small letter

◯ Spelling error

∧ Insert comma

Here are marked edits on a revised draft.

Composting: Black Gold for the Planet

Composting is a great way to get rid of plant waste because it is easy to do and has many benefits for the planet.

Composting uses the ^natural process that plant materials undergo when they die. Experts think composting is an (anceint) practice. Someone must have discovered that plants grew better in dirt covered by rotting leaves, grass, and manure. Growing more food meant more people could survive long winters or unexpected events. Today, compost can help people survive by reducing waste and pollution⊙

Compost involves mixing equal amounts of "browns" (carbon-rich dead leaves, wood chips, and manure) and "greens" (nitrogen-rich grass clippings and fruit and vegetable peelings). Add in a little soil, water, and air. Then microbes from the soil begin the process of respiration, breaking down the stuff into small parts, releasing carbon dioxide. Over time, a compost pile gets transformed into a dark, crumbly material called Humus. You can use it to enrich the soil. Because the material is so dark, rich∧ and full of nutrients, many gardeners refer to it as "black gold."

Composting helps with pollution. The Environmental Protection agency says that, "In 2011 alone, more than 36 tons of food waste was generated, with only 4 percent [composted]." The food (left waste) rotting in landfills generates methane. Cities that incinerate their waste create smoke that gets into groundwater and then into our drinking water.

¶One benefit to composting is personal. When people compost, they think about where their food comes from and where it goes. As they add banana peels or moldy bread to a compost pile, they might wonder who grew the food they ate and how and where it was grown.

Composting has has many benefits and no downside. It reduces pollution. It can inspire people to think about where food comes from. Composting truly is as precious as gold because of the value that it provides to the entire planet.

STEP 4: **Editing** *(continued)*

Editing Tips

The editing step is your last chance to make sure your writing is complete, coherent, and correct before you hand it in. These tips will help you make sure your writing is the best it can be.

■ **Using Spelling and Grammar Checkers:** When you write on a computer, you might think you can rely on spelling and grammar checkers to catch your errors—but that would be a mistake. If you use a word that is often confused but spell it correctly, your spellchecker probably will not highlight it. For example, if you wrote *The dogs wagged they're tails*, a spell checker probably won't identify *they're* as an error, since it's not misspelled, just not the correct word (*their*). A spellchecker also won't catch proper nouns that are not capitalized. If you leave out a word, the grammar checker might miss that, too. So, double-check for errors, and don't rely on spelling and grammar checkers.

■ **Using Quotations:** Weaving quotations into your own writing is a style issue but one worth thinking about as you edit. Placing a long quotation into the middle of a paragraph can sound awkward, because the author's voice probably sounds very different from your own voice. Instead, integrate quotations smoothly into your own writing:

■ **Original:** To make compost quickly, you want a balance of materials. "The best ratio is one green for every one brown."

■ **Revised:** According to the City of Springfield Waste Management Department's Web site, if you want to make compost quickly, "the best ratio is one green for every one brown."

Be sure that you keep quotation marks around the exact words another writer used, and that you make the source of the quotation clear. Using a quotation without giving credit is plagiarism—taking another writer's words and ideas and passing them off as your own.

■ **Citing Sources:** You will need to provide a list of all the sources you used to write your paper. A Works Cited or Bibliography should appear at the end of the body of your paper. There are several different source citation formats. Your teacher can tell you which one to use. Here are some basic rules:

- List your resources alphabetically by author's last name, or by title if the source has no author.

- Include all the relevant information—author or authors' names, title, publication information, online address.

- Indent all the lines after the first line of each citation.

Here are some source citations from "Composting: Black Gold for the Planet":

"Compost." *The Land Encyclopedia Online*. Land Encyclopedia, 2013. Web. 30 August 2013. <http://www.landencyclopedia.com/checked/topic/90675/compost.>

Freundlich, Calhoun. "Make Composting Work for You." *How Your Garden Grows Online Magazine*. Web. 28 August 2013. <http://www.howyourgardengrows.org/soil/methods_composting/.>

Clampett, Cissy. *Rotten Riches: Why Compost Is Black Gold*. Northampton, MA: Real Organic Matters Publishing Company, 2003. Print.

STEP 5 — Producing, Publishing, and Presenting

Now that you have edited your writing, making it clear and correct, you can publish it to share it with others. Think about ways you can improve the paper's visual presentation by adding images or text features.

- Photographs and illustrations downloaded from the Internet or created by you can add visual interest.

- Diagrams, graphs, charts, or maps can provide important information that is not easily explained in words. Think about where your writing can benefit from visual support.

- Headings and subheadings can help "chunk" ideas in your paper, making them easier for readers to find, understand, and remember.

- Visuals and text features can enhance your writing, but they can also make your pages more crowded. Don't overdo it! Be sure the way you present your final version best suits your purpose and audience.

- Once you have added the final touches, make a final copy of your paper. You can produce your final copy by using a computer or by neatly writing a clean copy by hand. It's important to show that you care about your work—and your audience—by creating a clean and legible final copy.

Online Publishing and Digital Slide Presentations

Another way to publish your writing is online. Perhaps your class or your school has a Web site where student writing can be published. If so, post the final copy of your work; you can scan in handwritten work if necessary. You might team up with other students to create a class anthology of student writings, or even use a special application to create e-book versions (complete with visuals) of student writings that can be viewed on computers or tablets.

Readers of online media often appreciate brevity, or conciseness. Consider transforming your report into a digital slide presentation. In such presentations, longer informative pieces are summarized and condensed. Each major section gets its own slide, with the most important points presented in bulleted lists.

Here's an example of a slide from "Composting: Black Gold for the Planet." This brief list of facts, along with before-and-after photos of a compost pile, would convey the information to readers effectively.

Process of Composting

- Equal amounts of "browns" and "greens" are mixed with soil, water, and air.
- Microbial respiration breaks down the items into small parts.
- Result is a rich, dark topsoil called humus, or "black gold."

SL.7.1.a, SL.7.1.c, SL.7.4, SL.7.5, SL.7.6, L.7.1, L.7.3

STEP 5: Producing, Publishing, and Presenting *(continued)*

Speaking Tips

Once you finish a piece of writing, you might be asked to share it with classmates in a speech or other oral presentation. Remember that written English and spoken English are different. Follow these rules to make your oral presentation effective.

- Use language that suits your audience and the occasion.

- Speak loudly and clearly so that everyone can hear and understand you.

- Speak in complete sentences, and pause between sentences to show the break in ideas.

- Change the pitch, rate, and volume of your voice to express your ideas.

- Make eye contact with your listeners and watch for audience feedback. If listeners appear confused or bored, change the pace at which you speak.

- If you include visuals, pause to allow your audience to view and respond to them. Clearly explain the connection between the visuals and your topic.

- Ask your listeners if they have any questions after you have finished speaking. Listen carefully and respectfully to the questions. Take time to think before you respond, and then answer politely.

DIGITAL CONNECTION

A digital slide presentation can be a great tool to use during a speech or oral presentation. Show the slides as you speak. Your presentation should expand on the information on the screen. Be sure to rehearse beforehand so that your slides and your talk work together seamlessly.

Listening Tips

When it's your turn to sit in the audience during a classmate's presentation, follow these tips:

- Keep your eyes on the presenter and focus your mind on the ideas.

- Make connections from what you hear to what you already know.

- Take notes. Include questions you want to ask.

- Try to picture what the speaker is describing.

- If you want to ask a question, wait until the speaker is ready. Keep your question brief and direct. Listen carefully to the answer.

There are three parts to this performance task. Your teacher will provide you with copies of one or more reading selections that go with each part.

- "River Rising" Genre: Drama

- "A Katrina Story" Genre: Realistic Fiction

- "The Cyclone" from *The Wizard of Oz* Genre: Fiction

- "Superstorms" Genre: Informational Article

- "Global Dimming" Genre: Informational Article

Part 1: Literary Analysis

☐ Carefully read "River Rising" and "A Katrina Story" and take notes about important events, ideas, and details. Then answer Items 1–9 on pages 312–314.

☐ Read the writing prompt in Item 10 on page 314. Review "River Rising" and "A Katrina Story" with the prompt in mind. You will use both passages in this task.

☐ Write an essay on your own paper in response to the prompt.

Part 2: Narrative Writing

☐ Carefully read "The Cyclone," an excerpt from *The Wizard of Oz*. As you read, take notes that help you understand the passage. Then answer Items 1–9 on pages 315–317.

☐ Read the writing prompt in Item 10 on page 317.

☐ Write a narrative on your own paper in response to the prompt.

Part 3: Research Simulation

☐ Carefully read "Superstorms" and *Global Dimming*. Take notes about important ideas and details. Then answer Items 1–9 on pages 318–320.

☐ Read the writing prompt in Item 10 on page 320. Then review "Superstorms" and "Global Dimming" with the prompt in mind. You will use both passages in this task.

☐ Write an essay on your own paper in response to the writing prompt.

Part 1 Literary Analysis

RL.7.1, RL.7.2, RL.7.3, RL.7.4, RL.7.10, W.7.2, W.7.4, W.7.9, W.7.10, L.7.1, L.7.3, L.7.4, L.7.5

Read all parts of the question before responding. Circle the correct answer to Items 1–9. Use your own paper to respond to Item 10.

Item 1

Part A How does the setting of "River Rising" shape the drama's conflict?

a. The farm setting creates a conflict between farmers and their neighbors.

b. The flooding river creates a conflict between the farmers and nature.

c. Sam is in conflict with Lois over his desire to move to Chicago.

d. Henry is in conflict with Lois over her demand that he move the mules.

Part B What text does NOT support the answer to Part A?

a. "The river must have overflowed the levee! This whole area is bound to flood!"

b. "Enough to swamp all that low-lying farmland."

c. "Even without another flood, sharecropping will never let us get ahead."

d. "If this flood is as bad as the last one, we won't get our crop in this year."

Item 2

Part A Which of the following sentences best states a key theme of "River Rising"?

a. Natural disasters can bring opportunities as well as suffering.

b. Human ingenuity always finds a way to prevent natural disasters.

c. There is no way to prepare for a natural disaster.

d. Natural disasters bring out the worst in human nature.

Part B What evidence supports the answer to Part A?

a. No one comes to warn Sam and Lois about the break in the levees.

b. Building scaffolding for the chickens and pigs can't save them from the flood.

c. Some parts of the levee may have broken, but Sam and Lois's farm will be protected.

d. The flood makes Sam realize that the family would be better off moving to Chicago.

Item 3

Part A What does the word *rupture* mean in "River Rising"?

a. a disaster

b. a confrontation

c. a crack or breach

d. a weakness

Part B Which context clues in the text support your answer in part A?

a. "the break is relieving pressure"

b. "on our side of the river"

c. "refugees are already swarming over the levee"

d. "It's the only high ground for miles."

Item 4

Part A How does the audience learn about the events as they unfold in "River Rising"?

a. mostly through description in the stage directions

b. by revealing the main characters' inner thoughts

c. almost entirely through dialogue between the characters

d. through language that mimics the rhythmic sound of raindrops

Part B What evidence supports the answer to Part A?

a. The italic text at the beginning of the play sets the scene.

b. Characters share news about events offstage as they appear onstage.

c. Most of the information about the flood comes from a long speech by Sam.

d. The rapid-fire dialogue between Lois and Henry sounds like rain.

Item 5

Part A When the neighbor cat *sidled up* to Isaac in paragraph 5 of "A Katrina Story," how did she move?

a. aggressively

b. secretively

c. curiously

d. clumsily

Part B Which detail from the text best supports the answer to Part A?

a. "he saw the next-door-neighbor sitting on the porch railing"

b. "her stealthy way of moving about the neighborhood"

c. "glistening ripples moved down the street"

d. "she reached out a delicate paw and batted at the door handle"

Item 6

Part A Which of the following best summarizes "A Katrina Story"?

a. A cat and a dog brave the pouring rain and fight a rat.

b. A dog and cat, abandoned in a flood, team up to find food.

c. A dog prevents a rat from stealing food from a starving cat.

d. A cat figures out how to release an abandoned dog from his leash.

Part B What evidence from the text does NOT support your response to Part A?

a. "he never knew where she would turn up"

b. "together they made a thorough survey of the kitchen"

c. "he wearily rose and followed her out the door"

d. "as Isaac once again heaved himself onto the counter, the cat waited"

Item 7

Part A What is the main conflict in "A Katrina Story"?

a. Isaac vs. the cat next door

b. Isaac and the cat vs. the rat

c. Isaac and the cat vs. the flood

d. Isaac and the cat vs. the rain storm

Part B Which evidence from the story best illustrates the answer to Part A?

a. Isaac is irritated by the cat's ability to sneak around undetected.

b. Taking the cat on his back, Isaac paddles through floodwater to find food.

c. Isaac cannot fight the rat because he doesn't have teeth.

d. The rain went on for a long time, preventing the cat from getting to Isaac earlier.

Item 8

Part A How does the conflict help reveal character in "A Katrina Story"?

a. by highlighting the pet owners' regret

b. by showing Isaac's laziness

c. by demonstrating the cat's ingenuity

d. by bringing out the city's rats

Part B What text supports the answer to part A?

a. Isaac's owner filled the bathtub with water in case the water pipes broke.

b. The cat figures out how to release the dog and finds the sliced meat.

c. Isaac is so tired that he just wants to rest on his comfortable bed.

d. The rat threatens to take the meat before the pets can eat it.

Item 9

Part A Which of the following conclusions can you draw about floods based on evidence in *both* selections?

a. Floods may occur even after the rain has stopped.

b. Cities are worse affected by flooding than rural areas.

c. People who leave their animals behind in a flood don't care about them.

d. Because of technology, today's floods are less destructive than those a century ago.

Part B Choose TWO pieces of evidence that support your answer to Part A.

a. "lead the mules up to the rise in the pasture" ("River Rising")

b. "It ain't going to flood. It ain't even raining out." ("River Rising")

c. "there's never been a safer time to live near the Mississippi" ("River Rising")

d. "during the height of the rainstorm, the water . . . hadn't risen this high" ("A Katrina Story")

e. "the street was deserted and water was up to the windows" ("A Katrina Story")

f. "At that moment, the pointy snout of a rat torpedoed toward them" ("A Katrina Story")

Item 10

In "A Katrina Story," Isaac noted that "the normal order of things was badly askew." Extreme weather has a way of reminding human beings that they can never fully control nature.

Write two or three paragraphs that analyze how the authors of both "River Rising" and "A Katrina Story" use flooding to show that nature, and not humankind, is in control. In your analysis, cite text evidence from both selections. Take care to organize your response logically, and use standard English.

Part 2 Narrative Writing

RL.7.1, RL.7.2, RL.7.3, RL.7.4, RL.7.6, RL.7.10, W.7.3, W.7.4, W.7.9, W.7.10, L.7.6

Read all parts of the question before responding. Circle the correct answer to Items 1–9. Use your own paper to respond to Item 10.

Item 1

Part A What does the word *garret* mean in these lines from "The Cyclone"?

"Their house was small. . . . There were four walls, a floor and a roof, which made one room; and this room contained a rusty looking cookstove. . . . There was no garret at all, and no cellar."

a. attic

b. basement

c. floorboards

d. kitchen area

Part B How do word relationships from the lines of text in Part A help you understand the meaning of *garret*?

a. "four walls, a floor, and a roof" are examples of *garret*

b. the words *small* and *one room* imply the meaning of *garret*

c. *garret* and *cellar* are probably opposites

d. *cookstove* and *garret* are probably synonyms

Item 2

Part A According to the story, why is the house that Dorothy shares with her aunt and uncle so small?

a. They are poor.

b. There is no lumber nearby.

c. Two-story buildings are not allowed in their neighborhood.

d. The house was built for a childless couple, not for three people.

Part B Choose the evidence from the list below that supports your response to Part A.

a. "Dorothy lived . . . with Uncle Henry, who was a farmer, and Aunt Em"

b. "for the lumber to build it had to be carried by wagon many miles"

c. "Uncle Henry and Aunt Em had a big bed in one corner"

d. "Dorothy had a little bed in another corner"

Item 3

Part A Which of the following words best describes the prairie setting of "The Cyclone"?

a. fertile and productive

b. dull and harsh

c. sunny and peaceful

d. noisy and overcrowded

Part B Which text supports the answer in Part A?

a. "the house had been painted"

b. "a small hole dug in the ground, called a cyclone cellar"

c. "the broad sweep of flat country that reached to the edge of the sky"

d. "the sun had baked the plowed land into a gray mass"

NARRATIVE WRITING

Item 4

Part A How has life on a prairie homestead affected Aunt Em?

a. She has risen to the challenge and thrived.

b. She enjoys the constant sunshine and cool breezes.

c. The harsh environment has been difficult for her.

d. She was fine until Dorothy came along.

Part B What evidence in the text supports the answer to Part A?

a. She runs to the storm cellar ahead of Uncle Henry and Dorothy.

b. Her eyes and skin are dull, her body is thin, and she never laughs.

c. When she first arrived on the homestead, she was young, pretty, and lively.

d. She has made the small cottage cheerful and cozy in spite of the harsh climate.

Item 5

Part A What does the narrator mean in saying that Uncle Henry "did not know what joy was"?

a. He is uneducated and has a limited vocabulary.

b. He is an immigrant from a foreign land and never learned that word.

c. His life is very hard, and he has no time for any kind of enjoyment.

d. He is happily married to Aunt Em.

Part B What evidence from the story best supports the answer to Part A?

a. "Uncle Henry . . . worked hard from morning till night"

b. "from his long beard to his rough boots"

c. "Uncle Henry sat upon the doorstep and looked anxiously at the sky"

d. "'There's a cyclone coming, Em'"

Item 6

Part A Which of the following character traits best describe Dorothy?

a. fearful and solitary

b. willful and stubborn

c. sensitive and generous

d. brave and levelheaded

Part B Select TWO pieces of evidence that support the answer to Part A.

a. She does not provide good company to her aunt and uncle.

b. She does not follow her aunt's instructions to head to the cyclone cellar.

c. She is aware of the danger of the tornado before her aunt and uncle are.

d. After rescuing Toto, she closes the trap door to prevent future accidents.

e. She decides to wait calmly and see where the cyclone takes her.

Item 7

Part A Which of the following conclusions can be drawn from this story?

a. Aunt Em would be happier if Dorothy were not living with her.

b. Tornados are a foreseeable danger of life on the prairie.

c. Uncle Henry is less successful at farming than his neighbors.

d. Dogs often sense dangerous weather events before humans do.

Part B Which evidence from the story supports the answer to Part A?

a. The family has a cyclone cellar in the event of a tornado.

b. Aunt Em used to be an attractive and vibrant woman.

c. Toto jumps out of Dorothy's arms and hides under the bed.

d. Uncle Henry works constantly.

Item 8

Part A Which of the following shifts occurs in "The Cyclone"?

a. The narration shifts from third person to first person.

b. The setting changes from Kansas to Oz.

c. Uncle Henry, once young and optimistic, becomes old and tired.

d. The realistic narrative details give way to fantasy.

Part B What details support the answer to part A?

a. Although Aunt Em is a frail and elderly woman, a younger version of her is described.

b. Howling winds and a darkening sky signal that a change is about to occur.

c. The description is realistic until the house is picked up, but not destroyed, by the tornado.

d. There is no dialogue until Uncle Henry says, "There's a cyclone coming, Em."

Item 9

Part A Which of the following best summarizes the story excerpt?

a. Aunt Em and Uncle Henry take care of their niece, but they lose her in a tragic storm.

b. Dorothy and her dog Toto enjoy many adventures on the prairie, including chasing storms.

c. Dorothy is a young girl living on a dreary farm until an extraordinary tornado whisks her away.

d. Aunt Em loves Dorothy, but her fear of tornados leads to a suffocating existence for the young girl.

Part B Select TWO pieces of evidence that support the correct summary in Part A.

a. Uncle Henry is stern and untalkative; Aunt Em is cheerless and tired.

b. From Dorothy's house, she can see nothing but gray prairie for miles in every direction.

c. Aunt Em would rather hide in a dark hole than "ride out" the tornado above ground.

d. Uncle Henry risks his life to save the farm animals before taking shelter with Aunt Em.

e. Toto is a small dog with sparkling eyes and silky fur.

f. Dorothy travels for hours in the house atop the tornado, wondering where it will go.

Item 10

As you have seen, weather can play a key role in the plot of a story. Rewrite the story you read in "The Cyclone," but change the setting and the extreme weather event. Show how the new setting and weather event affect the characters and the plot of the story.

To get started, think about extreme weather events you know something about, such as hurricanes, floods, blizzards, or wildfires. Then think about a setting where that kind of weather occurs. How would the new setting shape the characters? What would the extreme weather event bring to their lives? Use narrative elements like dialogue, description, and suspense to bring your story to life.

Part 3 Research Simulation

RI.7.1, RI.7.2, RI.7.3, RI.7.4, RI.7.10, RST.6.1, RST.6.2, RST.6.4, W.7.2, W.7.4, W.7.7, W.7.8, W.7.9, W.7.10, L.7.1, L.7.2, L.7.3, L.7.4

Read all parts of the question before responding. Circle the correct answer to Items 1–9. Use your own paper to respond to Item 10.

Item 1

Part A What does the word *exacerbated* mean in these lines from "Superstorms"?

"Rising sea levels *exacerbated* Sandy's storm surge, for example. And abnormally high sea surface temperatures in the Atlantic probably intensified the storm."

  a. relocated

  b. uprooted

  c. made worse

  d. decreased

Part B Which word relationship from the text in Part A helps you understand the meaning of *exacerbated*?

  a. *exacerbated* and *intensified* are synonyms

  b. *abnormally* describes *exacerbated*

  c. *exacerbated* and *surge* are antonyms

  d. "rising sea levels" are contrasted with "storm surge"

Item 2

Part A According to the article "Superstorms," what kind of weather disasters caused more than $1 billion in damage in the years 2011 and 2012?

  a. storms, including tornadoes and hurricanes

  b. all kinds, including drought, heat waves, and storms

  c. geological events such as earthquakes and tsunamis

  d. only the smallest thunderstorms

Part B What evidence supports the answer to Part A?

  a. The article says that most, but not all, of these weather events were storms.

  b. The article says that thunderstorms are the smallest type of storm.

  c. When earthquakes and tsunamis combine with storms, the damage is greater.

  d. The article says that all of these weather events were wind and rain storms.

Item 3

Part A According to "Superstorms," why might global warming lead to more intense storms?

  a. Drought-driven wildfires cause high winds.

  b. Carbon dioxide is building up in the atmosphere.

  c. Melting ice caps make storms wetter.

  d. Warmer air and oceans give storms more energy.

Part B What evidence in the text supports your response in Part A?

  a. data about decreased atmospheric water vapor

  b. data about increased global wind speeds and extreme downpours

  c. evidence about global increases in light but steady precipitation

  d. erosion from previous weather events, which increased Sandy's storm surge

Item 4

Part A What does the word *counterintuitive* mean in this passage from "Global Dimming"?

"Given what we know about global warming, this result may seem *counterintuitive*."

a. too good to be true

b. resulting from a simple logical process

c. the opposite of what one expects

d. easy to grasp

Part B Which example from the text best illustrates the correct answer to Part A?

a. Jet exhaust contains carbon dioxide.

b. Greenhouse gases contribute to global warming.

c. Global dimming is caused by tiny particles that float in the air.

d. Temperatures increased when a source of greenhouse gas was removed.

Item 5

Part A Which conclusion is NOT widely accepted by climate scientists?

a. Global dimming and global warming should not grow unchecked.

b. Global dimming occurs when aerosols reflect light back into space.

c. Global dimming is a significant contributor to climate change.

d. Carbon dioxide is a greenhouse gas.

Part B Which evidence from the text best supports the correct answer to part A?

a. "Scientists disagree about how much global dimming affects climate change."

b. "Many scientists believe . . . that global dimming must be addressed."

c. "Humans shouldn't count on global dimming to 'tone down' . . . warming."

d. "Most public health experts believe that eventually, Asia will have to come to grips with . . . pollution."

Item 6

Part A Which of these four conclusions that could be drawn from "Global Dimming" is best supported by evidence in the text?

a. Global dimming is a greater threat to the climate than global warming.

b. Deserts are mostly to blame for droughts caused by global dimming.

c. To prevent further environmental damage by global dimming, air traffic should stop.

d. The root cause of global dimming, aerosols, also causes serious health problems.

Part B What TWO pieces of evidence from "Global Dimming" support the answer to Part A?

a. "Aerosols . . . come from natural sources, like desert wind storms, and human sources"

b. "Recent changes in the annual monsoon season have hurt food production in Asia"

c. "The two animals might neutralize each other, but your personal danger would be high."

d. "Already the health hazard of aerosols has led the U.S. and other countries to pass clean air legislation."

e. "The negative health effects of air pollution in countries like China and India are also clear."

Item 7

Part A What is the likely origin of *radiation*, which appears in the sentence below?

"Scientists call the sunlight that reaches earth *surface solar radiation* (SSR)."

a. Latin *radix*, meaning "root"

b. Latin *radius*, meaning "ray"

c. Old French *rangier*, "to put in a line"

d. Old English *rād*, "riding, road"

Part B What evidence from "Global Dimming" supports your response to Part A?

a. *Radiation* is related to the rays of sunlight that reach the earth.

b. The causes of increased surface solar *radiation* are rooted in aerosols.

c. The aerosols that cause surface solar *radiation* come from a range of sources.

d. The earth's atmosphere is being warmed by greenhouse gases.

Item 8

Part A What conclusion can be drawn from "Superstorms" and "Global Dimming"?

a. Global dimming plays a larger role in climate change than was thought.

b. Global warming has caused devastating drought in Africa.

c. Changes in the water cycle include less evaporation from the earth's oceans.

d. Changes in the atmosphere have had a strong impact on the earth's climate.

Part B What evidence supports the answer to Part A?

a. Both articles discuss how disruptions in the water cycle relate to drought in Africa.

b. Both articles discuss the relation of increased storminess to pollution.

c. Both articles discuss changes in Earth's atmosphere that affect its climate.

d. Both articles discuss how clouds now produce more rain.

Item 9

Part A According to "Global Dimming," how might global dimming disrupt the water cycle?

a. As less sunlight reaches the ocean's surface, evaporation decreases.

b. As dimming creates a greenhouse effect, evaporation and precipitation increase.

c. As clouds contain more aerosols and rain, cloudiness decreases worldwide.

d. As precipitation increases, monsoons in Asia become more destructive.

Part B Which evidence from "Superstorms" may contradict the correct response in Part A?

a. "Heat waves and droughts have grown more likely and more extreme."

b. "extra water vapor in the atmosphere is making storms wetter"

c. "Concentration of . . . gases in the atmosphere [is] higher . . . ."

d. "Wind speeds have increased by . . . 5% over the past two decades."

Item 10

You have read two texts about different aspects of climate change. Think about how each article discusses climate change through an explanation of causes and effects.

Write an essay that analyzes the causes and effects of climate change. Think about changes that scientists have observed in the atmosphere, changes they have observed in Earth's climate, and their theories about why these changes are connected. Be sure to cite examples from each text to support your essay, and use standard English.

There are three parts to this performance task. Your teacher will provide you with copies of one or more reading selections that go with each part.

- *Paired Selection:* "Battle of the Bike Lane"   Genre: Realistic Fiction and "Film Fest Favorite"   Genre: Film Review

- *Paired Selection:* "An Inconvenient Girl"   Genre: Historical Fiction   and "Rebel Girl Provokes Massive Strike"   Genre: Historical Account

- "Meet Jill Schartner—Conservation Warden"   Genre: Personal Narrative

- *Paired Selection:* "NOHVU Keynote Address"   Genre: Speech   and "NOHVU Keynote Address Hits the Right Notes"   Genre: Review

- "Protecting Federal Lands for 'The Greatest Good'"   Genre: Magazine Article

Part 1: Literary Analysis

☐ Carefully read "Battle of the Bike Lane" and "Film Fest Favorite" and take notes about important events, ideas, and details. Then answer Items 1–4 on pages 322–323.

☐ Carefully read "An Inconvenient Girl" and "Rebel Girl Provokes Massive Strike" and take notes as you read. Then answer Items 5–9 on pages 323–324.

☐ Read the writing prompt in Item 10 on page 324. Review "Battle of the Bike Lane" and "An Inconvenient Girl" with the prompt in mind. You will use both passages in this task.

☐ Write an essay on your own paper in response to the prompt.

Part 2: Narrative Writing

☐ Carefully read "Meet Jill Schartner—Conservation Warden." As you read, take notes that help you understand the passage. Then answer Items 1–9 on pages 325–327.

☐ Read the writing prompt in Item 10 on page 327.

☐ Write a narrative on your own paper in response to the prompt.

Part 3: Research Simulation

☐ Carefully read "NOHVU Keynote Address," "NOHVU Keynote Address Hits the Right Notes," and "Protecting Federal Lands for 'The Greatest Good.'" Take notes about important ideas and details. Then answer Items 1–9 on pages 328–330.

☐ Read the writing prompt in Item 10 on page 330. Then review "NOHVU Keynote Address" and "Protecting Federal Lands for 'The Greatest Good.'"

☐ Write an essay on your own paper in response to the prompt.

RL.7.1, RL.7.2, RL.7.3, RL.7.7, RL.7.9, RL.7.10, RI.7.1, W.7.2, W.7.4, W.7.9, W.7.10, L.7.1, L.7.2, L.7.3, L.7.5, L.7.6

Part 1 Literary Analysis

Read all parts of the question before responding. Circle the correct answer to Items 1–9. Use your own paper to respond to Item 10.

Item 1

Part A Which of the following best describes the conflict in the short story "Battle of the Bike Lane"?

  a. Lorne vs. Dale

  b. Lorne vs. the young cyclist

  c. Lorne vs. the city transportation department

  d. all the residents of the street vs. the striping crew

Part B What text supports the answer to Part A?

  a. "all the new law requires is that you keep Loretta in your driveway"

  b. "Dale and his wife were weary of looking at Loretta"

  c. "these bicycle lanes are going to be insufferable"

  d. "the child snuffled, 'My pants got caught in my chain'"

Item 2

Part A Which of the following sentences best states a key theme of "Battle of the Bike Lane"?

  a. The government should do more to encourage physical fitness.

  b. Even a positive change can be difficult to accept.

  c. Minor disputes between neighbors can turn into bitter feuds.

  d. Senior citizens deserve to be exempt from certain rules.

Part B What text from the story supports the answer to Part A?

  a. "Dale had resided in the house opposite Lorne's since the neighborhood was constructed in the early 1970s"

  b. "they'd filed innumerable covert complaints with the city about the behemoth on the street"

  c. "he always seemed to know precisely when to navigate the RV back into his narrow driveway"

  d. "'I'm talking about custom, I'm taking about tradition!' said Lorne"

Item 3

Part A What does the word *conviviality* mean in these lines from "Battle of the Bike Lane"?

"Lorne Crawford attempted to join in the spirit of conviviality . . . but the meeting . . . had left him feeling prickly and defensive."

  a. friendliness

  b. rebellion

  c. compassion

  d. freedom

Part B The word relationship that helped you answer Part A was the relationship between *conviviality* and . . .

  a. "attempted to join"

  b. "he and his neighbors meandered out"

  c. "the meeting with city transportation officials"

  d. "prickly and defensive"

Item 4

Part A Based on information in "Film Fest Favorite," which of the following is used to focus on the film's conflict?

a. sound

b. costumes

c. makeup

d. contrast

Part B Which detail from the film review best supports the answer to Part A?

a. The film is in black and white.

b. The reviewer praises the film's sound editing.

c. The white bike lane stripe stands out against the black street.

d. The actor who plays Lorne gives a subtle and effective performance.

Item 5

Part A What can you infer about laws governing the workplace at the time "An Inconvenient Girl" is set?

a. There are no laws governing child labor.

b. Some laws govern child labor.

c. There are strict fire safety laws.

d. Employers are required to pay overtime.

Part B What text supports the answer to Part A?

a. "so they lock us in from dawn to dusk"

b. "the only time we get a chance to visit is at lunch"

c. "losing half a day's wages means no dinner for my whole family"

d. "only last week did I turn fourteen, the legal age of factory work"

Item 6

Part A Which of the following claims about the narrator of "An Inconvenient Girl" can be supported by text evidence?

a. The narrator realizes she has to work but would like fairer treatment.

b. The narrator wants the factory bosses and owners to be thrown in jail.

c. The narrator wants the law to require her to stop working.

d. The narrator wants to work more so she can earn more money.

Part B Which evidence from the story does NOT support the answer to Part A?

a. The workers are not allowed to talk while working.

b. The main character works eleven hours a day, six days a week.

c. Fourteen is the legal age for factory work.

d. Workers earn six dollars a week.

Item 7

Part A What connotation does the word *inconvenient* have in the title "An Inconvenient Girl"?

a. ill-timed

b. not handy

c. troublesome

d. uncomfortable

Part B What text supports the answer to Part A?

a. "for my six dollars, I work eleven hours a day, six days a week"

b. "my parents warn me not to cause trouble for the owners, but . . ."

c. "we have exactly one half hour to feel human"

d. "I shrug, trying to look braver than I feel"

LITERARY ANALYSIS

Item 8

Part A Which aspect of working in a garment factory is dealt with in "An Inconvenient Girl" but NOT in "Rebel Girl Provokes Massive Strike"?

   a. the fire hazards present in the garment factory

   b. the employment of underage workers

   c. the mind-numbing nature of the work

   d. the long hours in the workweek

Part B What quote from the text supports the answer to Part A?

   a. "The work is so repetitive, I feel I am nothing but an extension of the machine."

   b. "If it happens again, I'll send you home for half a day with no work and no wages."

   c. "Who but a child would accept $3.00 a week in wages?"

   d. "But you could get thrown in jail and beaten!"

Item 9

Part A Which word describes both the narrator from "An Inconvenient Girl" and Clara Lemlich in "Rebel Girl Provokes Massive Strike"?

   a. rash

   b. dreamy

   c. obedient

   d. determined

Part B Select TWO pieces of evidence (one from each text) that support your response to Part A.

   a. "Perhaps it was the fact that this girl has firsthand experience of work in these factories." ("Rebel Girl")

   b. "In a recent smaller strike, she was arrested no fewer than seventeen times." ("Rebel Girl")

   c. "It is doubtful whether women and girls can stand up to this kind of counterattack." ("Rebel Girl")

   d. "I dream we are all streaming into school, a school for girls." ("An Inconvenient Girl")

   e. "For my six dollars, I work eleven hours a day, six days a week." ("An Inconvenient Girl")

   f. "I've decided to join the union and the next strike." ("An Inconvenient Girl")

Item 10

Both of the fictional stories you have read deal with society's laws. "Battle of the Bike Lane" is about the law that gives a city government the right to say where bike lanes go. "An Inconvenient Girl" concerns labor laws for factory workers in the early 1900s.

Write an essay that analyzes how the law plays a part in each story and how the main characters react to the law. Cite evidence from each story to support your analysis. Be sure to follow the conventions of standard English.

Part 2 Narrative Writing

RL.7.1–4, RL.7.6, RL.7.10, W.7.3–4,
W.7.9–10, L.7.1–6, RH.7.4, RH.7.8

Read all parts of the question before responding. Circle the correct answer to Items 1–9. Use your own paper to respond to Item 10.

Item 1

Part A What does the word *culvert* mean in these lines from "Meet Jill Schartner—Conservation Warden"?

"From this location I can hear the walleyes splashing in the culverts, which run under the roadway."

   a. a natural creek or stream

   b. a ditch running parallel to a road

   c. a footpath passing under a bridge

   d. a sewer or drainpipe that passes beneath a road

Part B Which words from the lines of text in Part A help you understand the meaning of *culvert*?

   a. "from this location"

   b. "I can hear"

   c. "the walleyes"

   d. "which run under the roadway"

Item 2

Part A Choose two words that describe Jill Schartner, based on evidence from the text.

   a. brilliant and determined

   b. bold and dedicated

   c. brave and foolhardy

   d. sneaky and vengeful

Part B Choose TWO pieces of evidence that support your response to Part A.

   a. "Setting up surveillance . . . is one way we're able to do our job"

   b. "Now I need to find a place where I can watch the creek without being seen."

   c. "There is very little brushy area to conceal my location because of the road"

   d. "I decide to give it another hour. I know if I move now, my tracks will be seen."

   e. "I hear the noise of a loud muffler in the distance"

   f. "I move toward the driver and place my hands on his shoulders"

Item 3

Part A Which connotation does the word *discuss* carry in these lines from the narrative?

"Both men paid fines of more than $500.00 each and lost their hunting and fishing privileges for a 3-year period. As for the young boy, he and I were able to sit down and discuss the legal method of catching fish."

   a. argue about

   b. dispute bitterly

   c. debate heatedly

   d. talk over calmly

Part B What text supports the answer to Part A?

   a. "both men paid fines of more than $500.00"

   b. "lost their hunting and fishing privileges"

   c. "he and I were able to sit down"

   d. "the legal method of catching fish"

NARRATIVE WRITING

Item 4

Part A Why does the young boy fail to alert the two men to the presence of a conservation warden?

a. He is so surprised to see her that he is speechless.

b. He sees her but is not interested in her.

c. She signals to him not to make a sound.

d. He does not see her because he is looking at the men.

Part B Which detail from the text best supports the answer to Part A?

a. "I decide to try to conceal myself in a small clump of dogwood 20 feet from the water's edge"

b. "he is more interested in what the men are doing"

c. "I decide it is time to make my presence known"

d. "I'm now . . . behind the men, but they are so intent on making the fish look like it has been legally caught . . . "

Item 5

Part A What does Schartner mean when she says, "the game is about to begin" in these lines from the narrative?

"Something in his eyes tells me the game is about to begin, and in one quick movement, the driver bends down, grabs the net and takes one step toward the water's edge."

a. The driver will try to avoid being caught.

b. The driver wants to get home quickly to watch a football game.

c. The driver knows fishing and hunting season is about to start.

d. The driver will invite the warden to play a friendly game with him.

Part B What text supports the answer to Part A?

a. "something in his eyes tells me"

b. "in one quick movement"

c. "the driver bends down, grabs the net"

d. "toward the water's edge"

Item 6

Part A At the narrative's climax, which of the following themes emerges?

a. Female walleyes need protection to lay their eggs.

b. If you disobey the conservation warden, you'll be sorry.

c. A landing net or a fishing pole can pose a tripping hazard.

d. Good role models are found in unexpected places.

Part B Which evidence from the narrative supports the answer to Part A?

a. "they're busy releasing their eggs among the rocks in the shallow water"

b. "but he trips on some rocks and falls head first into the icy cold water"

c. "both men paid fines of more than $500.00 each and lost their hunting and fishing privileges for a 3-year period"

d. "he and I were able to sit down and discuss the legal method of catching fish"

Item 7

Part A Which meaning of the social studies word *conservation* applies in the job title "conservation warden"?

a. preserving with sugar

b. the process of using sparingly

c. relating to the protection of wildlife

d. maintenance of energy during a phase of changes

Part B What text from the narrative supports the answer to Part A?

a. "protecting natural resources"

b. "my job is the best job in the world"

c. "my thermos is empty"

d. "'C173, are you ready for a replacement?'"

Item 8

Part A Which of the following is a reasoned judgment, based on experience or logic?

a. "my job is the best job in the world"

b. "As I . . . reach into the creek, I am able to touch several of these large fish."

c. "because of the fresh snow, I decide to give [the surveillance] another hour"

d. "The young boy asks, 'Can I hold it? Can I get one like that?'"

Part B What text supports the answer to Part A?

a. "I know if I move now, my tracks will be seen"

b. "I think I am speaking for all of the wardens here in Wisconsin"

c. "they all laugh and point into the water as the driver yells excitedly"

d. "I can see as many as 50 walleyes swimming among the rocks in the shallow water"

Item 9

Part A Below are three claims about "Meet Jill Schartner." Which claim can be supported by evidence from the text?

a. She regrets that it is necessary to protect wildlife from poachers.

b. She believes more should be done to protect wildlife.

c. She enjoys enforcing Wisconsin's conservation laws.

d. She underwent extensive training to become a conservation warden.

Part B What text supports your response to Part A?

a. "the . . . cold damp air has been enough to keep me awake"

b. "at 2:00 A.M. . . . . my back is stiff and my thermos is empty"

c. "I decide it is time to make my presence known"

d. "he and I were able to sit down and discuss the legal method of catching fish"

Item 10

"Meet Jill Schartner—Conservation Warden" is a narrative told by Jill Schartner, reflecting her point of view and her feelings about the events she describes. Imagine this event from the point of view of one of the other participants—the driver who ends up in the water, his adult passenger, or even the young boy.

Write three or four paragraphs to tell the story of this incident from this other participant's point of view. Include his thoughts and feelings about the incident and his reactions to the events, taking care to show a different perspective than Jill Schartner's. Be sure to use details from "Meet Jill Schartner" in your story. End by having your narrator tell what conclusions he can draw about the incident, such as whether he did or did not learn anything.

Part 3 Research Simulation

RI.7.1, RI.7.2, RI.7.3, RI.7.4, RI.7.6, RI.7.9, RI.7.10, W.7.2, W.7.4, W.7.9, W.7.10, L.7.1, L.7.2, L.7.3, L.7.4

Read all parts of the question before responding. Circle the correct answer to Items 1–9. Use your own paper to respond to Item 10.

Item 1

Part A What does the word *emissions* mean in these lines from "NOHVU Keynote Address"?

"A lot of fuss has been made about the emissions of snowmobiles, ATVs, and dirt bikes. But I'm here to tell you that today's newer engines, whether 2-stroke or 4-stroke, are much less polluting than the old 2-stroke models."

a. substance released in the air

b. rapid rise in popularity

c. bans on public property

d. fuel efficiency

Part B Which words from the lines of text in Part A best help you understand the meaning of *emissions*?

a. "a lot of fuss"

b. "today's newer engines, whether 2-stroke or 4-stroke"

c. "much less polluting"

d. "the old 2-stroke models"

Item 2

Part A According to information in Bill Luckenbach's keynote address, which claim about the Wilderness Act is most accurate?

a. The Wilderness Act is a fundamentally flawed law that should not have been passed.

b. Through funds provided by the Wilderness Act, OHV users have built new trails.

c. The Wilderness Act has been used to prevent OHV users from going off trail.

d. Carrying out the Wilderness Act has led to unforeseen consequences.

Part B What text supports the answer to Part A?

a. "The Forest Service isn't the only agency threatening OHV use."

b. "25,000 acres of wilderness were closed under these rules"

c. "But in effect, three times that acreage is now unavailable to OHV users."

d. "We want to comply with the trail management rules"

Item 3

Part A According to the reaction to the speech, "NOHVU Keynote Address Hits the Right Notes," what part of the speech marked a dramatic change in the speaker's attitude?

a. The discussion of the economic impact of OHV retail sales.

b. The discussion of the effect of OHV tourism on local communities.

c. The imitation of the sound of a 2-stroke engine starting up.

d. The discussion of limits on OHV access to federal lands.

Part B What verbal element of Luckenbach's speech showed that his attitude had changed?

a. "his voice fairly booming"

b. "he shared good news with enthusiasm"

c. "he began at an unhurried pace"

d. "he reported on some of the injustices"

Item 4

Part A Based on "NOHVU Keynote Address Hits the Right Notes," which claim about Bill Luckenbach is accurate?

a. He is a clownish speaker whom the audience does not take seriously.

b. He is a relaxed speaker who connects with the audience.

c. He is a serious speaker who intimidates his audience.

d. He is a hesitant speaker who fails to leave an impression.

Part B Which of Luckenbach's verbal and nonverbal techniques, as reported in "NOHVU Keynote Address Hits the Right Notes," supports the claim from Part A?

a. He gets nostalgic, makes funny sounds, and pounds the podium.

b. He speaks in an unhurried tone and makes eye contact.

c. He stands straighter, pounds the podium, and glares at his audience.

d. He speaks softly, looks down, and fails to discuss important topics.

Item 5

Part A How does the author of "Protecting Federal Lands" feel about the Forest Service's Travel Management Rules?

a. She feels they do not go far enough to protect National Forests.

b. She defends the way the rules have been applied to OHV users.

c. She feels they are a long overdue response to President Nixon's original Executive Order.

d. She insists that the original rules should never have been revised.

Part B Which quotation from the text best supports the answer to Part A?

a. "this order required the Forest Service to create rules that would accomplish three goals"

b. "the 2005 revision was an attempt to stem the tide of destruction brought by OHVs"

c. "the rules still haven't slowed or reversed the damage"

d. "the growth of OHV use on our public lands has increased steadily"

Item 6

Part A Below are four claims about changes in OHV engine technology. Which claim does Bill Luckenbach make in his keynote address?

a. The EPA has no right to alter the signature sound of a two-stroke engine.

b. The engines in newer OHVs are cleaner, quieter, and less polluting.

c. Changes in OHV technology will not make any difference to our parklands.

d. OHV users were never fond of the conventional two-stroke engines anyway.

Part B Which quotation from "Protecting Federal Lands" best counters the claim above?

a. "the old-style OHV engines account for over half the OHVs in use today"

b. "the EPA has issued stricter emissions standards for the manufacturers of new OHVs"

c. "air pollution, of course, is another major problem with OHVs"

d. "many a bird-watcher knows the frustration that accompanies the ear-shattering blast of an OHV"

Item 7

Part A Which claim about the economic impact of OHV use does the author of "Protecting Federal Lands" make?

a. OHVs in public lands may discourage "human powered" tourists, which would hurt local economies.

b. OHV users, on a daily basis, spend about as much money on tourism as other users of federal lands.

c. In the future, the government will spend more money enforcing the regulation of OHVs in public lands.

d. OHV users will have to pay a fuel tax and a registration fee for the privilege of using their vehicles on public lands.

Part B What text from "NOHVU Keynote Address" could be used to argue against the correct claim in Part A?

a. "the value of the off-road retail market is $15 billion dollars"

b. "this economic downturn has an upside"

c. "through registration fees, user fees, and the fuel taxes we pay, we've shouldered the cost of using these lands"

d. "OHV users spend more on average than other park users in local economies"

Item 8

Part A In "Protecting Federal Lands," Susan Lund implies that federal land management suffers during economic downturns. How is Luckenbach's view of the economic downturn different from Lund's?

a. He sees it as negative because OHV users cannot afford new vehicles.

b. He sees it as negative because the government can't build new OHV trails.

c. He sees it as positive because OHV users can show their community spirit.

d. He sees it as positive because the government is less likely to enforce rules.

Part B What evidence supports the answer to Part A?

a. a Minnesota study showing the local impact of OHV tourist dollars

b. details about taxes and volunteer work OHV users have contributed

c. an example of how the government has stopped enforcing an OHV ban

d. statistics about a nationwide decline in retail OHV sales

Item 9

Part A Which meaning of *sustainable* best matches its use in these lines?

"This is the best possible kind of economic impact, generated by a sustainable industry that respects the land. What's more, wilderness region economies depend on it."

a. able to be maintained or prolonged

b. able to continue with little environmental damage

c. able to provide the necessities for living

d. able to be propped up from below

Part B Which word or phrase from the text in Part A supports your answer?

a. "economic impact"

b. "generated"

c. "respects the land"

d. "economies depend on it"

Item 10

You have read two texts dealing with the use of ATVs, snowmobiles, dirt bikes, and other off-highway vehicles (OHVs) on federal lands. Write an essay in which you compare what the authors say about the economic and environmental impact of OHV use on federal land. Then tell your opinion on this issue, based on the authors' arguments. Remember to use textual evidence to support your ideas.

A

accompany *(verb)* go with

accoutrement *(noun)* accessories; equipment

acknowledge *(verb)* to admit to be real or true

affected *(verb)* had an effect on; impacted

affinity *(noun)* fondness for; connection to

affirmatively *(adverb)* positively; in a way that expresses agreement

agile *(adjective)* moving and jumping easily; quick and well-coordinated

agitated *(adjective)* upset

allocated *(verb)* assigned when resources are divided up

altered *(verb)* changed

amulet *(noun)* an object that has symbolic meaning; a charm

anecdote *(noun)* brief story describing an event or person

animated *(adjective)* full of life or spirit; lively

apprised *(verb)* informed

aqueous *(adjective)* of water, or containing water; watery

archipelago *(noun)* group or chain of islands

arduous *(adjective)* difficult; hard

armory *(noun)* a place where weapons are kept

artifact *(noun)* an object of historical interest made by humans

aspect *(noun)* characteristic; part or side

assumed *(verb)* took on

atmospheric *(adjective)* of the atmosphere, the layer of air that surrounds Earth

atomic *(adjective)* having to do with atoms, the tiny, basic building blocks of matter

attempt *(verb)* to try; to make an effort at

authority *(noun)* the right to tell others what to do

authorized *(verb)* given permission or authority to do something

aviation *(noun)* the design, production, and use of aircraft

awe *(noun)* a strong feeling of admiration for something grand or powerful

B

bagpipes *(noun)* musical instrument made of a bag and connected pipes, often played in Scotland

beachhead *(noun)* base established on an enemy's shore during an invasion

bemoans *(verb)* complains about

bill *(noun)* a proposed law

biodiversity *(noun)* a great number and variety of plant and animal species in an environment

biofuel *(noun)* fuel created from renewable natural resources

bore *(verb)* carried

brink *(noun)* the edge or critical point after which success or catastrophe occurs

broadside *(noun)* the side of a ship above the water line

buckskin *(adjective)* made from the skin of a deer

buoyancy *(noun)* lightness; cheerfulness

bulb *(noun)* a rounded part, especially at the end of a cylinder

C

carbon footprint *(noun)* the amount of carbon dioxide a person, place, or activity releases into the atmosphere

cargo *(noun)* items transported on a ship, train, truck, etc.

canopy *(noun)* overhanging covering

cellular *(adjective)* relating to the system that uses radio waves to communicate telephone signals

certification *(noun)* official statement of competence or completion

chart *(verb)* to make a map of

chemist *(noun)* a scientist who works with chemicals

circumference *(noun)* the length of the outer boundary of a circle

civil disobedience *(noun)* political action in which participants peacefully break laws as a form of protest

classified *(verb)* placed in a group or category

climate *(noun)* typical weather conditions of an area

colleague *(noun)* coworker; person in a similar position

colony *(noun)* far-off area immigrated into and/or controlled by a country

combatant *(noun)* someone or something that fights against something else

commandeer *(verb)* take control of for military use

commencing *(verb)* beginning

communism *(noun)* form of government in which the leaders control the economy and many aspects of people's lives

compound *(noun)* combination of chemical elements

condensation *(noun)* process in which water collects into clouds or fog

confirm *(verb)* to check that something is true

conscientious *(adjective)* careful; exacting

considerable *(adjective)* significant

constellation *(noun)* group of objects in the sky

construction *(verb)* building

contaminant *(noun)* pollutant

contiguous *(adjective)* next to one another; touching

corded *(adjective)* lined with cords or cord-like lines

cosmic *(adjective)* having to do with space or the cosmos

countenance *(noun)* face

coveted *(verb)* became jealous of

crevasse *(noun)* crack in a rock or mountain

crewman *(noun)* a sailor; a worker on a ship

culvert *(noun)* drain crossing under a road

D

dais *(noun)* a raised platform

daunting *(adjective)* difficult and frightening; intimidating

decade *(noun)* a ten-year period

decimation *(noun)* the destruction of a great number of something

deforestation *(noun)* removal of forests and trees

delirium *(noun)* confusion caused by high fever

democracy *(noun)* form of government that recognizes the right of people to rule themselves through elected representatives

demon *(noun)* evil spirit

demonstrating *(verb)* protesting

depleted *(verb)* used up

deposit *(noun)* natural collection of a substance, usually a mineral

desolate *(adjective)* lonely and gloomy

devised *(verb)* thought up; created

diagnosis *(noun)* a medical decision about what illness or condition is affecting a person

diplomatic *(adjective)* involving relationships between countries

dissever *(verb)* to cut apart

disorder *(noun)* disease; disability

dispatched *(verb)* sent

dissipate *(verb)* scatter; spread out and away

diverges *(verb)* to move in a different direction from a common point; to branch off

documented *(adjective)* recorded in documents, as with evidence

duration *(noun)* length of time that something takes or lasts

duty *(noun)* tax

dwindling *(adjective)* becoming smaller or less

E

ecosystem *(noun)* the system of animals, plants, and other organisms that interact in an environment

electromagnetic *(adjective)* associated with the electric and magnetic fields and their interactions with each other

elements *(noun)* weather

eloquent *(adjective)* expressive; meaningful

emblem *(noun)* symbol; sign

emerged *(verb)* came out of

enabled *(verb)* allowed; let happen

encountered *(verb)* came across; met

encrypted *(verb)* placed in code

endurance *(noun)* ability or strength to keep going through difficulties

enterprise *(noun)* project; endeavor

entrepreneur *(noun)* a person who starts his or her own business

entrepreneurship *(noun)* development of a new business

environmental *(adjective)* having to do with nature and the natural world

equilibrium *(noun)* a state of balance

erosion *(verb)* wearing or washing away

estimation *(noun)* approximate calculation; judgment

estuary *(noun)* area where a river meets the sea

evaporation *(noun)* the natural process in which water is drawn up into the air

evidence *(noun)* proof; signs

evoke *(verb)* to cause people to think about; to call up memories or feelings about

exchange *(noun)* discussion

expanse *(noun)* an open, uninterrupted area

exploit *(verb)* take advantage of

exuberance *(noun)* enthusiasm; excitement and eagerness

eye *(noun)* the calm center of a hurricane

F

fateful *(adjective)* connected to the occurrence of something important or terrible

feat *(noun)* extraordinary act; accomplishment

federal *(adjective)* part of or from the national government

fertilizer *(noun)* a substance used to help plants grow, especially a chemical manure

filtration *(noun)* removal of dirt and debris

flight deck *(noun)* area where the astronauts sit to control the space shuttle

frigate *(noun)* a fast, heavily armed ship of the eighteenth century

forest canopy *(noun)* the highest layer of branches and leaves in a forest

forestry *(noun)* care and management of forests and the businesses that use them

forsake *(verb)* forget; abandon

founded *(verb)* began or started a business or other large effort

G

gallantly *(adverb)* bravely

garb *(noun)* clothing; style of clothing

gaudy *(adjective)* tastelessly showy; flashy

generate *(verb)* create; produce

genre *(noun)* style; type

gloss over *(verb)* to give a deceptively good appearance to something; to hide the negative aspects of something

greenhouse gases *(noun)* gases that lead to the warming of the Earth's atmosphere

H

hectare *(noun)* an area of land equal to about 2½ acres

helm *(noun)* place on a ship where the steering controls are located

heritage *(noun)* something one is born to

hide *(noun)* the skin of a large animal

highborn *(adjective)* aristocratic; of noble family

hue *(noun)* color

hurricane *(noun)* a large storm that develops over the ocean but can move inland

hydroelectric dam *(noun)* dam that uses falling water to create electricity

hygrometer *(noun)* instrument that measures humidity

I

immigrant *(noun)* a newcomer to a country or area

impaired *(adjective)* not working correctly

incident *(noun)* event; thing that happened

inclement *(adjective)* stormy; unpleasant

incomparable *(adjective)* better than the others; beyond comparison

indigenous *(adjective)* local; native

infrared *(adjective)* heat-sensing

inherent *(adjective)* existing as a natural or essential part of someone or something

innovation *(noun)* new idea; invention

inspiration *(noun)* something that encourages someone to strive for a goal

intricate *(adjective)* detailed; complex

instrument *(noun)* mechanical or electronic measuring device

intact *(adjective)* whole; in one piece

integral *(adjective)* essential

intense *(adjective)* having or showing great strength or feeling

invaluable *(adjective)* extremely valuable; beyond price

invigorating *(adjective)* energizing

isolated *(adjective)* separated from others; alone

J

joint *(adjective)* united; done by groups working together

jovial *(adjective)* happy and cheerful

K

kinsman *(noun)* relative

L

league *(noun)* a unit of distance equal to about 3 miles

legislator *(noun)* lawmaker

liberation *(noun)* the act of setting a nation or area free

long-standing *(adjective)* in place for a long time

lurches *(verb)* sways or rolls suddenly

luminous *(adjective)* shining

M

mandated *(verb)* stated as a law or rule

manifest *(noun)* list of passengers

manual *(adjective)* done by hand; physical

marshal *(verb)* bring together; gather

marvel *(noun)* an amazing thing

mass *(noun)* substance and weight of an object

meager *(adjective)* small or weak; puny

measure *(noun)* step; procedure

meet *(noun)* a sports competition

merchant *(adjective)* used in sales or trade

meteoroid *(noun)* small rock traveling through space

module *(noun)* small section; unit

momentary *(adjective)* lasting only for a moment; brief

musket *(noun)* an early type of rifle

mutually *(adverb)* done together

N

naïve *(adjective)* having a lack of experience or judgment

nanosecond *(noun)* 1/1,000,000,000 of a second

native *(adjective)* from the area; local

O

occurred *(verb)* happened; took place

onlooker *(noun)* person watching; spectator

oratorical *(adjective)* having to do with speaking and making speeches

orbit *(noun)* path one object takes around another object (such as a planet around the sun)

outfitted *(verb)* supplied; equipped

P

passage *(noun)* arrangements to travel as a passenger

patriot *(noun)* person loyal to a cause or country

peat *(noun)* soil that is thick with vegetable matter

perceived *(verb)* understood

permit *(noun)* official, written permission to do something

perpetuate *(verb)* to keep something going; support

perseveres *(verb)* keeps trying in spite of obstacles

pertinent *(adjective)* relevant; having to do with the matter at hand

philanthropist *(noun)* a person who gives money to do good works

philosophy *(noun)* system of belief

physical *(adjective)* relating to the substances something is made of

plantation *(noun)* a large farm

plummet *(verb)* drop suddenly and quickly

portion *(noun)* segment; piece of the whole

preservation *(noun)* protection; keeping something safe from harm

primary forest *(noun)* a forest in its original condition, mostly unaffected by human activities

processed food *(noun)* food changed from its natural state, usually made in factories

prolific *(adjective)* producing in abundance; fruitful

promontory *(noun)* high point; overlook

propelled *(verb)* pushed in a direction

propulsion *(noun)* a means of pushing something forward

prospect *(noun)* idea; possibility

provocation *(noun)* reason to take offense or be angry

Q

qualifications *(noun)* skills or experience that fits a person for a job, an office, etc.

R

rally *(noun)* public gathering; demonstration

receiver *(noun)* object that receives and processes signals

reconciliation *(noun)* process of becoming friends again

recuperate *(verb)* to recover after an illness

reeling *(verb)* staggering backward unsteadily, such as after being struck

refined *(adjective)* precise or exact

refute *(verb)* argue against; disprove

relapse *(verb)* to fall back into illness

related *(verb)* told; gave an account of

relative humidity *(noun)* a measure of the amount of moisture in the air, based on moisture possible at a given temperature

renewable resource *(noun)* resource of which more can be grown or produced

repose *(noun)* calmness; peacefulness

restraint *(noun)* holding back; control

restricting *(verb)* holding back; containing

routine *(adjective)* dull; ordinary

rude *(adjective)* roughly made; not fancy or refined

S

sabre *(noun)* a type of sword

safeguard *(verb)* protect; guard

sage *(noun)* wise and learned person who gives advice to others

satellite *(noun)* an object that travels around a planet

saturation *(noun)* the state of being as full of liquid as possible

scintillating *(adjective)* dazzling; brilliant

secondary forest *(noun)* a forest that has grown back after a destructive event

sedimentary *(adjective)* made of sand compacted together

seize *(verb)* take hold of something

sentry *(noun)* a soldier posted to stand guard or keep watch

sepulchre *(noun)* tomb

seraph *(noun)* angel

scout *(verb)* search for

sheer *(adjective)* straight and steep

singular *(adjective)* unique or extraordinary

sinew *(noun)* tendon

skirmish *(noun)* a fight between small numbers of opposing troops

smartphone *(noun)* a phone that includes a hand-held computer for Internet access, e-mail, and so on

so-called *(adjective)* known as

solace *(noun)* something that gives comfort or relief

solar array *(noun)* set of solar panels, which store energy from sunlight

soldiery *(noun)* soldiers; members of an army

sophisticated *(adjective)* complex or intricate

sounding *(adjective)* rumbling; booming

sphere *(noun)* a ball or rounded, ball-like form

spike *(noun)* pointed piece of metal like a giant nail

statesman *(noun)* experienced and wise government leader

steed *(noun)* horse

stockpiling *(verb)* storing up supplies

stoicism *(noun)* a lack of concern about pain or difficulty

storm surge *(noun)* flood of ocean water onto land during a hurricane

stowage *(noun)* storage

suborbital *(adjective)* not having the altitude to reach orbit

sultriness *(noun)* damp heat

summit *(noun)* top; peak

subsidizing *(verb)* paying part of the cost for another person or group

sustainable *(adjective)* able to last a long time, especially by using renewable resources and taking care of the environment

sustenance *(noun)* the state of being sustained, or kept going, for a long period

T

tailwind *(noun)* wind coming from behind a ship

talisman *(noun)* an object believed to have magical or protective properties

telescope *(noun)* tool used to magnify objects

temporary *(adjective)* not permanent; of short term

tense *(adjective)* stressed; difficult

theorized *(verb)* made an educated, informed guess or judgment

timber *(noun)* wood; lumber

timely *(adjective)* available at the right moment

tomb *(noun)* grave; place where a person is buried

torrential *(adjective)* falling with great force

toxin *(noun)* poison

trade route *(noun)* road or path used for trade between groups

tragedy *(noun)* terrible event; disaster

transcendentalist *(noun)* a philosopher who believes that true meaning lies beyond ordinary experiences

transform *(verb)* change completely

transmitted *(verb)* sent by signal

treaty *(noun)* an agreement between two groups, especially when they have been in conflict

trek *(noun)* a long walk or journey

tribulation *(noun)* severe trouble or difficulty

trilateration *(noun)* the process of using three data points to figure out a location

tugboat line *(noun)* a business that operates tugboats (small boats that tow or push ships)

tumultuous *(adjective)* wild and disordered; turbulent

tyranny *(noun)* unrestrained abuse of power and authority by a government

U

unassailable *(adjective)* unable to be argued with or attacked

urban sprawl *(noun)* the uncontrolled spread of cities and development into country areas

V

valor *(noun)* boldness in facing danger; bravery

venture *(noun)* an undertaking involving uncertainty as to the outcome

ventured *(verb)* attempted; tried

vessel *(noun)* ship

viable *(adjective)* able to live or grow correctly

vow *(noun)* solemn promise

W

wary *(adjective)* cautious; watchful

water cycle *(noun)* the cycle in which water evaporates from rivers, lakes, and oceans, falls as rain, and then again evaporates

waterfowl *(noun)* birds that live on and near the water

watershed *(noun)* the network of streams and rivers that flow into a lake or ocean

watt *(noun)* unit in which electricity is measured

wholesale *(adjective)* extensive

INDEX